Miss. Ella Ash

Forest, Ohio -

Hardin Co.,

Purchased at the State
Sunday School Convention
in Zanesville Ohio in 1912

Inspiring Hymns

for

THE CHURCH AND
SUNDAY - SCHOOL

EDITED *and* COMPILED
BY E. O. EXCELL

CHURCH HYMNS
SUNDAY-SCHOOL SONGS
RESPONSIVE READINGS
SOLOS *and* CHORUSES

Cloth Board Edition

PRICES: Cloth Boards, $35.00 the hundred, express not prepaid; Single copies 45 cents, post-paid.

Cloth, Limp Edition

PRICES: Cloth, Limp, $25.00 the hundred, express not prepaid; Single copies 35 cents, post-paid.

E. O. EXCELL, PUBLISHER
CHICAGO
The Fine Arts Building

A PSALM OF PRAISE

Praise ye the Lord.
Praise God in his
sanctuary: praise him
in the firmament of
his power.

Praise him for his mighty acts:
praise him according to his
excellent greatness.

Praise him with the sound
of the trumpet: praise him
with the psaltery and harp:
Praise him with the timbrel
and dance: praise him with
stringed instruments and
organs.

Praise him upon the loud
cymbals: praise him upon
the high sounding cymbals.
Let everything that hath
breath praise the Lord.
Praise ye the Lord.

Inspiring Hymns

No. 1. Joy to the World.
Isaac Watts.
C. F. Handel.
1. Joy to the world, the Lord is come! Let earth re - ceive her
2. No more let sin and sor - row grow, Nor thorns in - fest the
3. He rules the world with truth and grace, And makes the na - tions
King; Let ev - 'ry heart pre - pare Him room, And
ground; He comes to make His bless - ing flow Far
prove The glo - ries of His right - eous - ness, And
heav'n and na - ture sing, And heav'n and na - ture
as the curse is found, Far as the curse is
won - ders of His love, And won - ders of His
And heav'n and na - ture sing, And
sing, And heav'n, and heav'n and na - ture sing.
found, Far as, far as the curse is found.
love, And won-ders, and won - ders of His love.
heav'n and na - ture sing,

No. 2. Grace, Enough for Me.

E. O. E. | E. O. Excell.

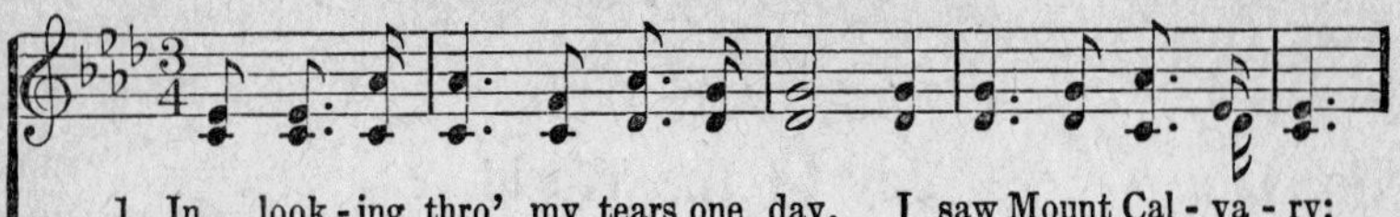

1. In looking thro' my tears one day, I saw Mount Calvary;
2. While standing there, my trembling heart, Once full of agony,
3. When I beheld my ev'ry sin Nailed to the cruel tree,
4. When I am safe within the veil, My portion there will be,

Beneath the cross there flowed a stream Of grace, enough for me.
Could scarce believe the sight I saw Of grace, enough for me. (enough for me.)
I felt a flood go thro' my soul Of grace, enough for me.
To sing thro' all the years to come Of grace, enough for me.

CHORUS.

Grace is flowing from Calvary, . . Grace as fathomless as the sea, . .
Grace is flow-ing from Cal-va-ry for me, Grace as fath-om-less as the roll-ing sea,

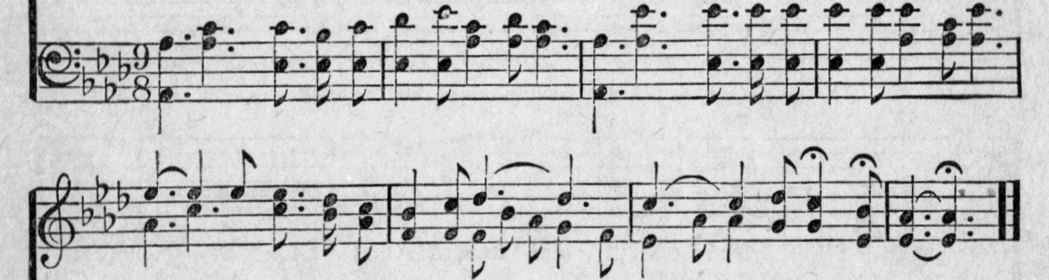

Grace for time and e-ter-ni-ty, . . . Grace, . . enough for me.
Grace for time and e-ter-ni-ty, His a-bun-dant grace I see, e-nough for me.

No. 3. The Touch of His Hand on Mine.

Jessie Brown Pounds. COPYRIGHT, 1913, BY CHAS. H. GABRIEL. E. O. EXCELL, OWNER. Henry P. Morton.

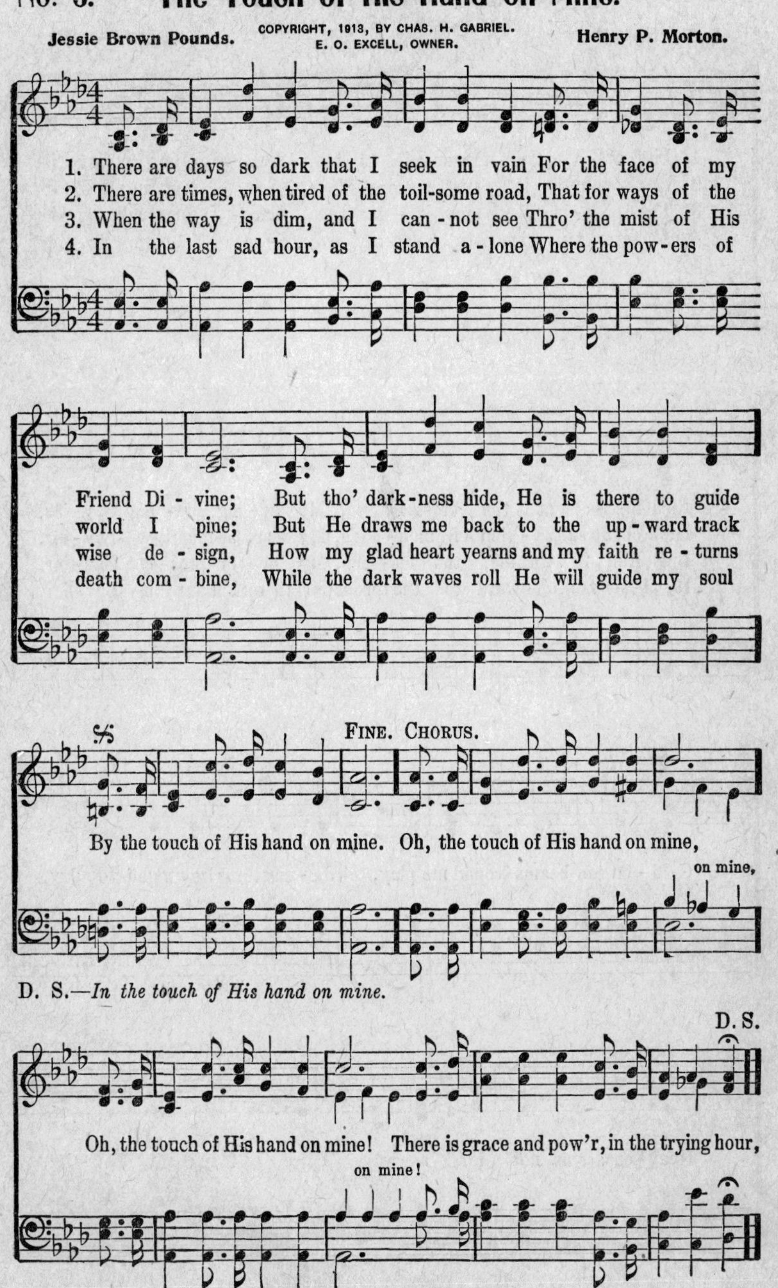
1. There are days so dark that I seek in vain For the face of my
2. There are times, when tired of the toil-some road, That for ways of the
3. When the way is dim, and I can-not see Thro' the mist of His
4. In the last sad hour, as I stand a-lone Where the pow-ers of
Friend Di-vine; But tho' dark-ness hide, He is there to guide
world I pine; But He draws me back to the up-ward track
wise de-sign, How my glad heart yearns and my faith re-turns
death com-bine, While the dark waves roll He will guide my soul
FINE. CHORUS.
By the touch of His hand on mine. Oh, the touch of His hand on mine,
on mine,
D. S.—In the touch of His hand on mine.
D. S.
Oh, the touch of His hand on mine! There is grace and pow'r, in the trying hour,
on mine!

No. 4. Since I Found My Savior.

E. E. Hewitt.
COPYRIGHT, 1892, BY JOHN R. SWENEY.
USED BY PERMISSION.
Jno. R. Sweney.
1. Life wears a dif - f'rent face to me, Since I found my Sav - ior;
2. He sought me in His wondrous love, So I found my Sav - ior;
3. The pass - ing clouds may in - ter-vene, Since I found my Sav - ior,
4. A strong hand kind - ly holds my own, Since I found my Sav - ior;
Rich mer - cy at the cross I see, My dy - ing, liv - ing Sav - ior.
He brought sal-va - tion from a - bove, My dear, al-might - y Sav - ior.
But He is with me, tho' un - seen, My ev - er-pres - ent Sav - ior.
It leads me on - ward to the throne; O there I'll see my Sav - ior.
Chorus.
Gold - en sun-beams 'round me play, Je - sus turns my night to day,
Heav - en seems not far a - way, Since I found my Sav - ior.

No. 5. It Was His Love.

Rev. E. A. Hoffman. | COPYRIGHT, 1913, BY E. O. EXCELL. WORDS AND MUSIC. | Chas. H. Gabriel.

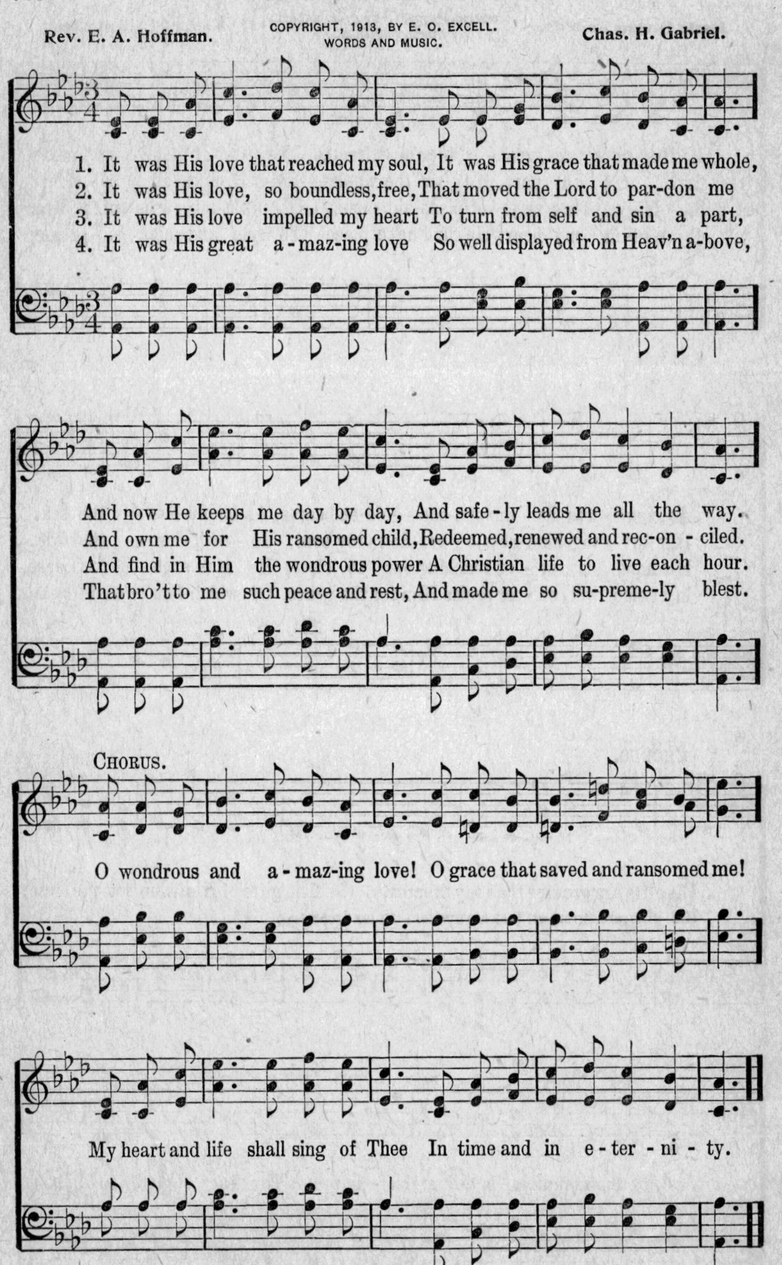
1. It was His love that reached my soul, It was His grace that made me whole,
2. It was His love, so boundless, free, That moved the Lord to par-don me
3. It was His love impelled my heart To turn from self and sin a part,
4. It was His great a-maz-ing love So well displayed from Heav'n a-bove,
And now He keeps me day by day, And safe-ly leads me all the way.
And own me for His ransomed child, Redeemed, renewed and rec-on-ciled.
And find in Him the wondrous power A Christian life to live each hour.
That bro't to me such peace and rest, And made me so su-preme-ly blest.
Chorus.
O wondrous and a-maz-ing love! O grace that saved and ransomed me!
My heart and life shall sing of Thee In time and in e-ter-ni-ty.

No. 6. The Gifts of God.

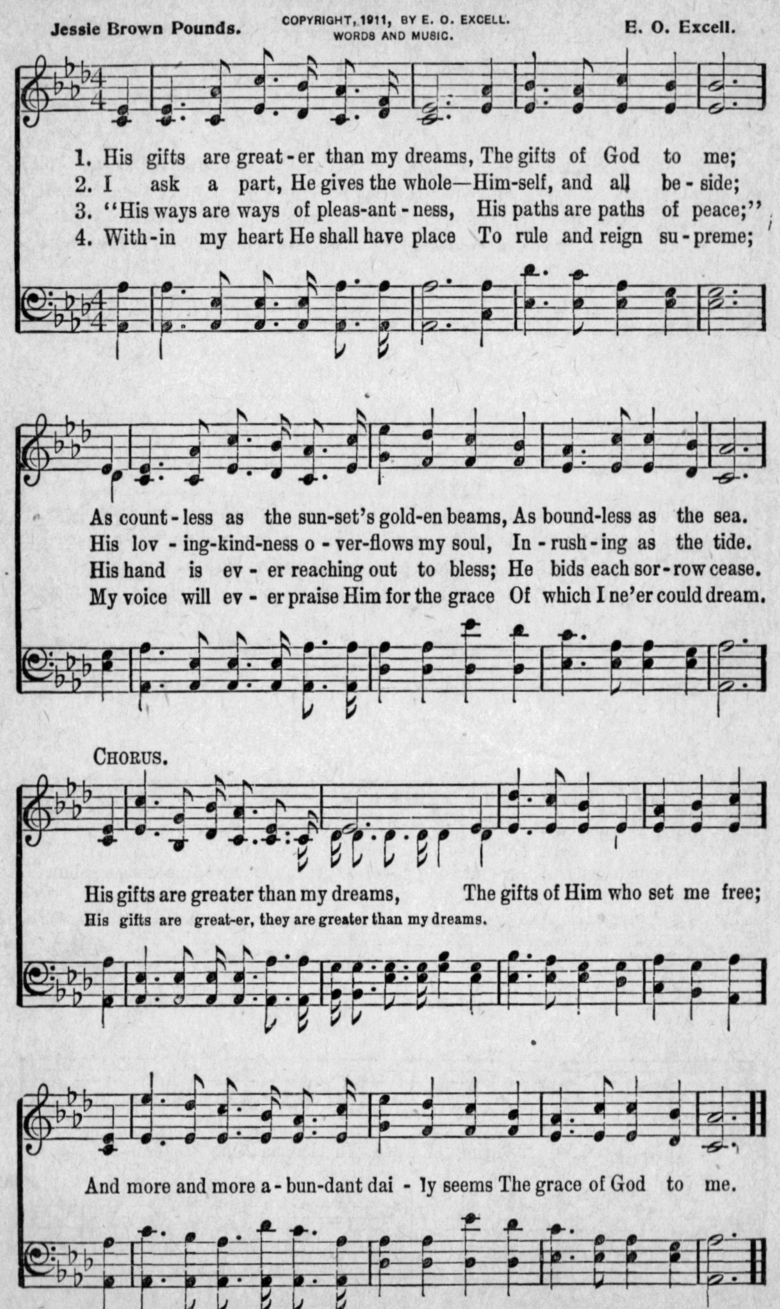
Jessie Brown Pounds.
COPYRIGHT, 1911, BY E. O. EXCELL.
WORDS AND MUSIC.
E. O. Excell.
1. His gifts are great-er than my dreams, The gifts of God to me;
2. I ask a part, He gives the whole—Him-self, and all be-side;
3. "His ways are ways of pleas-ant-ness, His paths are paths of peace;"
4. With-in my heart He shall have place To rule and reign su-preme;
As count-less as the sun-set's gold-en beams, As bound-less as the sea.
His lov-ing-kind-ness o-ver-flows my soul, In-rush-ing as the tide.
His hand is ev-er reaching out to bless; He bids each sor-row cease.
My voice will ev-er praise Him for the grace Of which I ne'er could dream.
CHORUS.
His gifts are greater than my dreams, The gifts of Him who set me free;
His gifts are great-er, they are greater than my dreams.
And more and more a-bun-dant dai-ly seems The grace of God to me.

No. 7. Just When I Need Him Most.

Rev. Wm. Pool.

Chas. H. Gabriel.

1. Just when I need Him, Je-sus is near, Just when I fal - ter, just when I fear;
2. Just when I need Him, Je-sus is true, Nev-er for-sak - ing all the way thro';
3. Just when I need Him, Je-sus is strong, Bearing my bur-dens all the day long;
4. Just when I need Him, He is my all, An-swer-ing when up-on Him I call;
Read - y to help me, read - y to cheer, Just when I need Him most.
Giv - ing for bur - dens pleasures a - new, Just when I need Him most.
For all my sor - row giv - ing a song, Just when I need Him most.
Ten - der - ly watch-ing lest I should fall, Just when I need Him most.
CHORUS.
Just when I need Him most, Just when I need Him most;
Je - sus is near to com-fort and cheer, Just when I need Him most.

No. 8. The Hour of Prayer.

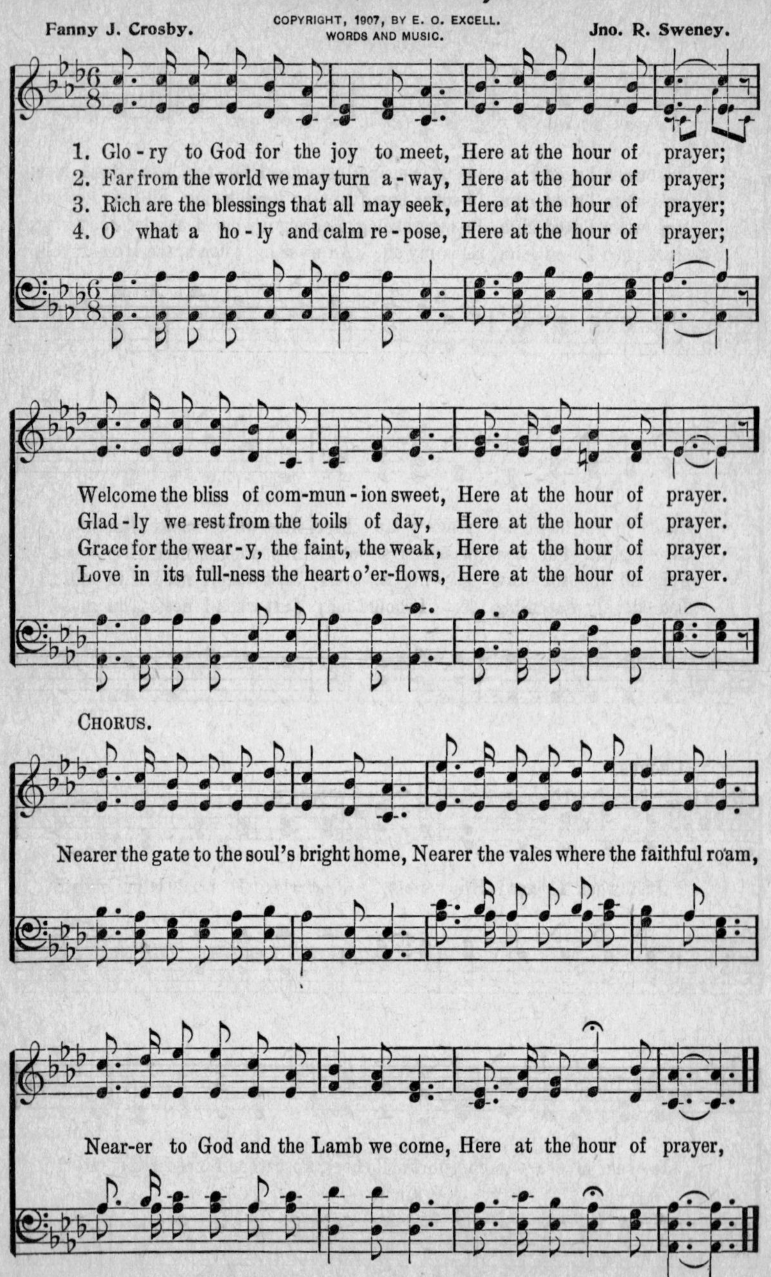

Fanny J. Crosby.
COPYRIGHT, 1907, BY E. O. EXCELL. WORDS AND MUSIC.
Jno. R. Sweney.
1. Glo - ry to God for the joy to meet, Here at the hour of prayer;
2. Far from the world we may turn a - way, Here at the hour of prayer;
3. Rich are the blessings that all may seek, Here at the hour of prayer;
4. O what a ho - ly and calm re - pose, Here at the hour of prayer;
Welcome the bliss of com-mun - ion sweet, Here at the hour of prayer.
Glad - ly we rest from the toils of day, Here at the hour of prayer.
Grace for the wear - y, the faint, the weak, Here at the hour of prayer.
Love in its full-ness the heart o'er-flows, Here at the hour of prayer.
CHORUS.
Nearer the gate to the soul's bright home, Nearer the vales where the faithful roam,
Near-er to God and the Lamb we come, Here at the hour of prayer,

No. 9. One Day for Thee.

Rev. W. C. Pool.

Chas. H. Gabriel.

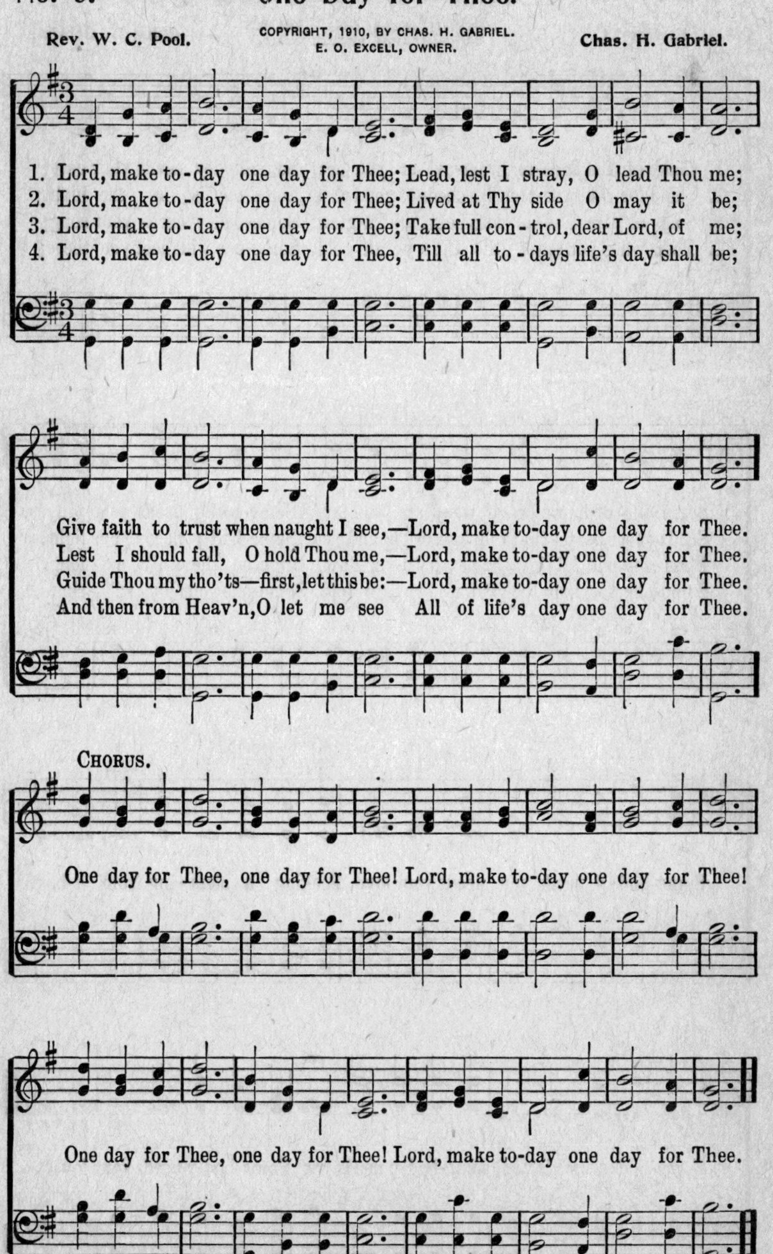
1. Lord, make to-day one day for Thee; Lead, lest I stray, O lead Thou me;
2. Lord, make to-day one day for Thee; Lived at Thy side O may it be;
3. Lord, make to-day one day for Thee; Take full con-trol, dear Lord, of me;
4. Lord, make to-day one day for Thee, Till all to-days life's day shall be;
Give faith to trust when naught I see,—Lord, make to-day one day for Thee.
Lest I should fall, O hold Thou me,—Lord, make to-day one day for Thee.
Guide Thou my tho'ts—first, let this be:—Lord, make to-day one day for Thee.
And then from Heav'n, O let me see All of life's day one day for Thee.
CHORUS.
One day for Thee, one day for Thee! Lord, make to-day one day for Thee!
One day for Thee, one day for Thee! Lord, make to-day one day for Thee.

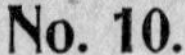

No. 10. Somebody Needs You.

E. E. Hewitt. | Chas. H. Gabriel.

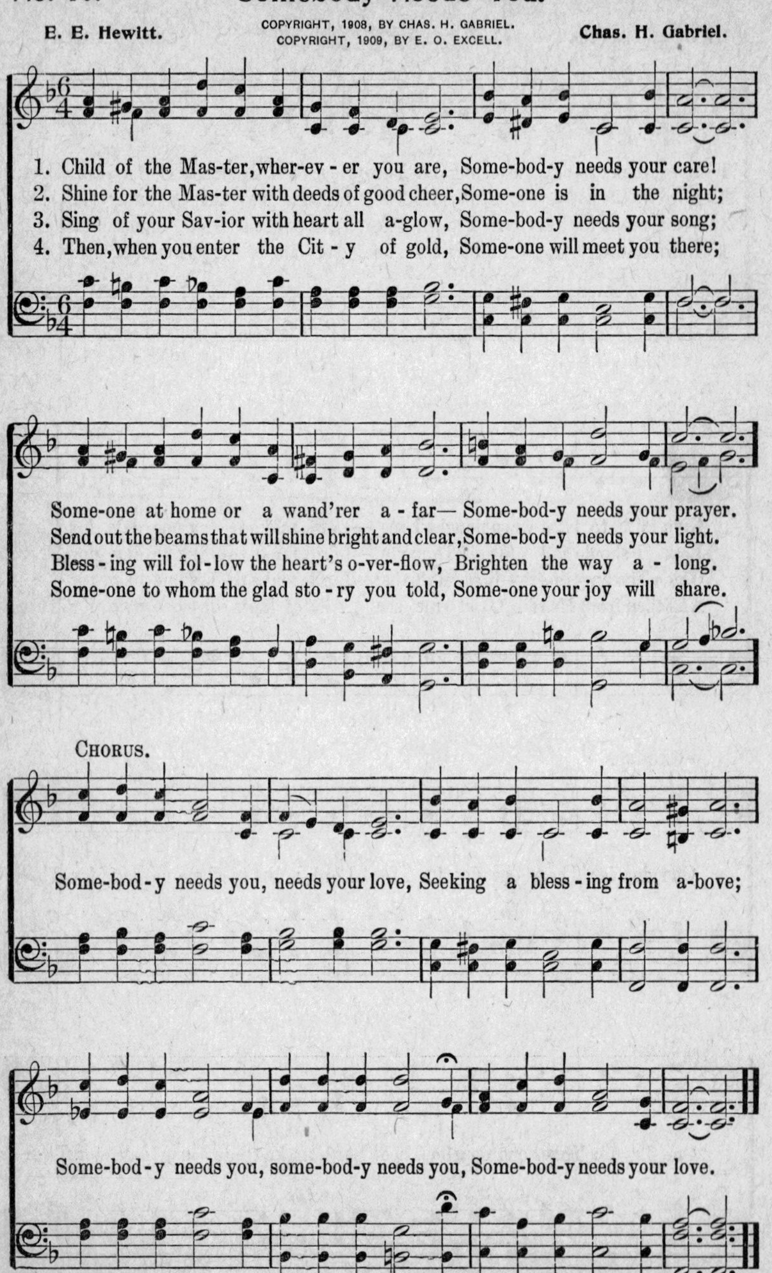
1. Child of the Mas-ter, wher-ev - er you are, Some-bod-y needs your care!
2. Shine for the Mas-ter with deeds of good cheer, Some-one is in the night;
3. Sing of your Sav-ior with heart all a-glow, Some-bod-y needs your song;
4. Then, when you enter the Cit - y of gold, Some-one will meet you there;
Some-one at home or a wand'rer a - far— Some-bod-y needs your prayer.
Send out the beams that will shine bright and clear, Some-bod-y needs your light.
Bless - ing will fol - low the heart's o-ver-flow, Brighten the way a - long.
Some-one to whom the glad sto - ry you told, Some-one your joy will share.
CHORUS.
Some-bod - y needs you, needs your love, Seeking a bless - ing from a-bove;
Some-bod - y needs you, some-bod-y needs you, Some-bod-y needs your love.

No. 11. All in All to Me.

C. H. G.

Chas. H. Gabriel.

1. All in all to me is Jesus! Ev-'ry need His grace supplies;
Day by day He guides and keeps me,— No good thing to me de - nies.

2. All in all to me is Je-sus, Lord, Redeemer, Savior, Friend;
Ten-der Shepherd, He will guard me, And from ev-'ry foe de - fend.

3. All in all to me is Je-sus, Bless - ed One of Cal-va - ry;
I will nev-er cease to love Him Who has done so much for me.

4. All in all to me is Je-sus, I am His, and He is mine;
To His love, and in His serv-ice, Ev-'ry-thing I now re - sign.

CHORUS.

In His love I am a - bid - ing, Ev-'ry-thing to Him con-fid - ing;
'Neath His wing my soul is hid - ing, He is all in all to me.

No. 12. Where Thou Callest Me.

James Apple. COPYRIGHT, 1910, BY E. O. EXCELL. WORDS AND MUSIC. Jno. R. Sweney.

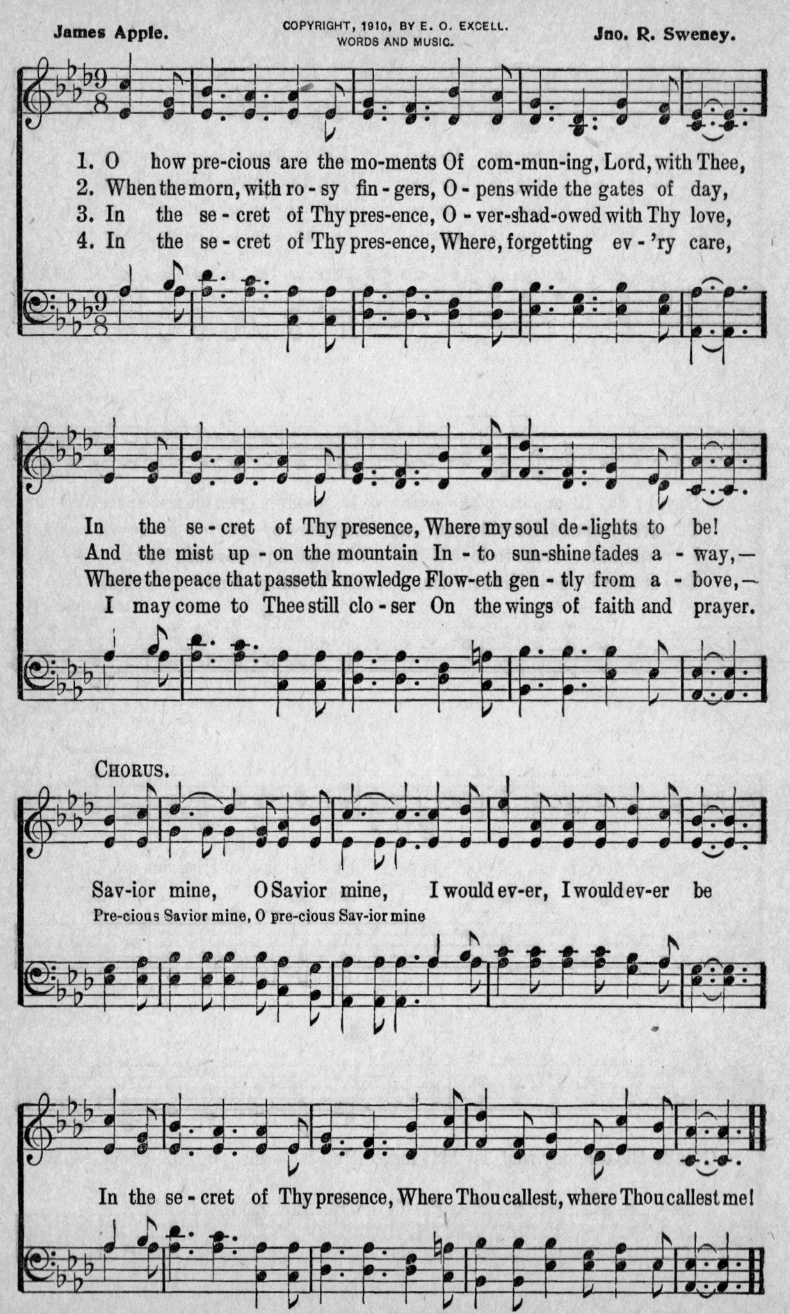

1. O how pre-cious are the mo-ments Of com-mun-ing, Lord, with Thee,
2. When the morn, with ro - sy fin - gers, O - pens wide the gates of day,
3. In the se - cret of Thy pres-ence, O - ver-shad-owed with Thy love,
4. In the se - cret of Thy pres-ence, Where, forgetting ev - 'ry care,
In the se - cret of Thy presence, Where my soul de - lights to be!
And the mist up - on the mountain In - to sun-shine fades a - way,—
Where the peace that passeth knowledge Flow-eth gen - tly from a - bove,—
I may come to Thee still clo - ser On the wings of faith and prayer.
CHORUS.
Sav-ior mine, O Savior mine, I would ev-er, I would ev-er be
Pre-cious Savior mine, O pre-cious Sav-ior mine
In the se - cret of Thy presence, Where Thou callest, where Thou callest me!

No. 13. I am Going on With Jesus.

Jessie Brown Pounds.
COPYRIGHT, 1913, BY E. O. EXCELL.
WORDS AND MUSIC.
Samuel W. Beazley.
1. I am go - ing on with Je - sus, Naught shall turn me from the way;
2. I am go - ing on with Je - sus, Tho' the world would call me back;
3. I am go - ing on with Je - sus; Safe - ly He thus far has led;
4. Past the shadows of the val - ley, Lo! the heights of glo - ry rise;
He will hold me lest I stum - ble, He will guide me lest I stray.
I will fol - low where He leads me, I will keep the blood-stained track.
Tho' He guide me thro' the val - ley, I can have no doubt or dread.
I am go - ing on with Je - sus To the hills of Par - a - dise.
CHORUS.
I am go - ing on with Je - sus, Go - ing on thro' shadows gray;
I am go - ing thro' the sun - shine, Go - ing with Him all the way.

No. 14. Help Somebody To-day.

Mrs. Frank A. Breck.

Chas. H. Gabriel.

1. Look all a-round you, find some one in need, Help some-bod-y to - day!
2. Man - y are wait-ing a kind, lov - ing word, Help some-bod-y to - day!
3. Man - y have bur-dens too heav - y to bear, Help some-bod-y to - day!
4. Some are dis-cour-aged and wear-y in heart, Help some-bod-y to - day!

Tho' it be lit - tle—a neigh-bor - ly deed—Help some-bod-y to - day!
Thou hast a mes-sage, O let it be heard, Help some-bod-y to - day!
Grief is the por - tion of some ev - 'ry-where, Help some-bod-y to - day!
Some one the jour - ney to heav - en should start, Help some-bod-y to - day!

CHORUS.

Help some-bod-y to - day, . . Some-bod-y a - long life's way; . . Let
to - day, home-ward way;

sor-row be end - ed, The friendless befriended, Oh, help somebody to - day!

No. 15. We Shall Be More Like Jesus.

James Rowe. B. D. Ackley.

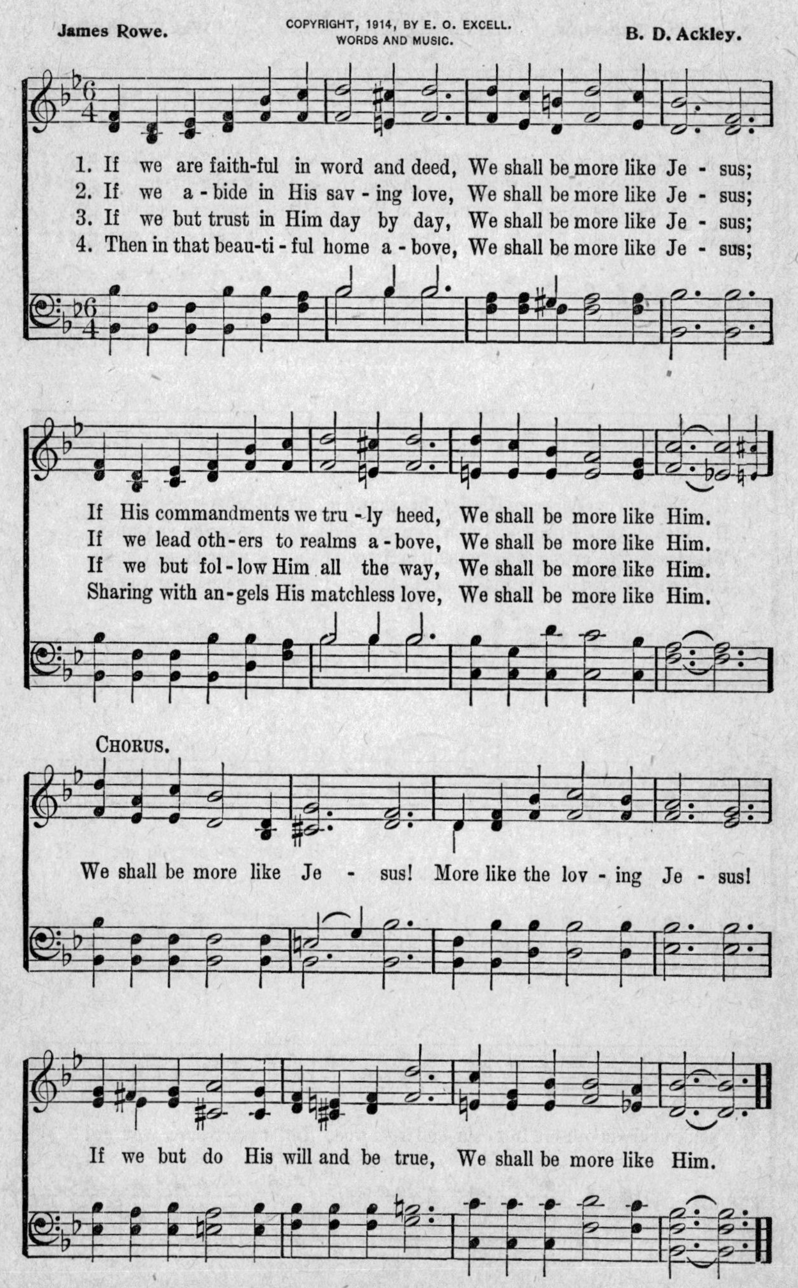
1. If we are faith-ful in word and deed, We shall be more like Je - sus;
2. If we a - bide in His sav - ing love, We shall be more like Je - sus;
3. If we but trust in Him day by day, We shall be more like Je - sus;
4. Then in that beau-ti - ful home a - bove, We shall be more like Je - sus;
If His commandments we tru - ly heed, We shall be more like Him.
If we lead oth - ers to realms a - bove, We shall be more like Him.
If we but fol - low Him all the way, We shall be more like Him.
Sharing with an - gels His matchless love, We shall be more like Him.
CHORUS.
We shall be more like Je - sus! More like the lov - ing Je - sus!
If we but do His will and be true, We shall be more like Him.

No. 16. Tell it Wherever You Go.

COPYRIGHT, 1907, BY CHAS. H, GABRIEL.
OWNED BY CHAS. REIGN SCOVILLE.
Rev. Johnston Oatman, Jr.
Wm. Edie Marks.
1. If Christ the Re-deem-er has pardoned your sin, Tell it wher-ev-er you go;
2. If now you are happy with Christ as your Guide, Tell it wher-ev-er you go;
3. When troubles as-sail do you trust in Him still? Tell it wher-ev-er you go;
4. If you are an heir to a man-sion on high, Tell it wher-ev-er you go;
If in-to your darkness His light has shown in, Tell it wher-ev-er you go.
If He is your Friend, and with Him you abide, Tell it wher-ev-er you go.
When sorrows o'erwhelm do you sink in His will? Tell it wher-ev-er you go.
Un-til you find rest in that home in the sky, Tell it wher-ev-er you go.
CHORUS.
Tell it, ... tell it, ... Tell it wher-ev-er you go; If
Tell it that oth-ers a-round you may know,
you would win oth-ers from sin and from woe, Tell it wher-ev-er you go!

No. 17. Teach Me.

Kate Ulmer. — Victor H. Benke.

1. Teach me, O, Thou Ho-ly Spir - it, How to do my Master's will;
2. Teach me how to be sub-miss - ive, Free - ly con - se-crat - ing all;
3. Teach me how to trust Him full - y, E'en when faith is sore - ly tried;
4. Teach me how to fol-low tru - ly, Nev - er run - ning on be - fore;
In o - be-dience to His bid - ding, Help me His commands ful - fill.
Fond-est hopes with joy re - sign - ing, In sur-ren - der to His call.
Teach me how to tell the sto - ry Of a Sav - ior cru - ci - fied.
Ev - er in His foot-steps walk - ing, Till my serv-ice here is o'er.
CHORUS.
Teach me, teach me, Teach me ev'ry day what to do and what to say;
Teach me, Ho-ly Spir - it, teach me, Ho-ly Spir-it,
Teach me, teach me How to do my Master's will. . .
Teach me, Ho-ly Spir-it, teach me, Ho-ly Spir-it,
my Master's will.

No. 18. Bring Peace to My Soul.

Helen M. Dungan. J. M. Dungan.

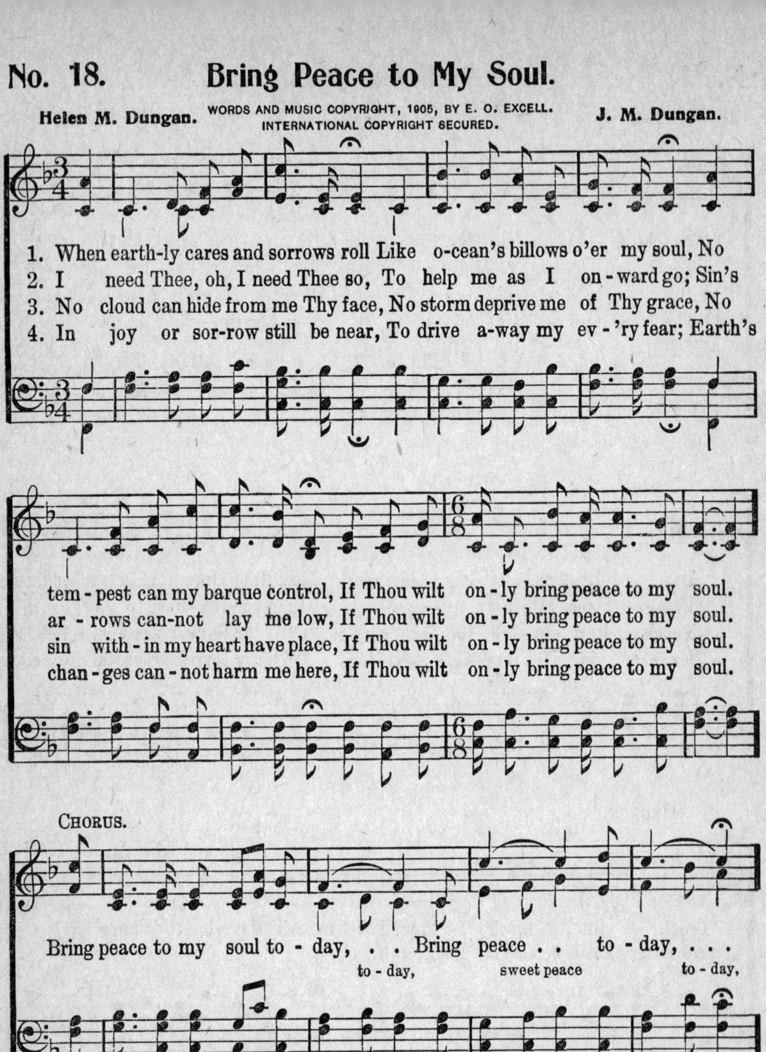
1. When earth-ly cares and sorrows roll Like o-cean's billows o'er my soul, No tem - pest can my barque control, If Thou wilt on - ly bring peace to my soul.
2. I need Thee, oh, I need Thee so, To help me as I on - ward go; Sin's ar - rows can-not lay me low, If Thou wilt on - ly bring peace to my soul.
3. No cloud can hide from me Thy face, No storm deprive me of Thy grace, No sin with - in my heart have place, If Thou wilt on - ly bring peace to my soul.
4. In joy or sor-row still be near, To drive a-way my ev - 'ry fear; Earth's chan - ges can - not harm me here, If Thou wilt on - ly bring peace to my soul.
CHORUS.
Bring peace to my soul to - day, . . Bring peace . . to - day, . . .
to - day, sweet peace to - day,

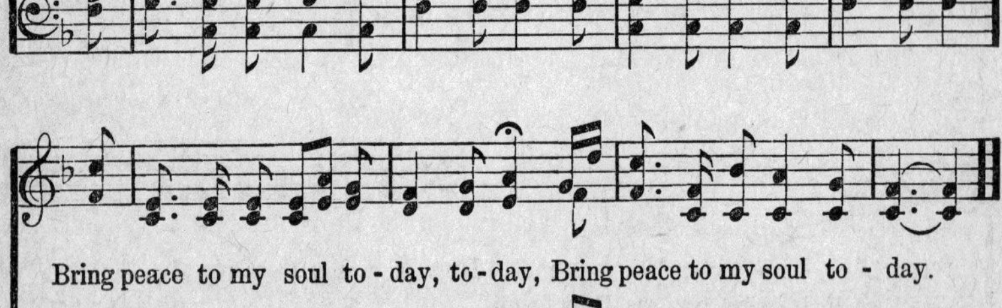

Bring peace to my soul to - day, to - day, Bring peace to my soul to - day.

No. 19. I Would Be Like Jesus.

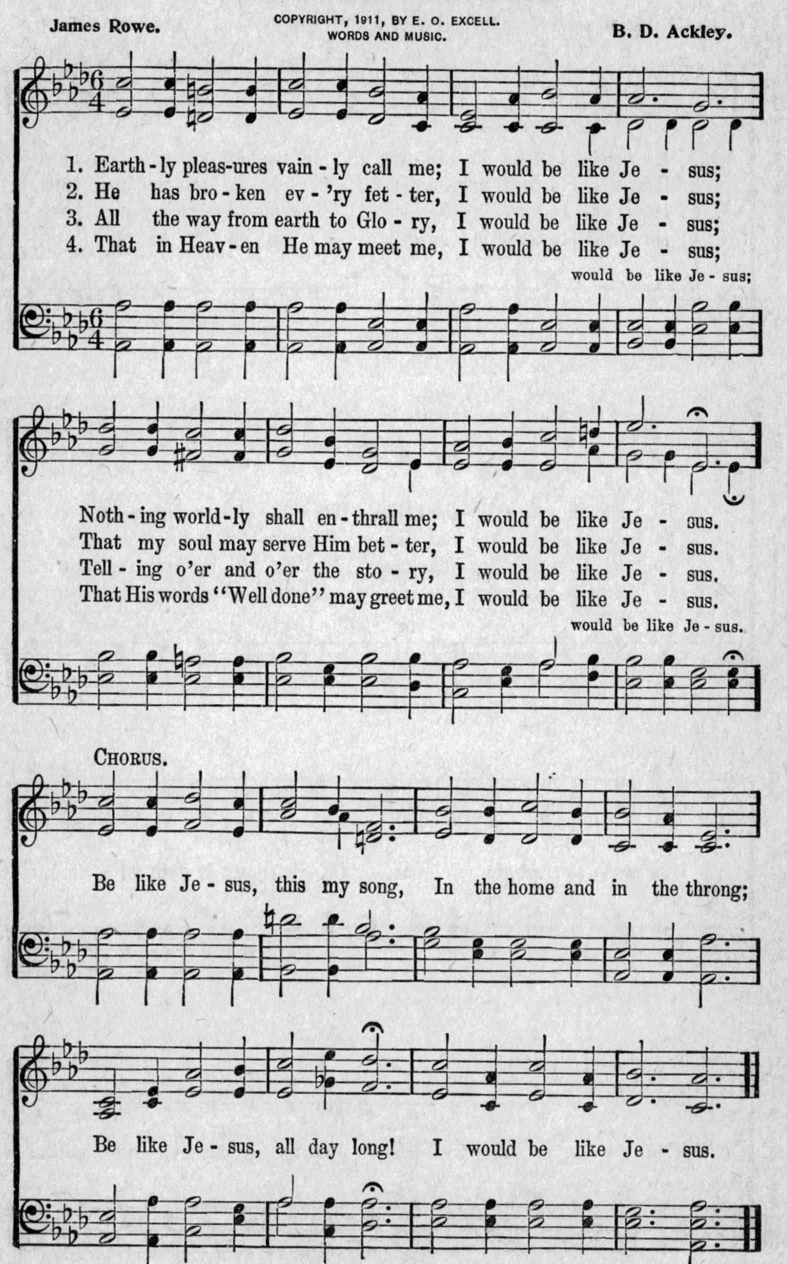
James Rowe.
COPYRIGHT, 1911, BY E. O. EXCELL. WORDS AND MUSIC.
B. D. Ackley.
1. Earth-ly pleas-ures vain-ly call me; I would be like Je - sus;
2. He has bro-ken ev-'ry fet-ter, I would be like Je - sus;
3. All the way from earth to Glo-ry, I would be like Je - sus;
4. That in Heav-en He may meet me, I would be like Je - sus;
would be like Je-sus;
Noth-ing world-ly shall en-thrall me; I would be like Je - sus.
That my soul may serve Him bet-ter, I would be like Je - sus.
Tell-ing o'er and o'er the sto-ry, I would be like Je - sus.
That His words "Well done" may greet me, I would be like Je - sus.
would be like Je-sus.
CHORUS.
Be like Je-sus, this my song, In the home and in the throng;
Be like Je-sus, all day long! I would be like Je - sus.

No. 20. How Sweet to Trust in Jesus.

Dr. M. Victor Staley. COPYRIGHT, 1914, BY E. O. EXCELL. WORDS AND MUSIC. Chas. H. Gabriel.

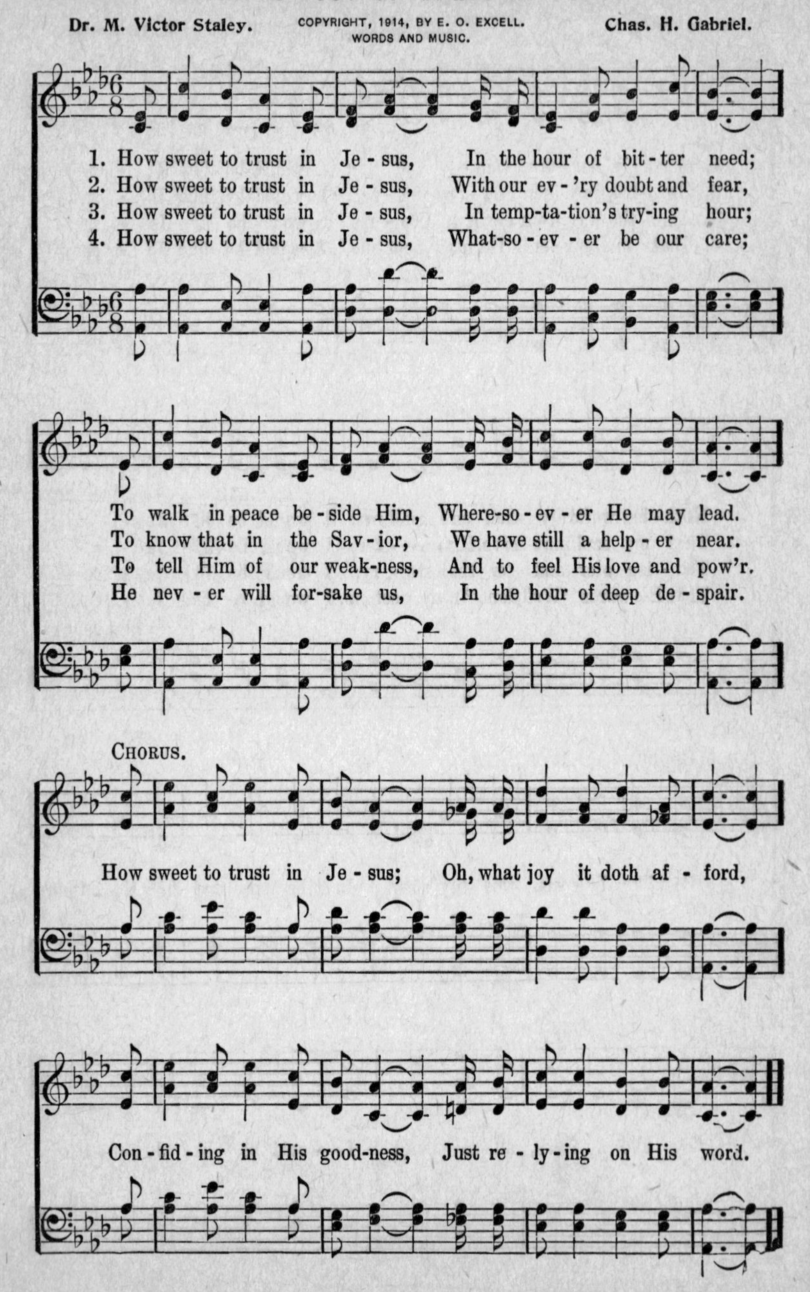
1. How sweet to trust in Je - sus, In the hour of bit - ter need;
2. How sweet to trust in Je - sus, With our ev - 'ry doubt and fear,
3. How sweet to trust in Je - sus, In temp-ta-tion's try-ing hour;
4. How sweet to trust in Je - sus, What-so - ev - er be our care;
To walk in peace be - side Him, Where-so - ev - er He may lead.
To know that in the Sav - ior, We have still a help - er near.
To tell Him of our weak-ness, And to feel His love and pow'r.
He nev - er will for-sake us, In the hour of deep de - spair.
CHORUS.
How sweet to trust in Je - sus; Oh, what joy it doth af - ford,
Con - fid - ing in His good-ness, Just re - ly - ing on His word.

No. 21. I Shall Always Need Thee.

James Rowe.
COPYRIGHT, 1914, BY E. O. EXCELL.
WORDS AND MUSIC.
B. D. Ackley.
1. I shall al - ways need Thee, Sav - ior, hold my hand,
2. I shall al - ways need Thee, Foes are ev - er near,
3. I shall al - ways need Thee, For I know not when
4. I shall al - ways need Thee, For Thou art a part
Lest I wan - der from Thee In this bar - ren land.
Try - ing hard to win me From my Sav - ior dear.
Life's tem - pes - tuous bil - lows May o'er-whelm a - gain.
Of my cling - ing spir - it, Of my trust - ing heart.
CHORUS.
I shall al - ways need Thee, I shall al - ways need Thee,—
Stay be side me, Safe - ly guide me, I shall al - ways need Thee.

No. 22. God Will Take Care of You.

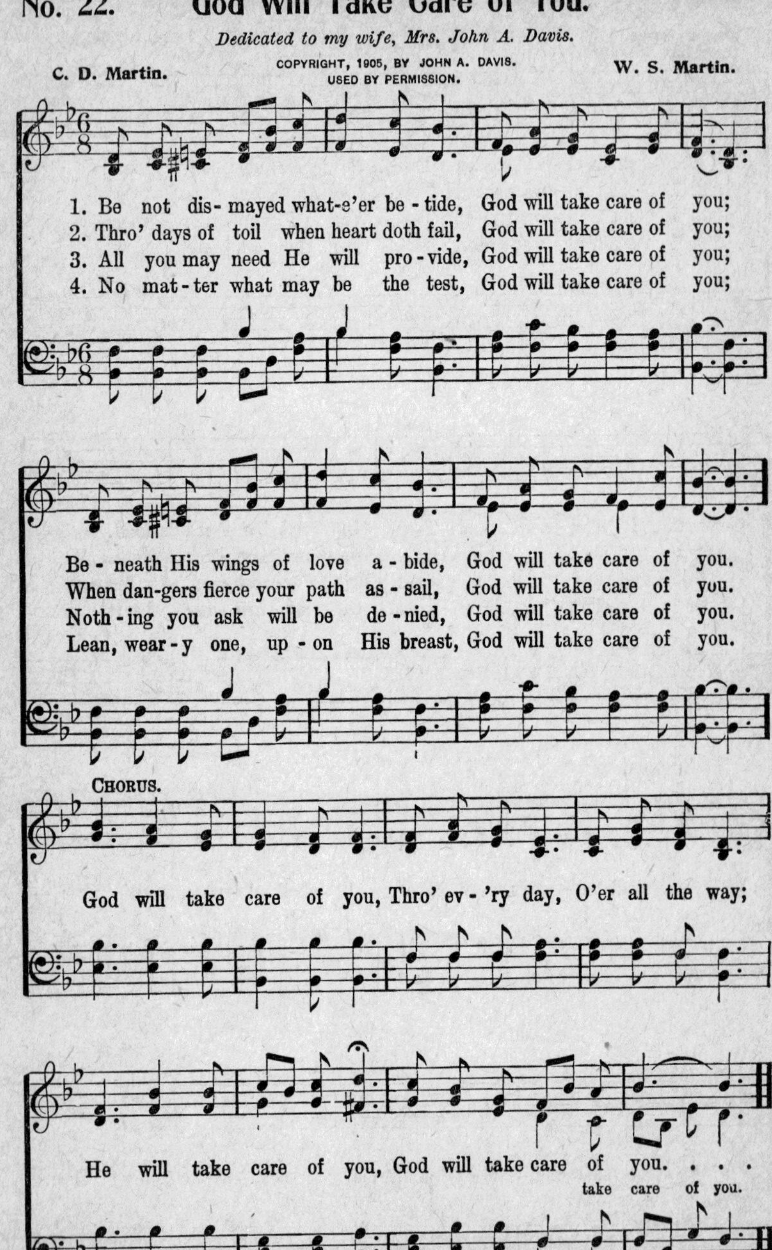

Dedicated to my wife, Mrs. John A. Davis.
C. D. Martin.
COPYRIGHT, 1905, BY JOHN A. DAVIS.
USED BY PERMISSION.
W. S. Martin.
1. Be not dis- mayed what-e'er be - tide, God will take care of you;
2. Thro' days of toil when heart doth fail, God will take care of you;
3. All you may need He will pro - vide, God will take care of you;
4. No mat - ter what may be the test, God will take care of you;
Be - neath His wings of love a - bide, God will take care of you.
When dan-gers fierce your path as - sail, God will take care of you.
Noth - ing you ask will be de - nied, God will take care of you.
Lean, wear - y one, up - on His breast, God will take care of you.
CHORUS.
God will take care of you, Thro' ev - 'ry day, O'er all the way;
He will take care of you, God will take care of you. . . .
take care of you.

No. 23. The Love of Jesus.

COPYRIGHT, 1906, BY CHAS. H. GABRIEL.
James Rowe.
Chas. H. Gabriel.
1. The love of Je - sus fills my soul, And makes me sing for joy;
2. The love of Je - sus is my light, My guide from day to day;
3. The love of Je - sus is my shield When en - e - mies as - sail;
4. The love of Je - sus draws me on To rest and joys un - told,
It helps me bear with pa-tience all The troub-les which an - noy.
My com - fort in the cheer-less night, My song a - long the way.
It gives me strength the sword to wield, And helps me to pre - vail.
To that blest land of fade-less dawn, Be-yond the gates of gold.
CHORUS.
O pre-cious love, O love di-vine, A - bide with-in this soul of mine,
And I will sing with joy thy praise, Still more and more thro' endless days.

No. 24. Jesus Only.

W. I. Coburn.
COPYRIGHT, 1914, BY E. O. EXCELL.
WORDS AND MUSIC.
B. D. Ackley.
1. When temp - ta - tion fierce as - sails, When my soul be - fore it quails,
2. When the world with proud ar - ray, With its wealth or pleas-ures gay,
3. When the judg-ment day ap - pears, Rise the deeds of all the years,
4. When the eyes grow dim and fail, When the lips turn cold and pale,
rit.
When my cour-age al - most fails, Je - sus on - ly let me see.
Tempts me from my trust a - way, Je - sus on - ly let me see.
Fill the soul with quak-ing fears, Je - sus on - ly let me see.
When I pass with-in the veil, Je - sus on - ly let me see.
Chorus.
Je - sus on - ly, this my plea, That will be e - nough for me;
rit.
Sa - tan, sin, the world will flee, If Je - sus on - ly I can see.

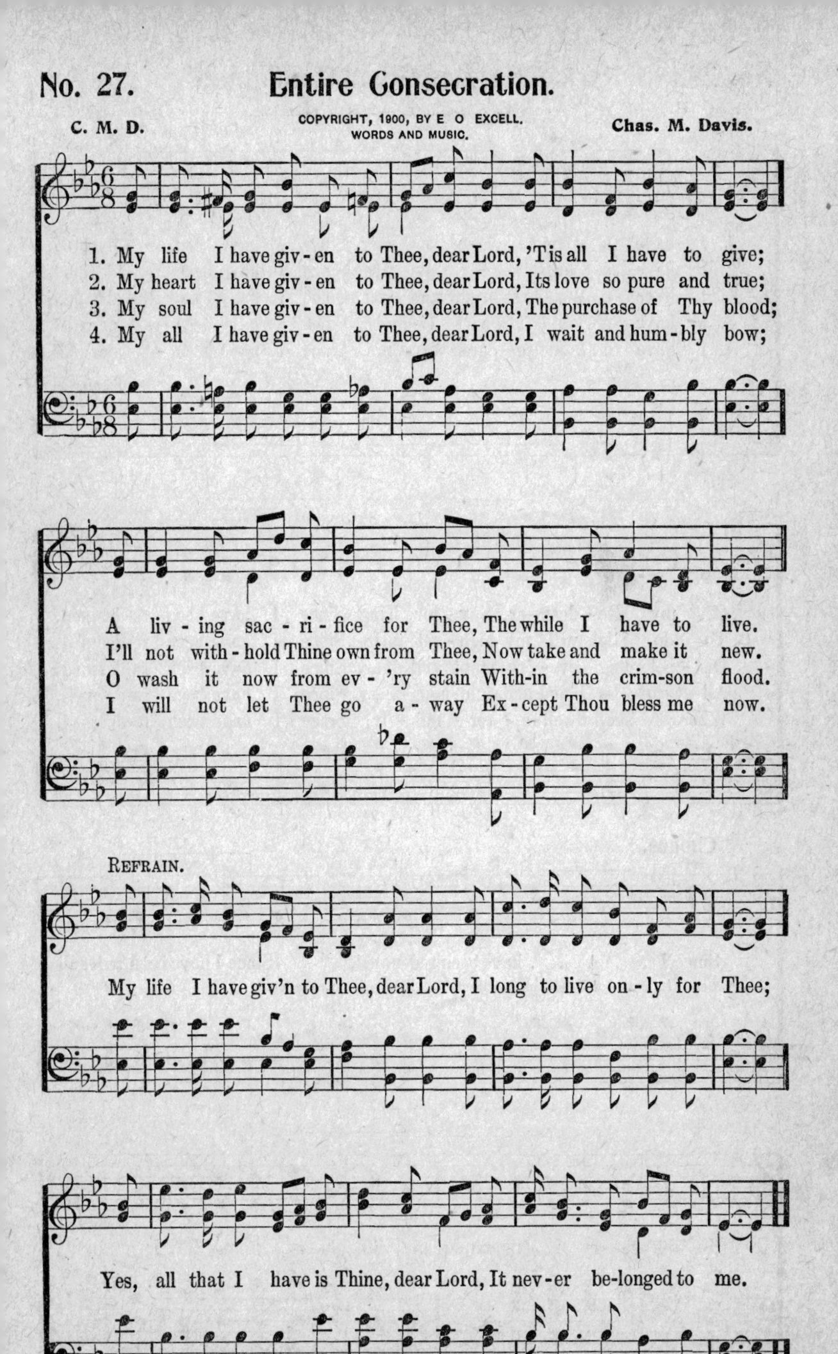
No. 27. Entire Consecration.
C. M. D.
COPYRIGHT, 1900, BY E. O. EXCELL. WORDS AND MUSIC.
Chas. M. Davis.
1. My life I have giv-en to Thee, dear Lord, 'Tis all I have to give;
2. My heart I have giv-en to Thee, dear Lord, Its love so pure and true;
3. My soul I have giv-en to Thee, dear Lord, The purchase of Thy blood;
4. My all I have giv-en to Thee, dear Lord, I wait and hum-bly bow;
A liv-ing sac-ri-fice for Thee, The while I have to live.
I'll not with-hold Thine own from Thee, Now take and make it new.
O wash it now from ev-'ry stain With-in the crim-son flood.
I will not let Thee go a-way Ex-cept Thou bless me now.
REFRAIN.
My life I have giv'n to Thee, dear Lord, I long to live on-ly for Thee;
Yes, all that I have is Thine, dear Lord, It nev-er be-longed to me.

No. 28. Since I Have Been Redeemed.
E. O. E.
COPYRIGHT, 1912, BY E. O. EXCELL. RENEWAL.
E. O. Excell.
1. I have a song I love to sing, Since I have been re - deemed,
2. I have a Christ that sat - is - fies, Since I have been re - deemed,
3. I have a Wit - ness bright and clear, Since I have been re - deemed,
4. I have a joy I can't ex-press, Since I have been re - deemed,
5. I have a home pre-pared for me, Since I have been re - deemed,
Of my Re - deem-er, Sav - ior, King, Since I have been re-deemed.
To do His will my high - est prize, Since I have been re-deemed.
Dis - pel - ling ev - 'ry doubt and fear, Since I have been re-deemed.
All thro' His blood and right-eous - ness, Since I have been re-deemed.
Where I shall dwell e - ter - nal - ly, Since I have been re-deemed.
CHORUS.
Since I . . . . . . have been redeemed, Since I have been redeemed,
Since I have been redeemed, Since I have been redeemed,
I will glo - ry in His name; I will glo - ry in my Sav-ior's name.

No. 29. What Wondrous Love.

COPYRIGHT, 1914, BY E. O. EXCELL.
John Newton.
E. O. Excell.
1. I saw One hang-ing on a tree, In ag-o-ny and blood;
2. Sure, nev-er, till my lat-est breath, Can I for-get that look:
3. My conscience felt and owned the guilt, And plunged me in de-spair;
4. A-las! I knew not what I did,—But now my tears are vain:
5. A sec-ond look He gave, which said, "I free-ly all for-give:
He fixed His lan-guid eyes on me, As near His cross I stood.
It seemed to charge me with His death, Tho' not a word He spoke.
I saw my sins His blood had spilt And helped to nail Him there.
Where shall my trem-bling soul be hid? For I the Lord have slain.
This blood is for thy ran-som paid, I die that thou may'st live."
CHORUS.
What wondrous love! Thy life to give That I might ran-somed be;
Had I a thou-sand lives to live I'd live them all for Thee.

No. 30.
Glory in the Cross.
Rev. Dwight Williams.
COPYRIGHT, 1913, BY E. O. EXCELL.
Chas. H. Gabriel.
1. In the cross shall be my glo - ry! This a - lone my boast shall be;
2. I be - held it in the dis-tance, And it seemed to draw me near,
3. Then my heart grew strangely light - er, And a beau - ty fell on me;
I can nev - er tell the sto - ry, What the cross has done for me!
Till I felt my soul's re-sist-ance All with-in me dis - ap - pear.
All the world was sweeter, brighter, For the cross had set me free.
CHORUS.
I will sing.............. of it for - ev - er, In the
I will sing of the cross, will sing of the cross for - ev - er,
land.......... to which I go;........... In the beautiful land,......... be-
In the beau-ti-ful land, the land to which I go; In the beau-ti-ful land,
yond the riv - er, This shall be........... my song, I know.
the land be-yond the riv - er, This shall be my hap - py song, I know.

No. 31.
O That Will Be Glory.
C. H. G.
COPYRIGHT, 1900, BY E. O. EXCELL.
WORDS AND MUSIC.
Chas. H. Gabriel.
1. When all my la-bors and tri-als are o'er, And I am safe on that beau-ti-ful shore, Just to be near the dear Lord I a-dore, Will thro' the a-ges be glo-ry for me . .
2. When, by the gift of His in-fin-ite grace, I am ac-cord-ed in heav-en a place, Just to be there and to look on His face,
3. Friends will be there I have loved long a-go; Joy like a riv-er a-round me will flow; Yet, just a smile from my Sav-ior, I know,
Rit.
CHORUS.
O that will be glo-ry for me, Glo-ry for me, glo-ry for me; When by His grace I shall look on His face, That will be glo-ry, be glo-ry for me.
O . . . . . . that will be glo-ry for me, Glo-ry for me, glo-ry for me; . . . .
rit.

No. 32. Satisfied.

A. H. Ackley.

B. D. Ackley.

1. When I have fin - ished my pil - grim - age here, When shall have vanished temp - ta - tion and fear, As in the arms of His love I a - bide,
2. When I am troub - led by grief and de - spair, Grace nev - er fail - ing a - waits me up there; Will - ing to trust Him what - ev - er be - tide,
3. When I have traveled the way with my Lord, Count - ing the mile - posts by faith in His word, Liv - ing and dy - ing with Him at my side,
I shall be sat - is - fied.
CHORUS.
I.......... shall be sat - is - fied, I.......... shall be sat - is - fied;
I shall be sat - is - fied, I shall be sat - is - fied; I shall be sat - is - fied;
rit.
Sheltered a - bove by His in - fin - ite love, I shall be sat - is - fied.

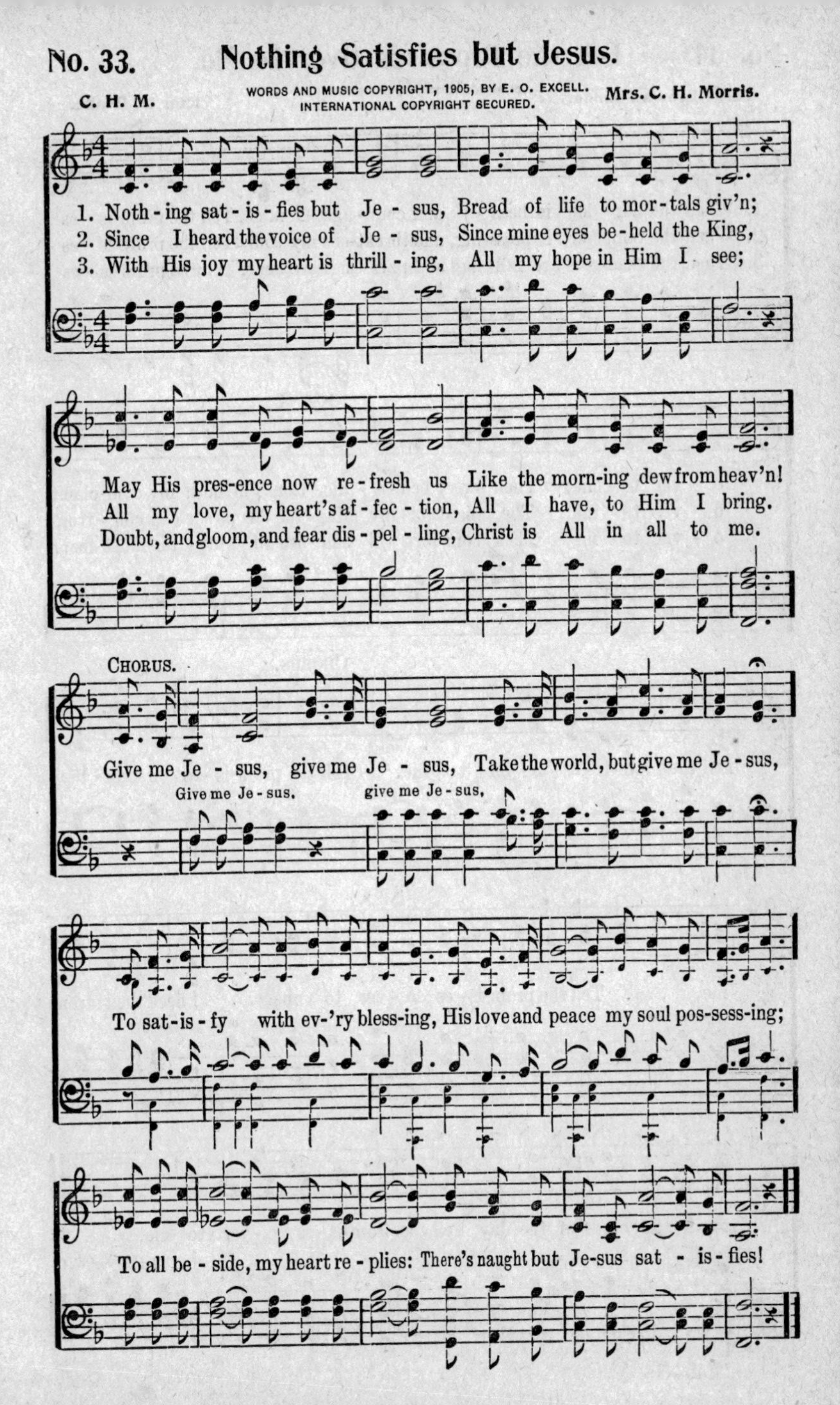
No. 33. Nothing Satisfies but Jesus.
C. H. M.
WORDS AND MUSIC COPYRIGHT, 1905, BY E. O. EXCELL.
INTERNATIONAL COPYRIGHT SECURED.
Mrs. C. H. Morris.
1. Noth-ing sat-is-fies but Je-sus, Bread of life to mor-tals giv'n;
2. Since I heard the voice of Je-sus, Since mine eyes be-held the King,
3. With His joy my heart is thrill-ing, All my hope in Him I see;
May His pres-ence now re-fresh us Like the morn-ing dew from heav'n!
All my love, my heart's af-fec-tion, All I have, to Him I bring.
Doubt, and gloom, and fear dis-pel-ling, Christ is All in all to me.
CHORUS.
Give me Je-sus, give me Je-sus, Take the world, but give me Je-sus,
Give me Je-sus, give me Je-sus,
To sat-is-fy with ev-'ry bless-ing, His love and peace my soul pos-sess-ing;
To all be-side, my heart re-plies: There's naught but Je-sus sat-is-fies!

No. 34. Tell the Promises Over to Me.

Jesse Brown Pounds. Victor H. Benke.

1. When the bur - den is heav - y and cour - age is faint, Tell the prom - is - es
2. When the tempt - er is press - ing, and threat - ens my soul, Tell the prom - is - es
3. When the shad - ows are fall - ing and part - ings are near, Tell the prom - is - es
o - ver to me; Their sweet ben - e - dic - tion will hush my com - plaint;
o - ver to me; The might of my Mas - ter his pow'r can con - trol,
o - ver to me; Their com - fort will ban - ish life's ut - ter - most fear,
CHORUS.
Tell the prom - is - es o - ver to me. Tell the prom - is - es o - ver to
me, . . Tell the prom - is - es o - ver to me, . . I need their strong
o - ver to me,
to me,
stay for the cares of the day, Tell the prom - is - es o - ver to me. . .
o - ver to me.

No. 35. Faith Will Bring the Blessing.
James Rowe.
COPYRIGHT, 1912, BY W. E. BIEDERWOLF.
B. D. Ackley.
1. If you need up - lift-ing, if you need a song, Strength to help your soul to
2. In some hour un-guard-ed, if the foe as - sail, Tho' you feel your weakness,
3. On the Lord de-pend-ing, sing a - long the way, Naught can ev-er harm you
tri-umph o - ver wrong, Put your faith in Je - sus, He is true and strong;
let not cour-age fail; Trust in Je - sus on - ly and you shall pre - vail;
if He is your stay; Lean up - on His promise till the bet - ter day;
CHORUS.
Faith will bring the blessing ev-'ry time . . Faith will bring the blessing
yes, ev'ry time.
ev'ry time, Tho' your faith be simple or sublime; For the Savior knows the heart,
Ev-'ry need He will impart; Faith will bring the blessing ev'ry time. . .
ev-'ry time.

No. 36. Blessed Be the Fountain.

W. A. O. — COPYRIGHT, 1889, BY E. O. EXCELL. WORDS AND MUSIC. — W. A. Ogden.

1. Bless-ed be the foun-tain of life to-day, Flowing free, flow-ing free!
2. Man-y have been cleansed in that fount of sin,
3. Lin-ger not a-way from this foun-tain pure,
Flow-ing free, flow-ing free, so free!
There the soul may wash all its guilt a-way, In that foun-tain of life, flow-ing free!
Man-y yet will come and will wash there-in, Bless-ed
For the guilt-y soul 'tis a wond'rous cure, Bless-ed
CHORUS.
Oh, ... the bless-ed foun-tain of life, free-ly flow-ing!
Oh, the bless-ed fount, the bless-ed fount
To . . . . . that blessed foun-tain I'll go and I'll wash and be clean. (be clean.)
To that blessed fount, the fount of life,
rit.

No. 37. * Only Remembered.
Bonar.
COPYRIGHT, 1899, BY E. O. EXCELL.
Mrs. Carrie B. Adams.
1. Fad-ing a-way like the stars of the morn-ing, Los-ing their light in the glo-ri-ous sun; So let me steal a-way gen-tly and lov-ing-ly,
2. So let my name and my place be for-got-ten, On-ly my life-race be lov-ing-ly run; So let me pass a-way peace-ful-ly, si-lent-ly,
3. So in the har-vest if oth-ers may gath-er Sheaves from the fields that in spring I have sown; Who ploughed or sowed matters not to the reap-er,
On-ly re-mem-bered by what I have done.
CHORUS.
On-ly re-mem-bered, On-ly re-mem-bered, On-ly re-mem-bered as the years roll on; On-ly re-mem-bered, for-ev-er remembered, On-ly remembered by what I have done.
On-ly remembered,
On-ly re-mem-bered,
f
rit.
* While visiting the late Ira D. Sankey, "A sweet singer in Israel," a few days before his death, he repeated to me the words of this beautiful hymn. —E O. E.

No. 38. The Home of Endless Years.
John R. Clements.
COPYRIGHT, 1902, BY JOHN R. CLEMENTS. USED BY PERMISSION.
John R. Sweney.
1. Tho' bur-dens heav-y we here must bear, And the eyes are made dim with tears, There'll be naught of sor-row "o-ver there" In the "home of the end-less years."
2. With toil-some ef-fort in faith we sow, Tho' no har-vest our vi-sion cheers; We will not lose heart, 'twill all be plain, In the
3. We'll la-bor with a smile and a song, And we'll give to the winds our fears, For the day of tri-als can't be long, Soon the
CHORUS.
In the bet-ter land, In that sun-ny land, In that E-den land, safe by and by; In that bet-ter land, In that sun-ny land, In that E-den land, safe by and by.

No. 39. The Trumpet Call.
Eleanor W. Long.
COPYRIGHT, 1914, BY E. O EXCELL. WORDS AND MUSIC.
Chas. H. Gabriel.
1. Hark! the call To arms! To arms! Faith-ful sol-diers, brave and true!
2. In the bat-tle for the right, Pur-pose firm must rule and guide,
3. Blow the trump-et loud and long! Let it nev-er call re-treat!
Let there be no turn-ing back—'T is the time to dare and do.
For the foe is bold and strong, Press-ing in from ev-'ry side.
For-ward! tho' the march be long— On-ward, tho' with wear-y feet.
Chorus.
Then let the trumpet call ring clear, Let it give no un-cer-tain sound
ring clear,
wav-'ring sound
A-mid the grim war-rat-tle; Let ev-'ry sol-dier, great and small,
sol-dier, great and small,
When he shall hear the Lead-er's call, Pre-pare him-self for the bat-tle!
hear the call,

No. 40. The Way of the Cross Leads Home.

Jessie Brown Pounds.

Chas. H. Gabriel.

1. I must needs go home by the way of the cross, There's no oth - er
2. I must needs go on in the blood-sprinkled way, The path that the
3. Then I bid fare - well to the way of the world, To walk in it
way but this; I shall ne'er get sight of the Gates of Light,
Sav - ior trod, If I ev - er climb to the heights sub - lime,
nev - er more; For my Lord says "Come," and I seek my home,
If the way of the cross I miss.
Where the soul is at home with God.
Where He waits at the o - pen door.
CHORUS.
The way of the cross leads
home, The way of the cross leads home; It is
leads home,
leads home;
sweet to know, as I on - ward go, The way of the cross leads home.

No. 41.
Christ Shall Be King.
W. C. Poole.
COPYRIGHT, 1913, BY CHAS. H. GABRIEL.
E. O. EXCELL, OWNER.
Chas. H. Gabriel.
1. Christ shall be King of the whole wide world, He shall be King, let prais-es ring!
2. Christ shall be King o - ver land and sea, He shall be King, let prais-es ring!
3. Christ shall be King in my heart to - day, He shall be King, let prais-es ring!
Un-der His banner of love unfurled, There shall be gathered the whole wide world,
He who redeemed us and made us free, King of the world shall for-ev - er be,
O-ver each tho't and each purpose sway, All that I have shall be His al - way,
rit.
CHORUS.
And Christ shall be the King. O - ver all the world Christ shall be the King;
Yes, Christ shall be the King.
For Christ shall be the King.
O - ver all the world Christ shall be the King;
O - ver all the world let His praises ring; Ev'ry land and nation Shall
O - ver all the world let His prais-es ring;
know His great sal-va-tion; Christ shall be the King, He shall be the King.

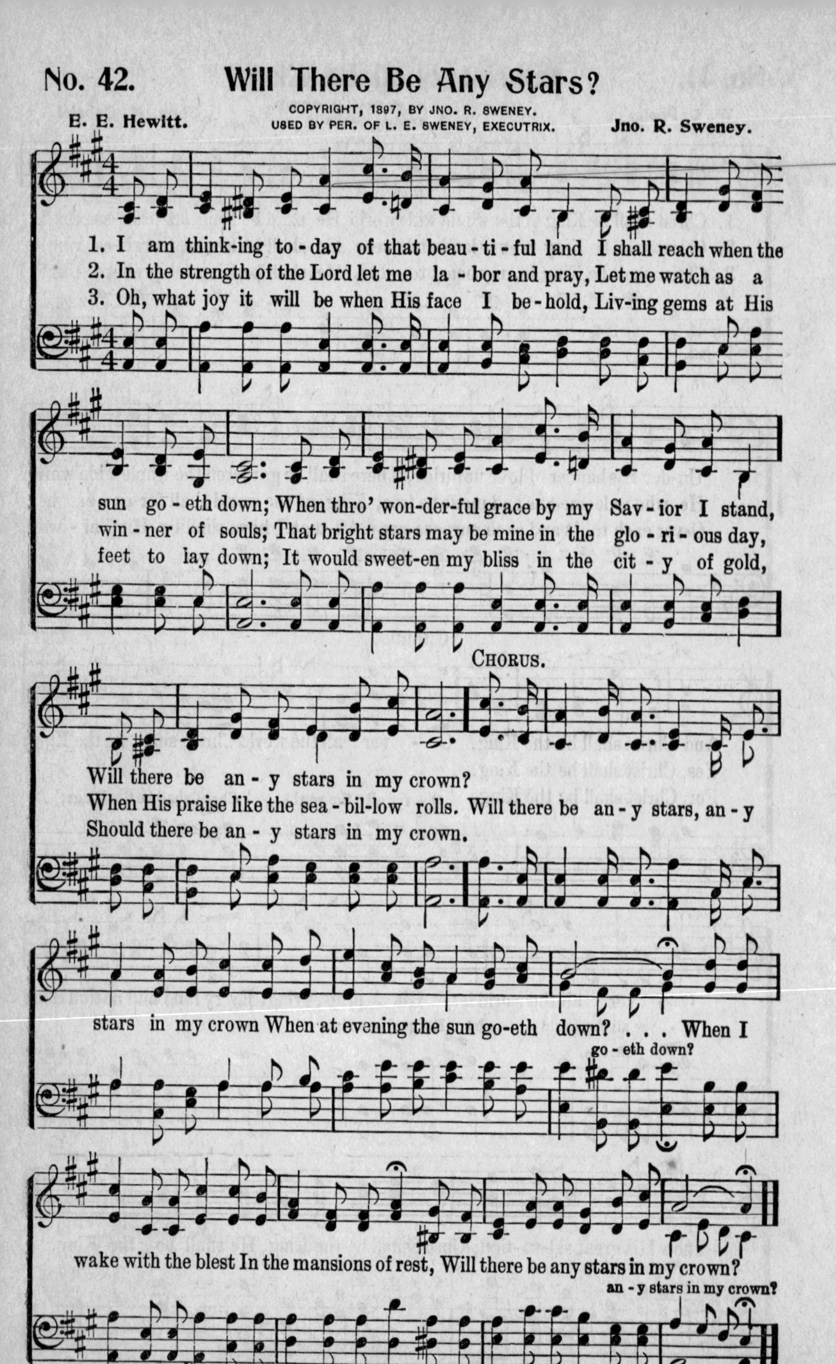
No. 42. Will There Be Any Stars?
E. E. Hewitt.
COPYRIGHT, 1897, BY JNO. R. SWENEY.
USED BY PER. OF L. E. SWENEY, EXECUTRIX.
Jno. R. Sweney.
1. I am think-ing to-day of that beau-ti-ful land I shall reach when the sun go-eth down; When thro' won-der-ful grace by my Sav-ior I stand,
2. In the strength of the Lord let me la-bor and pray, Let me watch as a win-ner of souls; That bright stars may be mine in the glo-ri-ous day,
3. Oh, what joy it will be when His face I be-hold, Liv-ing gems at His feet to lay down; It would sweet-en my bliss in the cit-y of gold,
Will there be an-y stars in my crown?
When His praise like the sea-bil-low rolls.
Should there be an-y stars in my crown.
CHORUS.
Will there be an-y stars, an-y stars in my crown When at evening the sun go-eth down? . . . When I wake with the blest In the mansions of rest, Will there be any stars in my crown?
go-eth down?
an-y stars in my crown?

No. 43. If It Were Not So.
Jessie Brown Pounds.
COPYRIGHT, 1913, BY E. O. EXCELL. WORDS AND MUSIC.
Samuel W. Beazley.
1. If it were not so, my Mas-ter would have told me; Like a mother's arms the
2. If it were not so,—if He pre-pares no dwell-ing,—He would ne'er to men the
3. If it were not so, would He dare hush our sigh-ing? If it were not so, would
prom-ise seems to hold me; With a love com-plete, it seems to wrap and fold me:
word of hope be tell-ing; He who has the Truth, in-carn-ate and ex-cel-ling,
He de-ceive the dy-ing? On His ho-ly word my spir-it is re-ly-ing—
"If it were not so I would have told you."
If it were not so He would have told me.
If it were not so He would have told me.
CHORUS.
If it were not so He would have
told me,
If it were not so He would have told me; Jesus ne'er would grieve me,
He would ne'er deceive me— If it were not so He would have told me.

No. 44. All Glory Be Thine.

Fanny J. Crosby.
COPYRIGHT, 1909, BY E. O. EXCELL. WORDS AND MUSIC.
Jno. R. Sweney.
1. Thou on - ly art ho - ly, Thou on - ly the Lord; Truth, mer-cy, and
2. Thou on - ly art ho - ly; In Thee is our trust; Thy laws are un -
3. Thou on - ly art ho - ly; The an-gels in light With prophets and
judg - ment Shine forth in Thy word. Thou rul - est and reign - est
chang-ing, Thy stat-utes are just. All na - tions and peo - ple
mar - tyrs Their an-thems u - nite. Thou on - ly art ho - ly,
All oth-ers a - bove; Thy throne is e - ter - nal, Thy scep-ter is love.
Be-fore Thee shall fall, The Fa-ther, Re-deem-er, And Sav-ior of all.
O An-cient of days; The boundless cre - a - tion Is filled with Thy praise.
CHORUS.
Thy reign ev - er - last - ing, Thy king - dom di - vine,
Hence - forth and for - ev - er All glo - ry be Thine.

No. 45. Memories of Galilee.
Robert Morris, LL. D.
USED BY PERMISSION.
H. R. Palmer.
1. Each coo-ing dove . . . and sigh-ing bough . . . That makes the eve . . . so blest to me, . . . Has something far . . . di-vin-er now, . . . It bears me back . . . to Gal-i-lee . . .
2. Each flow-'ry glen . . . and moss-y dell, . . . Where hap-py birds . . in song a-gree . . . Thro' sunny morn . . . the praises tell . . . Of sights and sounds . . . in Gal-i-lee . . .
3. And when I read . . . the thrill-ing lore, . . . Of Him who walked . . up-on the sea, . . . I long, oh, how . . . I long once more . . . To fol-low Him . . . in Gal-i-lee . . .
CHORUS.
O Gal-i-lee! sweet Gal-i-lee! Where Je-sus loved so much to be; O Gal-i-lee! blue Gal-i-lee! Come, sing thy song a-gain to me!

No. 46. The King's Business.
Dr. E. T. Cassel.
COPYRIGHT, 1902, BY E. O. EXCELL. WORDS AND MUSIC.
Flora H. Cassel.
1. I am a stran-ger here, with-in a for-eign land; My home is
2. This is the King's command: that all men, ev-'ry-where, Re-pent and
3. My home is bright-er far than Shar-on's ro-sy plain, E-ter-nal
far a-way, up-on a gold-en strand; Am-bas-sa-dor to be of
turn a-way from sin's se-duc-tive snare; That all who will o-bey, with
life and joy thro'-out its vast do-main; My Sov'reign bids me tell how
realms be-yond the sea, I'm here on business for my King.
Him shall reign for aye, And that's my business for my King. This is the
mor-tals there may dwell, And that's my business for my King.
CHORUS.
mes-sage that I bring, A message angels fain would sing; "Oh, be ye
reconciled," Thus saith my Lord and King, "Oh, be ye rec-on-ciled to God."

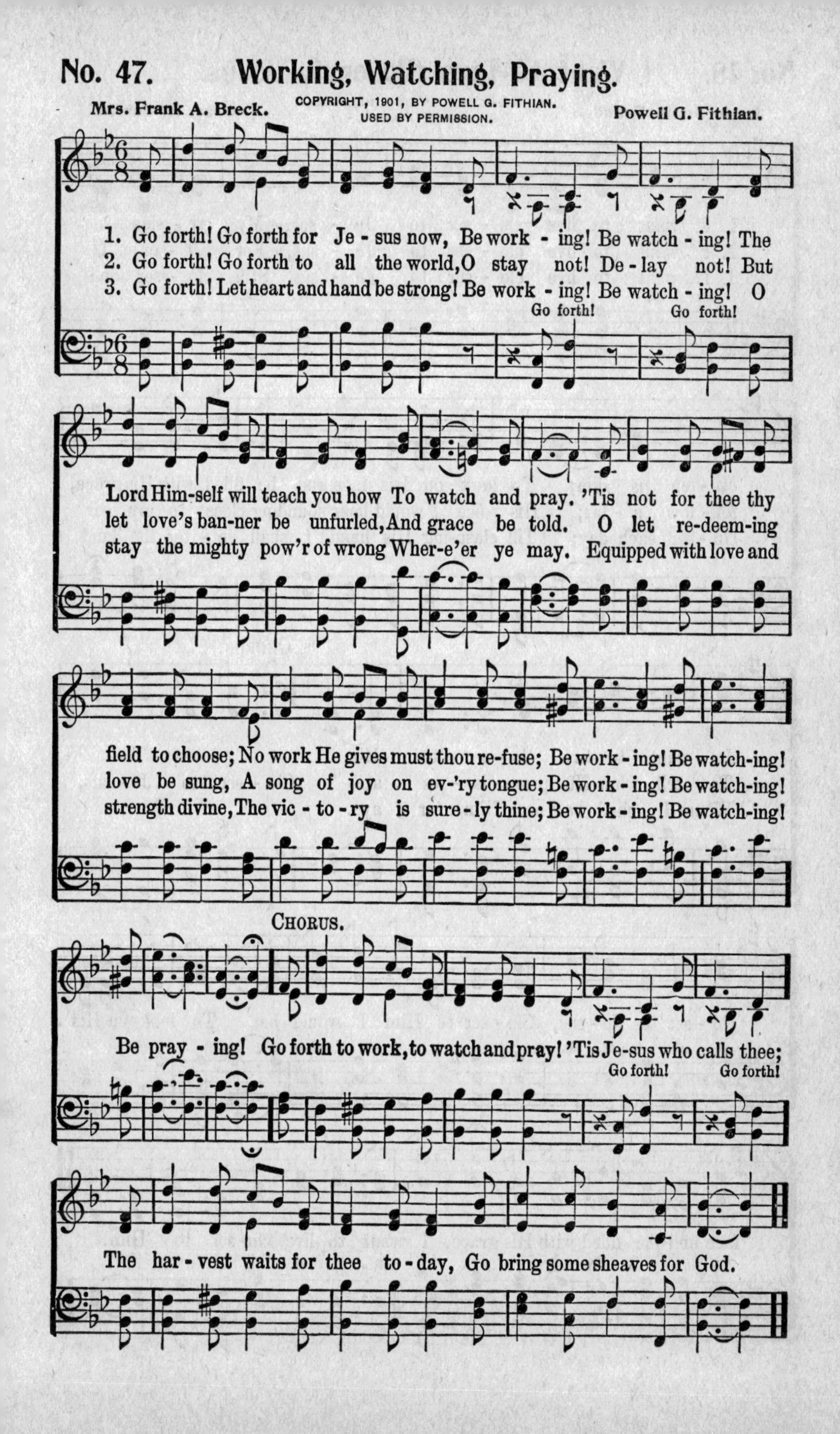
No. 47. Working, Watching, Praying.
Mrs. Frank A. Breck.
COPYRIGHT, 1901, BY POWELL G. FITHIAN.
USED BY PERMISSION.
Powell G. Fithian.
1. Go forth! Go forth for Je - sus now, Be work - ing! Be watch - ing! The
2. Go forth! Go forth to all the world, O stay not! De - lay not! But
3. Go forth! Let heart and hand be strong! Be work - ing! Be watch - ing! O
Go forth! Go forth!
Lord Him-self will teach you how To watch and pray. 'Tis not for thee thy
let love's ban-ner be unfurled, And grace be told. O let re-deem-ing
stay the mighty pow'r of wrong Wher-e'er ye may. Equipped with love and
field to choose; No work He gives must thou re-fuse; Be work - ing! Be watch-ing!
love be sung, A song of joy on ev-'ry tongue; Be work - ing! Be watch-ing!
strength divine, The vic - to - ry is sure - ly thine; Be work - ing! Be watch-ing!
CHORUS.
Be pray - ing! Go forth to work, to watch and pray! 'Tis Je-sus who calls thee;
Go forth! Go forth!
The har - vest waits for thee to - day, Go bring some sheaves for God.

No. 48. I Want to Live Closer to Jesus.

Jessie Brown Pounds.

Chas. H. Gabriel.

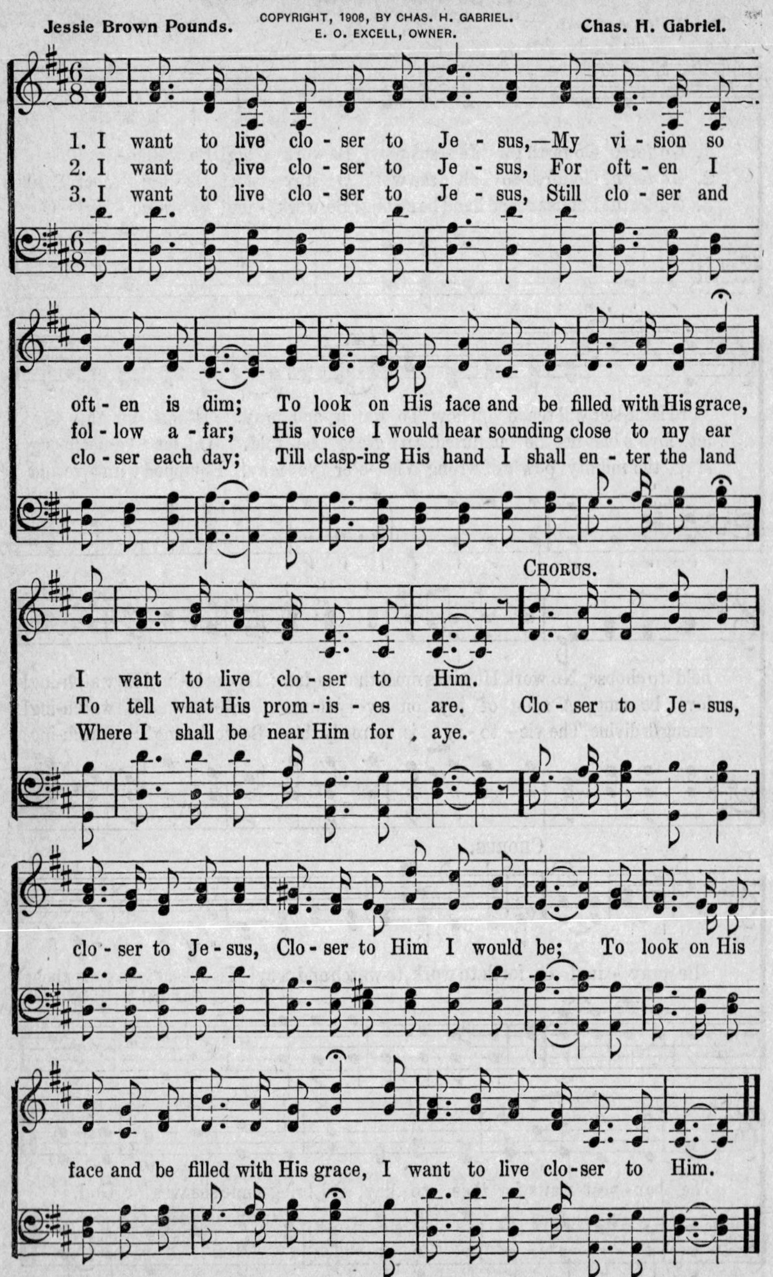
1. I want to live clo - ser to Je - sus,—My vi - sion so oft - en is dim; To look on His face and be filled with His grace, I want to live clo - ser to Him.
2. I want to live clo - ser to Je - sus, For oft - en I fol - low a - far; His voice I would hear sounding close to my ear To tell what His prom - is - es are.
3. I want to live clo - ser to Je - sus, Still clo - ser and clo - ser each day; Till clasp-ing His hand I shall en - ter the land Where I shall be near Him for , aye.
CHORUS.
Clo - ser to Je - sus, clo - ser to Je - sus, Clo - ser to Him I would be; To look on His face and be filled with His grace, I want to live clo - ser to Him.

No. 49. I Will Not Forget Thee.
C. H. G.
COPYRIGHT, 1889, BY E. O. EXCELL.
WORDS AND MUSIC.
Chas. H. Gabriel.
1. Sweet is the promise—"I will not forget thee," Nothing can mo-lest or
2. Trust-ing the promise—"I will not forget thee," Onward will I go with
3. When at the gold-en por-tals I am standing, All my trib-u-la-tions,
turn my soul a-way; E'en tho' the night be dark with-in the val-ley,
songs of joy and love; Tho' earth de-spise me, tho' my friends forsake me,
all my sorrows past, How sweet to hear the bless-ed proc-la-ma-tion,
Just be-yond is shining one e-ter-nal day.
I shall be remembered in my home above.
"Enter, faithful servant, welcome home at last!"
CHORUS.
I...... will not forget thee or
I will not forget thee, I will nev-er
leave thee; In my hands I'll hold thee, in my arms I'll fold thee; I........ will
leave thee;
I will not for-get
not for-get thee or leave thee; I am thy Re-deem-er, I will care for thee.
thee, for-get

No. 50.
In His Sunlight.
James Rowe.
COPYRIGHT, 1914, BY E. O. EXCELL. WORDS AND MUSIC.
B. D. Ackley.
1. In the light and glo - ry of His life and sto - ry There is ev - 'ry-thing that I can need; That is why I'm cling-ing and His prais - es sing-ing, As the lost to Him I lead.
2. O my bless - ed Sav - ior! He is mine for - ev - er, And will be my near - est, dear - est Friend; That is why I love Him, hav - ing naught above Him, And shall trust Him to the end.
3. Oh, the peace and pleas - ure, oh, the price - less treas - ure Of the love of Him who died for me! Thro' that day e - ter - nal, in the world su - per - nal, Love Di - vine my song shall be.
CHORUS.
In His sunlight, His precious sun - light, I am al - ways hap - py, yes, in - deed! In His sun - light, His pre - cious sun - light, There is ev - 'ry - thing I need.

No. 51. Hiding, Safely Hiding.

E. O. E. and A. B. — COPYRIGHT, 1896, BY E. O. EXCELL. WORDS AND MUSIC. — E. O. Excell.

1. 'Neath the shad-ow of th' Al-might-y, In the pres-ence of my King, I am
2. When the storms of life are rag-ing, Clo-ser to His side I cling; I am
3. All my life, my love, my service, All I have to Him I bring; I am
hid - - ing, hid - ing, Hid-ing in the shadow of His wing.
hid-ing, safely hid-ing, hid-ing, safely hid-ing, Hid-ing in the shad-ow of His wing.
In the se-cret place a-bid-ing, In con-tent-ment I can sing; I am
In His love I'm safe-ly sheltered, Peace and qui-et He doth bring; I am
He will hide me, safe-ly hide me Till in Heav'n this song I sing: I am
hid - ing, hid - ing, Hid-ing in the shadow of His wing; . .
hiding, safely hiding, hiding, safely hiding,
I'm hiding, hiding;
Hid - ing, hid - ing, Hid-ing in the shadow of His wing.
Hiding, safely hiding, hiding, safely hiding,

No. 52. I Would Not Live Without Him.

A. W. S.
COPYRIGHT, 1909, BY E. O. EXCELL. WORDS AND MUSIC.
Arthur Willis Spooner.
1. Je - sus is a Friend so kind, Tru - er Friend you can-not find; O, I
2. If you turn this Friend a-way, He will fol - low you each day; O, I
3. When your head is bowed with grief, Then this Friend will bring relief; O, I
would not live with-out Him if I could;—He will help you to the end,
would not live with-out Him if I could;—When you fall, this Friend is near,
would not live with-out Him if I could;—When you stand before the throne,
D. S.—He is lov-ing, ten-der, kind,
On His love you may de-pend; O, I would not live with-
Call on Him, you need not fear; O, I would not live with-
He will claim you for His own; O, I would not live with-
Tru - er Friend you can - not find; O, I would not live with-
FINE. CHORUS.
out Him if I could. O, I would not live with-out Him if I
out Him if I could.
D. S.
could, if I could, O, I would not live with-out Him if I could;—

No. 53. Savior, Go With Me.

Rev. Johnson Oatman, Jr. — Chas. H. Gabriel.

1. As Thou once the host pre-ced-ed, Sav-ior, go with me! Guid-ing, when a guide they needed, Sav-ior, go with me! As with pillar Thou didst head them, Thro' the rag-ing bil-lows led them, Dai-ly on Thy man-na fed them, Sav-ior, go with me.
2. In this world I'm but a stran-ger, Sav-ior, go with me! Thro' its dark-ness and its dan-ger, Sav-ior, go with me! Guide me, O my Sav-ior, guide me! And when e-vil doth be-tide me, In Thine own pa-vil-ion hide me,
3. Thou who art of life the giv-er, Sav-ior, go with me! When I'm called to cross death's river, Sav-ior, go with me! When these earthly ties are riv-en, Thou best friend to mor-tals giv-en, Thro' the shin-ing gates of Heav-en,
CHORUS.
Sav-ior, go with me, All the way with me! With Thy presence lead me, For so much I need Thee, Savior, go with me.

No. 54. In the Shadow of His Wings.
Rev. J. B. Atchinson.
COPYRIGHT, 1910, BY E. O. EXCELL RENEWAL.
E. O. Excell.
1. In the shad-ow of His wings There is rest, sweet rest; There is
2. In the shad-ow of His wings There is peace, sweet peace, Peace that
3. In the shad-ow of His wings There is joy, glad joy; There is
rest from care and la - bor, There is rest for friend and neighbor; In the
pass - eth un - der-stand-ing, Peace, sweet peace that knows no ending; In the
joy to tell the sto - ry, Joy ex - ceed-ing, full of glo - ry; In the
shad-ow of His wings There is rest, sweet rest, In the shadow of His wings
shad-ow of His wings There is peace, sweet peace, In the shadow of His wings
shad-ow of His wings There is joy, glad joy, In the shadow of His wings
CHORUS.
There is rest (sweet rest). There is rest, There is peace, There is
There is peace (sweet peace).
There is joy (glad joy).
sweet rest,
sweet peace,
joy, In the shad-ow of His wings; shad-ow of His wings.
glad joy,

No. 55.
Come To-day.
R. L. B.
WORDS AND MUSIC COPYRIGHT, 1905, BY E. O. EXCELL.
INTERNATIONAL COPYRIGHT SECURED.
R. L. Blowers.
1. Do you hear the Savior's voice so sweet-ly call-ing, Come to-day, come to-day? He will wipe the tear-drops now so swift-ly fall-ing, All a-way, all a-way; Come to Him now with all your sor-row, No lon-ger turn from Him a-way:
2. If you trust Him He will take a-way your sor-row, Day by day, day by day; And in safe-ty lead you to that bright to-mor-row, All the way, all the way; His arms are o-pen to re-ceive you; From sin and darkness turn a-way:
3. He a-lone can give you par-don and sal-va-tion, Full and free, full and free; "Who-so-ev-er," is the bless-ed in-vi-ta-tion, 'Come to Me, come to Me;" Then wait no lon-ger, night is fall-ing, Too late, too late, He soon may say:
CHORUS.
Lis-ten to His lov-ing voice so sweet-ly call-ing, "Come to-day, come to-day."

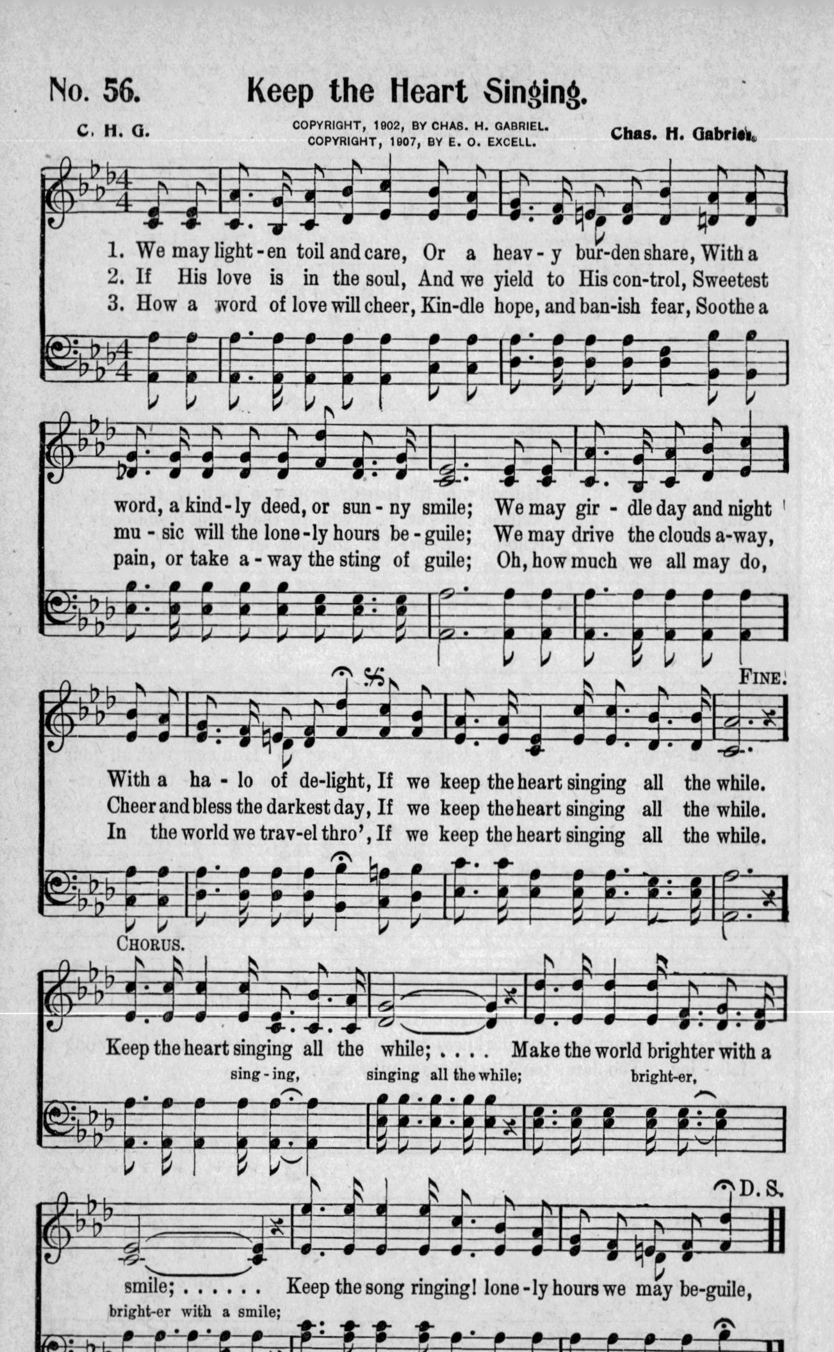
No. 56. Keep the Heart Singing.
C. H. G.
COPYRIGHT, 1902, BY CHAS. H. GABRIEL.
COPYRIGHT, 1907, BY E. O. EXCELL.
Chas. H. Gabriel.
1. We may light-en toil and care, Or a heav-y bur-den share, With a word, a kind-ly deed, or sun-ny smile; We may gir-dle day and night With a halo of de-light, If we keep the heart singing all the while.
2. If His love is in the soul, And we yield to His con-trol, Sweetest mu-sic will the lone-ly hours be-guile; We may drive the clouds a-way, Cheer and bless the darkest day, If we keep the heart singing all the while.
3. How a word of love will cheer, Kin-dle hope, and ban-ish fear, Soothe a pain, or take a-way the sting of guile; Oh, how much we all may do, In the world we trav-el thro', If we keep the heart singing all the while.
FINE.
CHORUS.
Keep the heart singing all the while; . . . . Make the world brighter with a smile; . . . . . . Keep the song ringing! lone-ly hours we may be-guile,
sing-ing, singing all the while; bright-er, bright-er with a smile;
D. S.

No. 57. Held by My Savior's Mighty Hand.
COPYRIGHT, 1913, BY E. O. EXCELL. WORDS AND MUSIC.
E. E. Hewitt.
B. D. Ackley.
1. On-ward will I jour-ney, thro life's rain or shine, Held by my Sav-ior's might-y hand;...... Guid-ed by His Spir-it, kept by pow'r di-vine, Held by my Sav-ior's might-y hand...........
2. In the paths ap-point-ed, led by change-less love, Held by my Sav-ior's might-y hand;...... Serv-ing Him with gladness, strengthened from a-bove, Held by my Sav-ior's might-y hand...........
3. In the Sav-ior's car-ing, I will fear no ill, Held by my Sav-ior's might-y hand;...... In the si-lent val-ley, He'll be with me still, Held by my Sav-ior's might-y hand...........
His mighty hand;
His might-y hand.
CHORUS. UNISON.
Onward, forward, at the King's command, Trusting when I cannot understand,
HARMONY.
rit.
Till I see His beauty in the Bet-ter Land, Held by my Savior's mighty hand.

No. 58.
Saints in Glory.
C. Bissett.
COPYRIGHT, 1889, BY E. O. EXCELL.
WORDS AND MUSIC.
Chas. H. Gabriel.
1. Thy saints all stand in glo - ry Before Thy throne, O God, And sing un - to their Sav - ior, Who bo't them with His blood; And there in Heaven's glo - ry, From sin and sor-row free, They reign with God their Father, To all e - ter-ni-ty.
2. All clothed in robes of whiteness, They worship and a-dore, And fall be - fore their Sav - ior, And praise Him ev - er - more; There, lifting up their voi - ces, With one accord they raise Un-to the Lamb that liv - eth An ev-er-last-ing praise.
3. Je - sus, my Lord and Sav - ior, Who bled and died for me, Who bore my sins and sor - rows On the ac - curs-ed tree; I, too, shall stand in glo - ry, And sing of Thy great love; And at Thy feet a - dore Thee With all Thy saints above.
CHORUS.
There is joy . . . a-mong the ransomed o - ver there, There is joy . . . o - ver there; . . There is joy for - ev - er o - ver there.
There is joy,
There is joy
o - ver there;

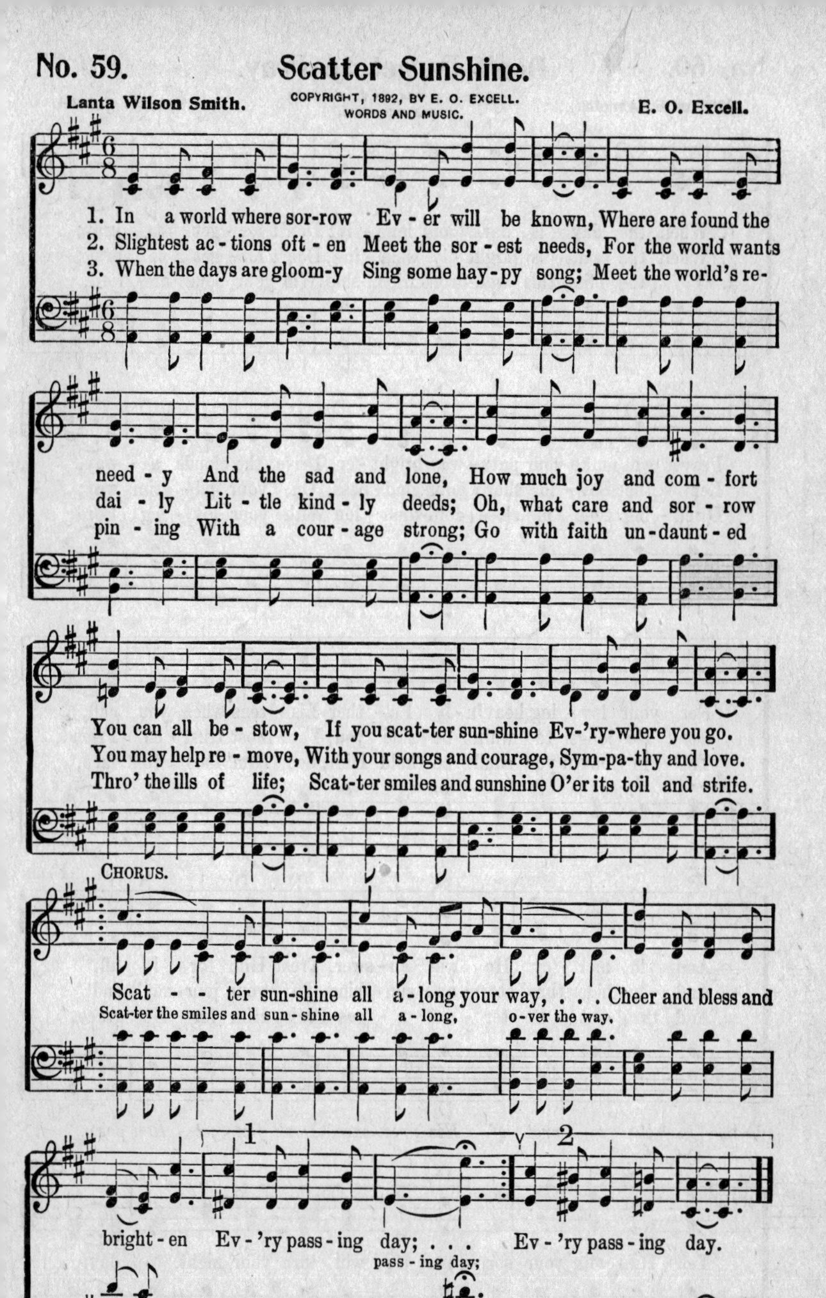
No. 59. Scatter Sunshine.
Lanta Wilson Smith.
COPYRIGHT, 1892, BY E. O. EXCELL. WORDS AND MUSIC.
E. O. Excell.
1. In a world where sor-row Ev - er will be known, Where are found the need - y And the sad and lone, How much joy and com - fort You can all be - stow, If you scat-ter sun-shine Ev-'ry-where you go.
2. Slightest ac - tions oft - en Meet the sor - est needs, For the world wants dai - ly Lit - tle kind - ly deeds; Oh, what care and sor - row You may help re - move, With your songs and courage, Sym-pa-thy and love.
3. When the days are gloom-y Sing some hay - py song; Meet the world's re- pin - ing With a cour - age strong; Go with faith un-daunt - ed Thro' the ills of life; Scat-ter smiles and sunshine O'er its toil and strife.
CHORUS.
Scat - - ter sun-shine all a - long your way, . . . Cheer and bless and bright - en Ev - 'ry pass - ing day; . . . Ev - 'ry pass - ing day.
Scat-ter the smiles and sun - shine all a - long, o - ver the way.
pass - ing day;

No. 60. Don't Forget to Pray.
Miriam E. Arnold.
COPYRIGHT, 1914, BY E. O. EXCELL. WORDS AND MUSIC.
Chas. H. Gabriel.
1. When the day is dark and lone-ly, Don't for-get to pray;
2. When the sun is bright-ly shin-ing, Don't for-get to pray;
3. O the bliss this won-drous friend-ship Will your soul af-ford,
Prayer will make your path-way bright-er, Drive the clouds a-way.
Let the Sav-ior share your glad-ness, On your pil-grim way;
Dwell-ing thus in close com-mun-ion With your lov-ing Lord;
For your lov-ing heav'n-ly Fa-ther Lis-tens when you call,
For He longs to walk be-side you, Your most trust-ed Friend,
Till in Heav'n you shall be-hold Him, See Him face to face,
FINE.
And in mer-cy He will an-swer, Trust Him for it all.
And a-bide thro' storm and sun-shine To your jour-ney's end.
And thro'-out e-ter-nal a-ges Praise Him for His grace.
D.S.—"In the se-cret of His pres-ence," Don't for-get to pray.
CHORUS.
D. S.
Tell Him all your sor-rows, He will turn your night to day,

No. 61. Tell Me the Old, Old Story.
Birdie Bell.
COPYRIGHT, 1894, BY E. O. EXCELL.
WORDS AND MUSIC.
E. O. Excell.
1. Tell me the old, old sto - ry, Tell it, for 'tis al - ways new;
2. Tell me the old, old sto - ry, Tell it, for it is so sweet;
3. Tell me the old, old sto - ry, Tell it so I'll ne'er for - get;
Tell me of a Sav-ior's par - don, Tell it, for I know 'tis true;
Tell me why He came from Heav - en, Tell it, ev - 'ry word re - peat;
Tell me, tho' I oft of - fend Him, Tell it, that He loves me yet;
Tell me how He died for sin - ners, Tell it to me o'er and o'er,
Tell me, 'tis my on - ly com - fort, Tell it, for I love it so,
Tell me when in deep - est sor - row, Tell it, He will be my stay,
FINE.
For I am long-ing to hear it, Long-ing for it more and more.
And I will tell it to oth - ers, Tell it ev - 'ry-where I go.
And by and by, when in glo - ry, I shall reign with Him for aye.
D. S.—For I am long-ing to hear it, Long-ing for it more and more.
CHORUS.
D. S.
Tell me the old, old sto - ry, Tell it to me o'er and o'er;

No. 62. Open the Door for the Children.

Mary E. Kidder. COPYRIGHT, 1885, BY E. O. EXCELL. E. O. Excell.

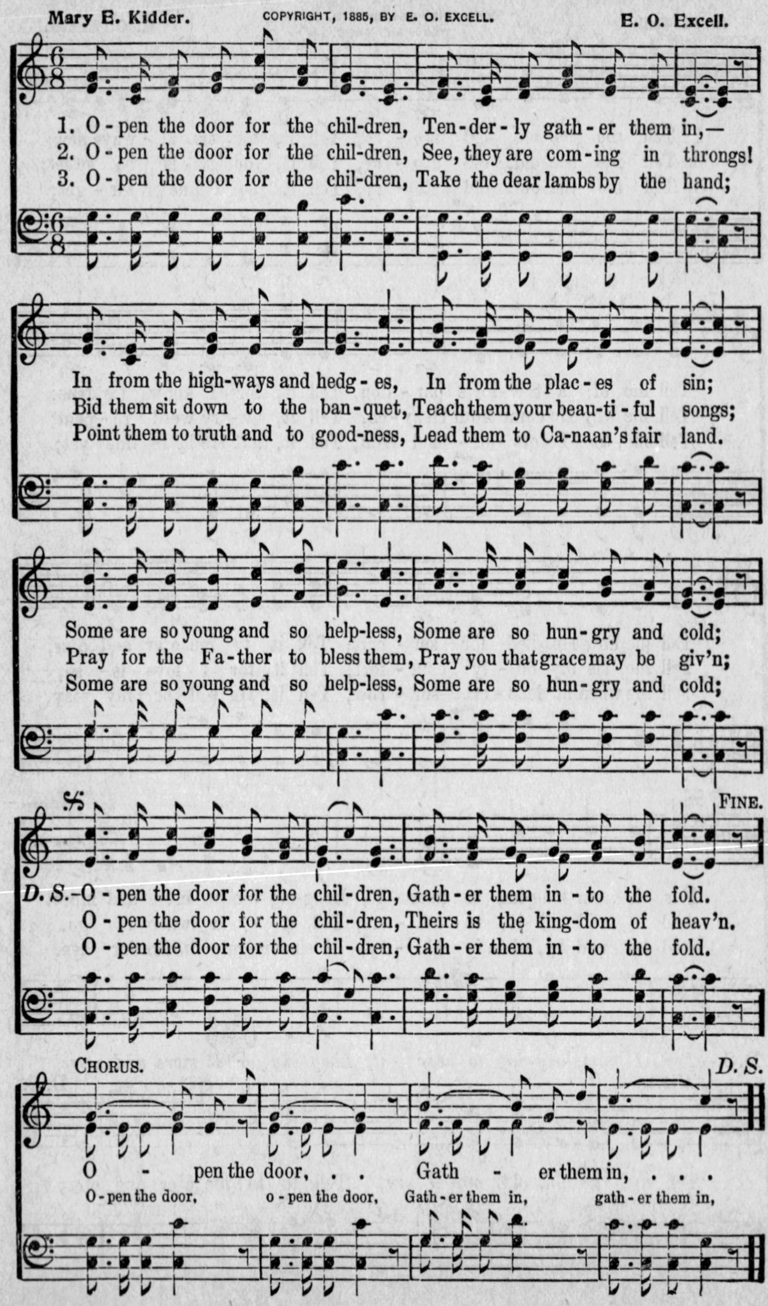
1. O-pen the door for the chil-dren, Ten-der-ly gath-er them in,—
2. O-pen the door for the chil-dren, See, they are com-ing in throngs!
3. O-pen the door for the chil-dren, Take the dear lambs by the hand;
In from the high-ways and hedg-es, In from the plac-es of sin;
Bid them sit down to the ban-quet, Teach them your beau-ti-ful songs;
Point them to truth and to good-ness, Lead them to Ca-naan's fair land.
Some are so young and so help-less, Some are so hun-gry and cold;
Pray for the Fa-ther to bless them, Pray you that grace may be giv'n;
Some are so young and so help-less, Some are so hun-gry and cold;
FINE.
D. S.-O-pen the door for the chil-dren, Gath-er them in-to the fold.
O-pen the door for the chil-dren, Theirs is the king-dom of heav'n.
O-pen the door for the chil-dren, Gath-er them in-to the fold.
CHORUS.
D. S.
O - pen the door, . . Gath - er them in, . . .
O-pen the door, o-pen the door, Gath-er them in, gath-er them in,

No. 63. The Field is the World.
C. H. G.
COPYRIGHT, 1907, BY CHAS. H. GABRIEL.
E. O. EXCELL, OWNER.
Chas. H. Gabriel.
1. The reap-ers are loud - ly sing - ing, As out in the har - vest - field
2. "The field is the world," O reap - er, There's plenty for all to do;
3. The Mas-ter hath us com-mand - ed To la - bor and watch and pray;
They gath-er the grain from val-ley and plain, With willing and tire-less hand;
A - rise and be - gin the work that shall win For you an im-mor - tal crown;
To dil - i - gent be, and faith-ful, if we Would share in the vict'ries won;
The winds from a - far come bring - ing Glad news of a - bun-dant yield,
The Lord is thy Guide and Keep - er, He'll car - ry you safe - ly thro';
Then why will you emp - ty - hand - ed Ap - pear, at the close of day,
FINE.
Of work to be done, of souls to be won For God at His own com-mand.
He calls you to-day, then trust and o-bey, And reap till the sun goes down.
Ac-count-ing to give, and hope to re-ceive A blessing for noth - ing done?
D.S.—And gather the grain from hill and from plain For garners beyond the sky.
CHORUS.
D. S.
Join . . in the song . . that is waft - ed a - long, . .
Join in the song, Join in the song that is waft-ed a - long, waft - ed a - long,

No. 64. Hold My Hand Fast, O Savior.

Florence Jones Hadley.
COPYRIGHT, 1913, BY E. O. EXCELL.
WORDS AND MUSIC.
Roger Cox.
SOLO OR DUET.
1. The night shadows gather a - round me, And I am weary, sad and lone,
2. 'T is the hand that was pierced on Cal-va-ry, So ten-der and strong and true;
3. Then straightway the shadows are lift - ed, The fear and the doubts de-part;
But a hand reaches out of the darkness And lov-ing-ly folds o'er my own. . .
o'er my own.
A hand that will lift me when I fall, And safe - ly lead me thro'. . .
lead me thro'.
I know that a Friend is close beside me Whose presence gives strength to my heart.
to my heart.
CHORUS.
Then hold my hand fast, O Sav - ior, Lest I fal - ter and lose the way;
O, hold my hand fast till the dark-ness Gives place to e - ter - nal day;
O, hold my hand fast till the dark-ness Gives place to e - ter - nal day.

No. 65. Follow Your Leader.

Lizzie DeArmond. COPYRIGHT, 1913, BY E. O EXCELL WORDS AND MUSIC Rev. C. B. Widmeyer.

1. Fol-low your Leader! His cross marks the way; Gird on your ar-mor, haste forth to the fray; Je-sus has called you His sol-diers to be; From earth-ly fet-ters your souls shall be free.
2. Fol-low your Leader wher-ev-er He goes; Bold-ly press for-ward in spite of your foes; Aft-er the con-flict with Sa-tan and sin, Crowns of re-joic-ing you sure-ly shall win.
3. Fol-low your Leader, the march has be-gun, Stead-fast of pur-pose till vic-t'ry is won; All will be well if by Him you are led; Bright with His glo-ry the cross gleams a-head.
CHORUS.
Fol-low your Leader! 't is Je-sus, the King; Fol-low your Leader, and joy-ful-ly sing; Grace will be giv-en to con-quer each foe; Fol-low your Leader wher-ev-er you go.

No. 66. He is So Precious to Me.
C. H. G.
COPYRIGHT, 1902, BY CHAS. H. GABRIEL.
COPYRIGHT, 1907, BY E. O. EXCELL.
Chas. H. Gabriel.
1. So pre-cious is Je - sus, my Sav-ior, my King, His praise all the day long
2. He stood at my heart's door 'mid sunshine and rain, And pa-tient-ly wait - ed
3. I stand on the moun-tain of bless - ing at last, No cloud in the heav-ens
4. I praise Him be-cause He ap-point-ed a place Where, some day, thro' faith in
with rap - ture I sing; To Him in my weak-ness for strength I can cling,
an en-trance to gain; What shame that so long He en - treat - ed in vain,
a shad - ow to cast; His smile is up - on me, the val - ley is past,
His won - der - ful grace, I know I shall see Him—shall look on His face,
CHORUS. Faster.
For He is so pre-cious to me. For He is so pre-cious to
so
pre-cious to me,
so pre-cious to me;
me, . . . For He is so pre-cious to me; . . . 'T is heaven be-
rit. - - - -
low My Re-deem - er to know, For He is so pre-cious to me.

No. 67. Jesus On the Cross.
COPYRIGHT, 1914, BY E. O. EXCELL.
WORDS AND MUSIC.
Ina Duley Ogdon.
B. D. Ackley.
1. A vi - sion goes be - fore me, day by day, Je - sus, bless - ed
2. And when I see Him there in ag - o - ny, Je - sus, bless - ed
3. For me He came from glo - ry to the grave, Je - sus, bless - ed
4. Hence-forth that I my grat - i - tude may prove, Je - sus, bless - ed
Je-sus on the cross! It keeps me in the straight and nar - row way,
Je-sus on the cross! I mar - vel at His sac - ri - fice for me,
Je-sus on the cross! To save my soul His life for me He gave,
Je-sus on the cross! I con - se-crate to Him my heart of love,
Je-sus, bless-ed Je-sus on the cross!
REFRAIN.
I see my lov-ing Sav-ior thro' my tears; (thro' my tears;) His mem-o-ry I cher-ish all the years; (all the years;) My heart no lon-ger fears, since His sac-ri-fice ap-pears, Je-sus, blessed Je-sus on the cross!

No. 68. Land of the Unsetting Sun.

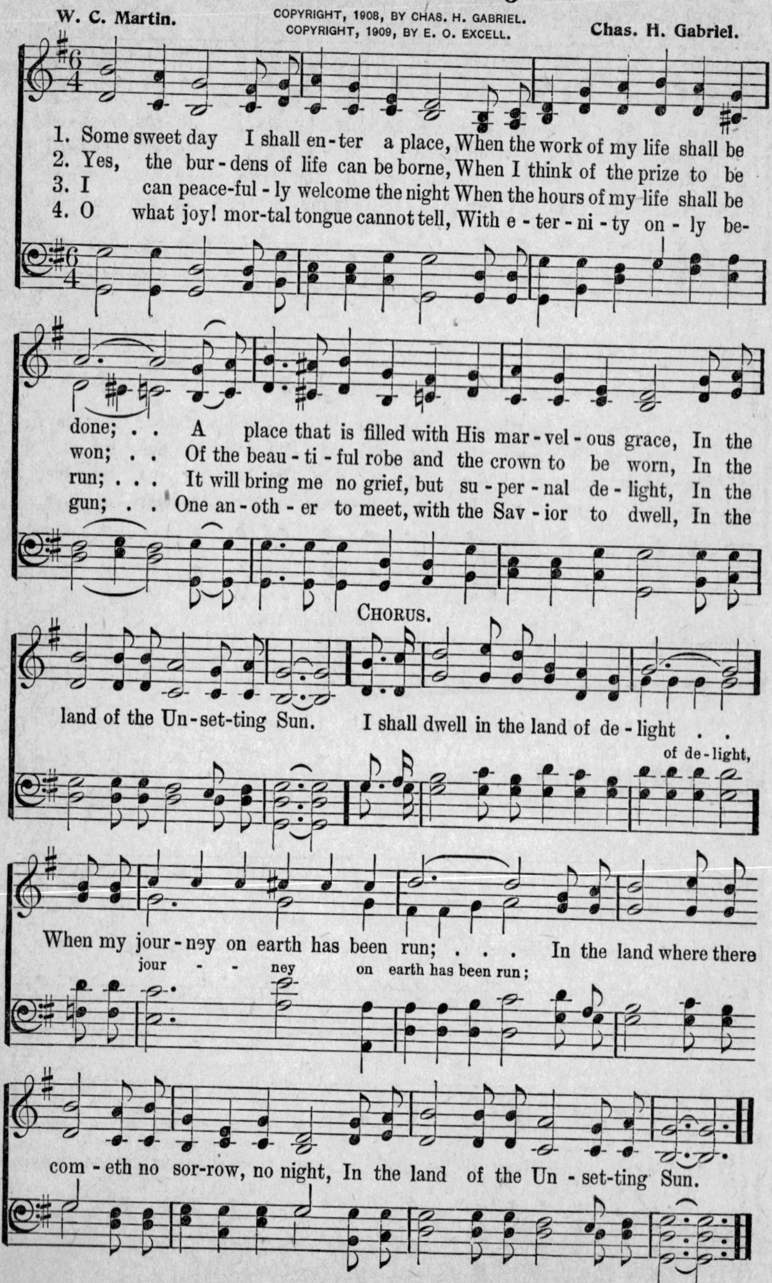
W. C. Martin.
COPYRIGHT, 1908, BY CHAS. H. GABRIEL.
COPYRIGHT, 1909, BY E. O. EXCELL.
Chas. H. Gabriel.
1. Some sweet day I shall en-ter a place, When the work of my life shall be
2. Yes, the bur-dens of life can be borne, When I think of the prize to be
3. I can peace-ful-ly welcome the night When the hours of my life shall be
4. O what joy! mor-tal tongue cannot tell, With e-ter-ni-ty on-ly be-
done; . . A place that is filled with His mar-vel-ous grace, In the
won; . . Of the beau-ti-ful robe and the crown to be worn, In the
run; . . . It will bring me no grief, but su-per-nal de-light, In the
gun; . . One an-oth-er to meet, with the Sav-ior to dwell, In the
CHORUS.
land of the Un-set-ting Sun. I shall dwell in the land of de-light . .
of de-light,
When my jour-ney on earth has been run; . . . In the land where there
jour - - ney on earth has been run;
com-eth no sor-row, no night, In the land of the Un-set-ting Sun.

No. 69.
Alone With God.
G. H. C.
COPYRIGHT, 1913, BY E. O. EXCELL.
WORDS AND MUSIC.
George H. Carr.
1. I love to be a-lone with God, And to lis-ten to His lov-ing voice;
2. I tell Him of my doubts and fears, And He stills the tempest in my breast,
3. I tell Him of my weak-ness-es, Of my sins, my hopes, my fond de-sires;
4. Then let me nev-er seek to know Sweeter friendship than with Him I find,
As He bids my ev'-ry care depart, How His presence makes my heart rejoice!
Bids the raging storms of passion cease, Calms my anxious tho't with quiet rest.
And He cheers my heart to onward press To gain the goal my soul as-pires.
As I choose the qui-et hours with Him, Leav-ing all the bus-y world be-hind.
CHORUS.
A-lone with God, No oth-er friend so dear, A-lone with
A-lone with God, A-
God, What joy when He is near! My heart with rap-ture thrills,
lone with God,
My cup of bless-ing fills, When all a-lone with God.
When all a-lone with God.

No. 70. Nobody Told Me of Jesus.

Mrs. Frank A. Breck. COPYRIGHT, 1908, BY CHAS. H. GABRIEL. COPYRIGHT, 1909, BY E. O. EXCELL. Chas. H. Gabriel.

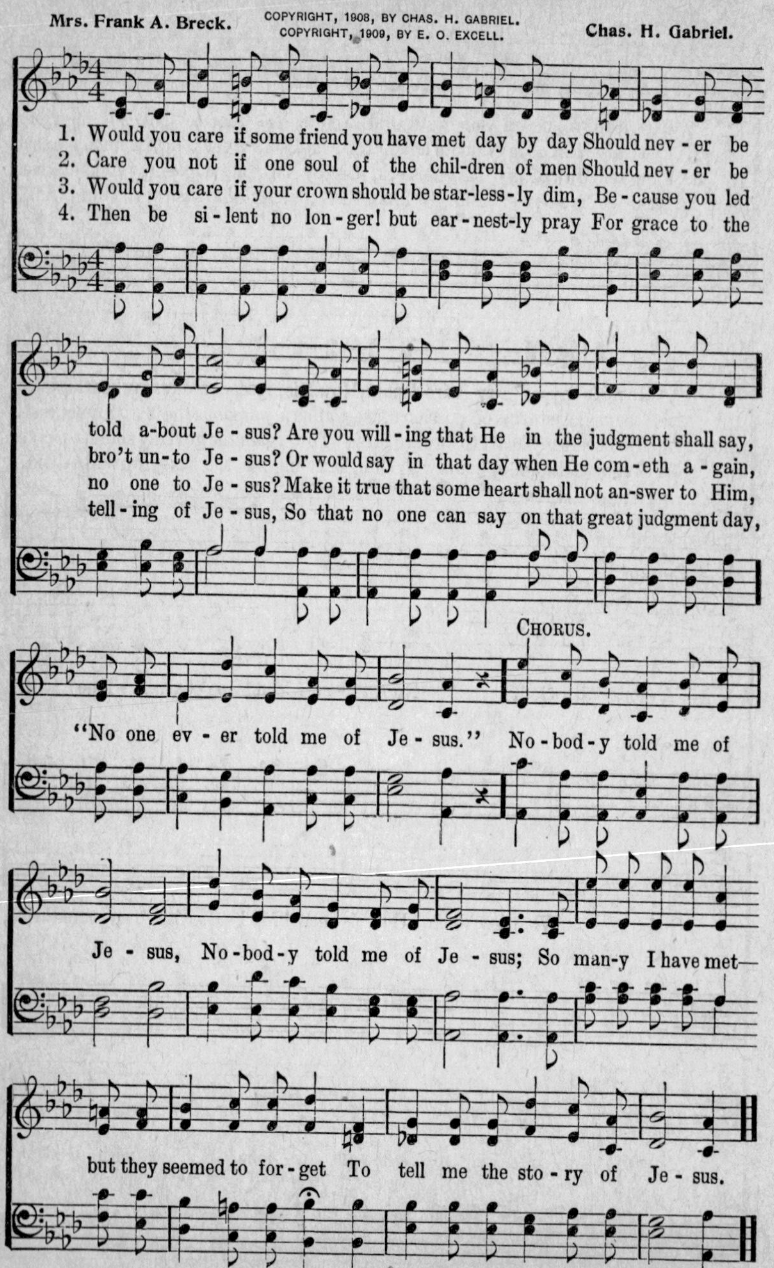

1. Would you care if some friend you have met day by day Should nev - er be told a-bout Je - sus? Are you will - ing that He in the judgment shall say,
2. Care you not if one soul of the chil-dren of men Should nev - er be bro't un-to Je - sus? Or would say in that day when He com - eth a - gain,
3. Would you care if your crown should be star-less-ly dim, Be - cause you led no one to Je - sus? Make it true that some heart shall not an-swer to Him,
4. Then be si - lent no lon - ger! but ear - nest-ly pray For grace to the tell - ing of Je - sus, So that no one can say on that great judgment day,
"No one ev - er told me of Je - sus."
CHORUS.
No - bod - y told me of Je - sus, No - bod - y told me of Je - sus; So man - y I have met— but they seemed to for - get To tell me the sto - ry of Je - sus.

No. 71. I Am Satisfied With Jesus.
S. W. B.
COPYRIGHT, 1913, BY E. O. EXCELL
WORDS AND MUSIC.
Samuel W. Beazley.
1. The love of Je - sus, oh, how sweet, His name is mu - sic to re-peat,
2. The way may dark and drear - y be, His hand I know is lead - ing me,
3. The world may tempt my feet to stray, But I can nev - er lose my way,
4. The storms of life I will not fear, For He hath said "Be of good cheer;"
His presence makes my joy complete; I am sat - is - fied with Je - sus.
No oth - er friend so good as He; I am sat - is - fied with Je - sus.
For He is with me night and day; I am sat - is - fied with Je - sus.
And since I find Him al - ways near, I am sat - is - fied with Je - sus.
Chorus.
I am sat - is - fied, I am sat - is - fied, I am
sat - is - fied with Je - sus: On the cross of Cal - va - ry, By His
death He ransomed me, I am sat - is - fied with Je - sus.

No. 72. Because I Love Jesus.

James Rowe. COPYRIGHT, 1902, BY CHAS. H. GABRIEL. E. O. EXCELL, OWNER. Chas. H. Gabriel.

1. My path may be lone - ly, and dark be the night, The clouds may be
2. Be - cause I love Je - sus, my Sav - ior and thine, There's peace in my
3. Tho' loved ones be ta - ken a - way from my side, Tho' rich - es and
4. Tho' all that is e - vil a - gainst me com-bine, Tho' Sa - tan a-
hid - ing the sun from my sight, Yet I have as-sur-ance that all will be right,
soul, there is comfort di-vine; 'T will al-ways abide, for the promise is mine,
hon - or to me be de - nied, Yet if I but trust Him no ill can be-tide,
round me his snares should entwine, Yet if I am faith-ful a crown will be mine,
REFRAIN.
Be - cause...... I love Je - sus. Be - cause I love Je - sus,
Be - cause
Je - sus, Be - cause...... I love Je - sus; My soul is at
Be - cause
rest, and in Him I am blest, Be - cause...... I love Je - sus.
Be - cause

No. 73. We Shall See the King Some Day.

L. E. J.
COPYRIGHT, 1906, BY CHAS. H. GABRIEL.
W. E. M. HACKLEMAN, OWNER.
L. E. Jones.
1. Tho' the way we jour-ney may be oft - en drear, We shall see the
2. Aft - er pain and an-guish, aft - er toil and care, We shall see the
3. Aft - er foes are conquered, aft - er bat - les won, We shall see the
4. There with all the loved ones who have gone be-fore, We shall see the
King some day (some day); On that bless-ed morning clouds will dis - ap-pear;
King some day (some day); Thro' the end-less a - ges joy and blessing share,
King some day (some day); Aft - er strife is o - ver, aft - er set of sun,
King some day (some day); Sor-row past for-ev - er, on that peaceful shore,
We shall see the King some day.
CHORUS.
We shall see the King some day (some day),
We will shout and sing some day (some day); Gathered round the throne,
When He shall call His own, We shall see the King some day.

No. 74. Someone is Looking to You.

W. M. Lighthall.

Chas. H. Gabriel.

1. Let your light shine where-so-e'er you go, Some-one is look-ing to you! Bright-er each day let it gleam and glow, Some-one is look-ing to you!
2. Some-one is grop-ing his way to God, Some-one is look-ing to you! Fol-low-ing on where your feet have trod, Some-one is look-ing to you!
3. Some-one your coun-sel will sure-ly take, Some-one is look-ing to you! And by your life his de-ci-sion make, Some-one is look-ing to you!
4. Some-one has al-most ac-cept-ed Him, Some-one is look-ing to you! And may be lost if your light grows dim, Some-one is look-ing to you!
CHORUS.
Look-ing to you, yes, look-ing to you!
Let your light shine the dark-ness through;
O be faith-ful, be loy-al, and true,
For some-one is look-ing to you!

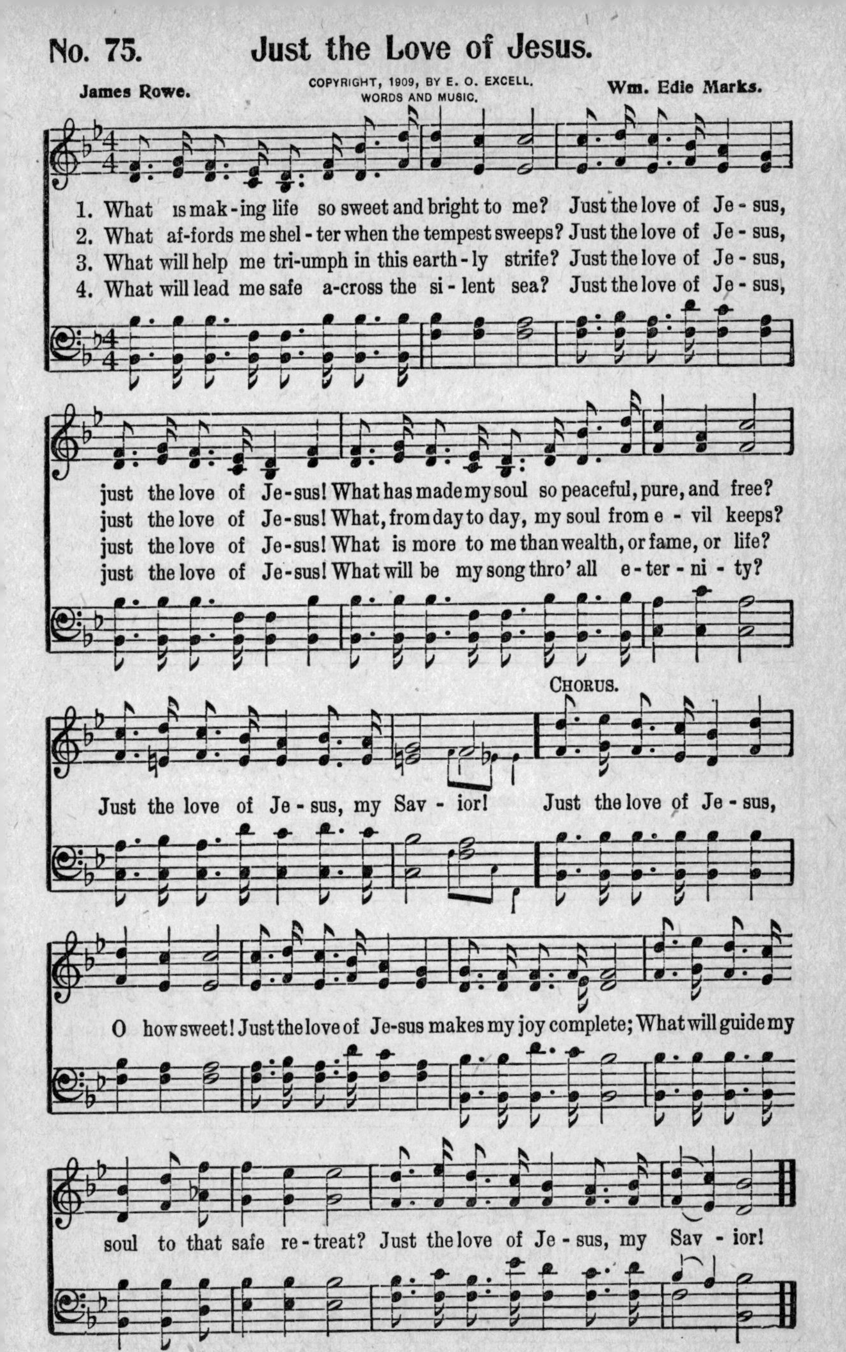
No. 75. Just the Love of Jesus.
James Rowe.
COPYRIGHT, 1909, BY E. O. EXCELL.
WORDS AND MUSIC.
Wm. Edie Marks.
1. What is mak-ing life so sweet and bright to me? Just the love of Je-sus,
2. What af-fords me shel-ter when the tempest sweeps? Just the love of Je-sus,
3. What will help me tri-umph in this earth-ly strife? Just the love of Je-sus,
4. What will lead me safe a-cross the si-lent sea? Just the love of Je-sus,
just the love of Je-sus! What has made my soul so peaceful, pure, and free?
just the love of Je-sus! What, from day to day, my soul from e-vil keeps?
just the love of Je-sus! What is more to me than wealth, or fame, or life?
just the love of Je-sus! What will be my song thro' all e-ter-ni-ty?
Just the love of Je-sus, my Sav-ior!
CHORUS.
Just the love of Je-sus,
O how sweet! Just the love of Je-sus makes my joy complete; What will guide my
soul to that safe re-treat? Just the love of Je-sus, my Sav-ior!

No. 76.
God is Calling Yet.
Gerhard Tersteegen.
COPYRIGHT, 1887, BY E. O. EXCELL.
E. O. Excell.
1. God call-ing yet! shall I not hear? Earth's pleasures shall I still hold dear?
2. God call-ing yet! shall I not rise? Can I His lov-ing voice de-spise,
3. God call-ing yet! and shall He knock, And I my heart the clo-ser lock?
4. God call-ing yet! I can-not stay, My heart I yield with-out de-lay;
Shall life's swift pass-ing years all fly, And still my soul in slum-ber lie?
And base-ly His kind care re-pay? He calls me still; can I de-lay?
He still is wait-ing to re-ceive, And shall I dare His Spir-it grieve?
Vain world, farewell, from thee I part; The voice of God has reached my heart.
CHORUS.
Call - - ing, oh, hear Him call - - ing, oh, hear Him, God is
God is call-ing yet,
God is call-ing yet,
rit.
call-ing yet, oh, hear Him call-ing, call-ing; Call - - ing, oh, hear Him,
a tempo.
God is call-ing yet,
rit.
call - - ing, oh, hear Him, God is call-ing yet, oh, hear Him calling yet.
God is call-ing yet,

No. 77. Christ at the Door.

J. Grigg. COPYRIGHT, 1889, BY E. O. EXCELL. Frank A. Simpkins.

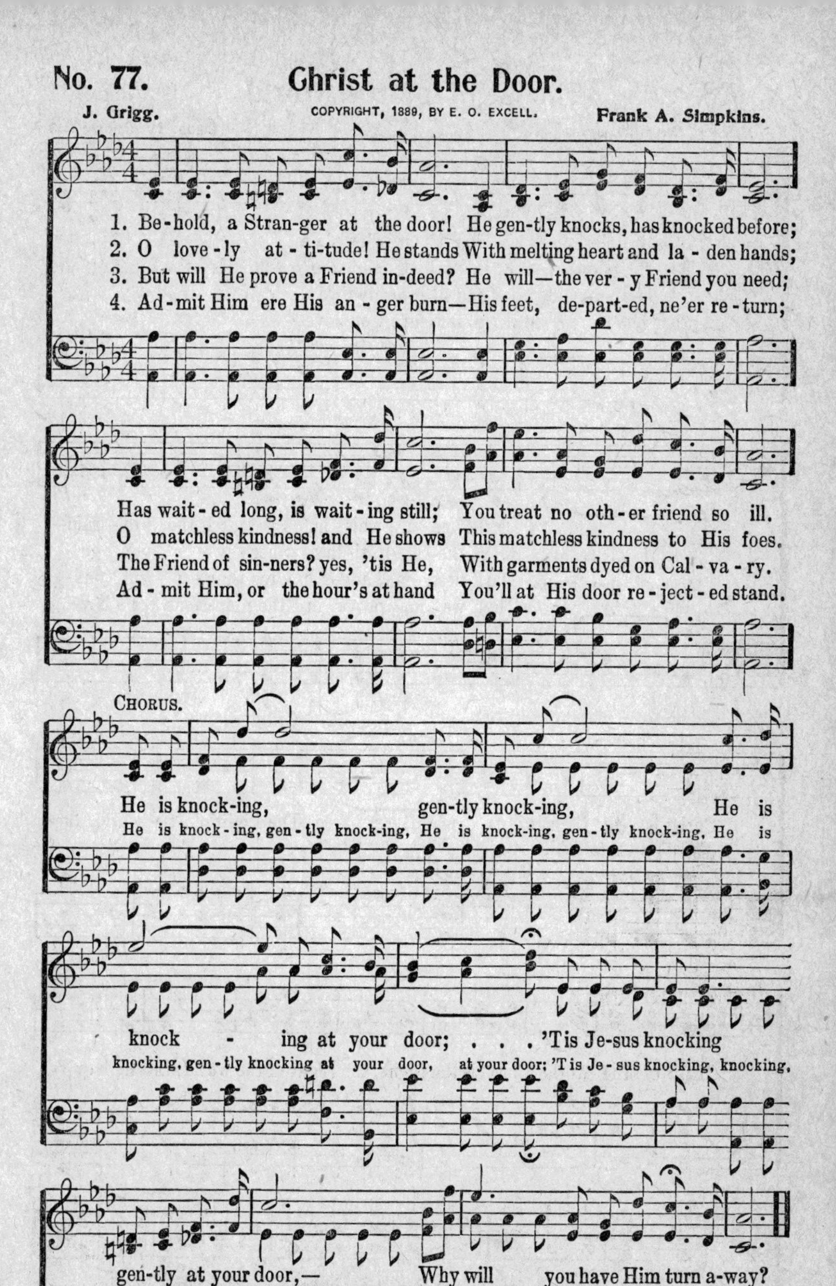

1. Be-hold, a Stran-ger at the door! He gen-tly knocks, has knocked before;
2. O love-ly at-ti-tude! He stands With melting heart and la-den hands;
3. But will He prove a Friend in-deed? He will—the ver-y Friend you need;
4. Ad-mit Him ere His an-ger burn—His feet, de-part-ed, ne'er re-turn;
Has wait-ed long, is wait-ing still; You treat no oth-er friend so ill.
O matchless kindness! and He shows This matchless kindness to His foes.
The Friend of sin-ners? yes, 'tis He, With garments dyed on Cal-va-ry.
Ad-mit Him, or the hour's at hand You'll at His door re-ject-ed stand.
CHORUS.
He is knock-ing, gen-tly knock-ing, He is
He is knock-ing, gen-tly knock-ing, He is knock-ing, gen-tly knock-ing, He is
knock - ing at your door; . . . 'Tis Je-sus knocking
knocking, gen-tly knocking at your door, at your door; 'Tis Je-sus knocking, knocking,
gen-tly at your door,— Why will you have Him turn a-way?
gen-tly at your door. He is knocking,—Why will, why will you have Him turn a-way?

No. 78. The Light of the World.

Rev. J. Oatman, Jr.
COPYRIGHT, 1914, BY E. O. EXCELL.
WORDS AND MUSIC.
Chas. H. Gabriel.
1. Tell it o'er mountain, and tell it o'er plain,
2. Tell the poor sin - ner in darkness and woe, Christ is the Light of the
3. I - dols of gold, wood and sil - ver give way, Christ is the light, the
4. Then let us fol - low in patience and love—
Mil-lions are wait - ing to catch the re - frain—
world! . . . Shout the glad ti-dings wher - ev - er you go—
Light of the world! Dark-ness is changed in - to beau - ti - ful day—
That we may prove, in the man-sions a - bove,
CHORUS.
Christ is the Light of the world! . . . The Light of the world, the
Christ is the Light, the Light of the world!
Light of the world, Christ is the Light, the Light of the world; Lift high ev'ry
voice, oh, sing and re - joice, For Christ is the Light of the world!

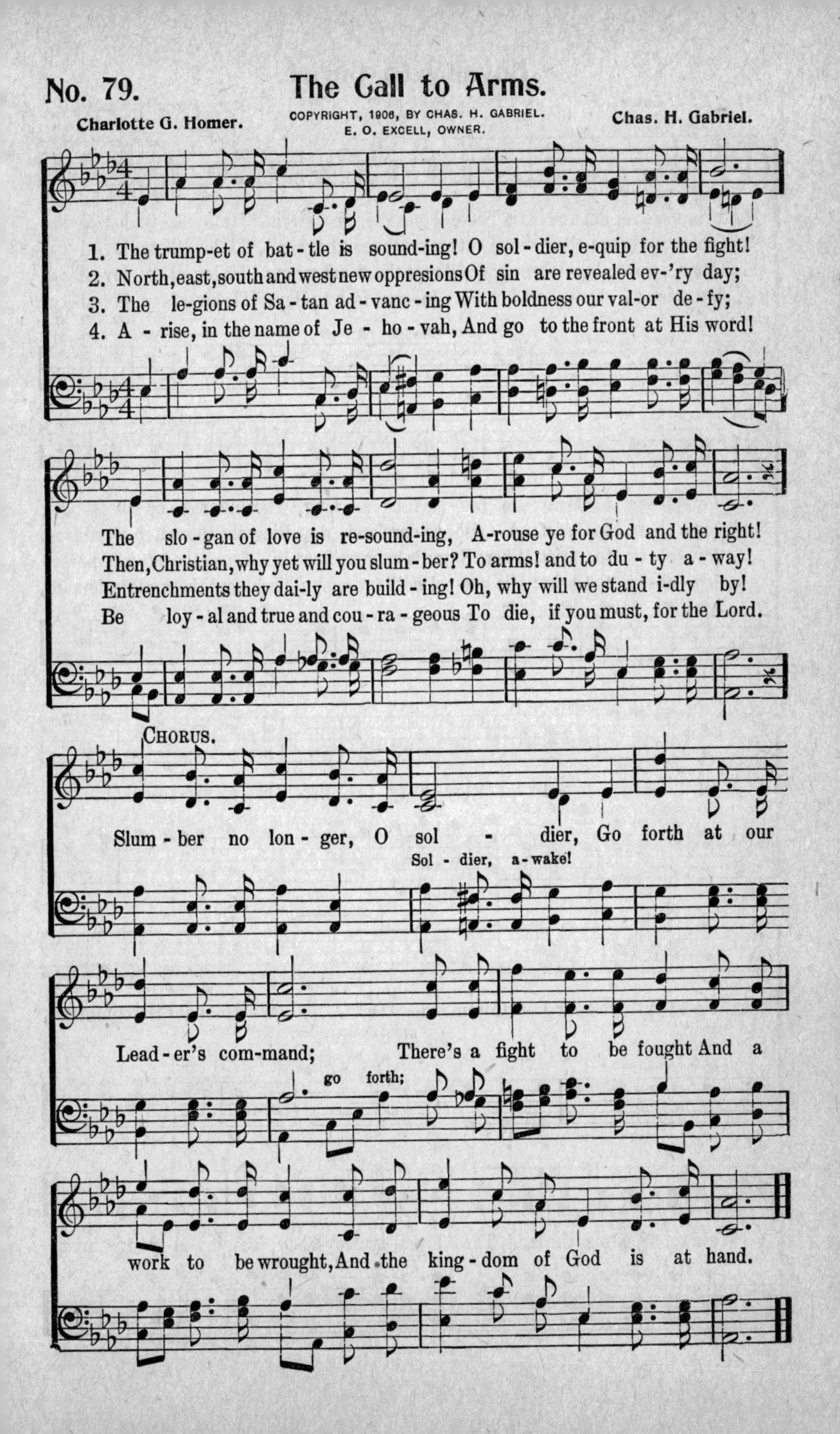

No. 79.
The Call to Arms.
Charlotte G. Homer.
COPYRIGHT, 1906, BY CHAS. H. GABRIEL.
E. O. EXCELL, OWNER.
Chas. H. Gabriel.
1. The trump-et of bat-tle is sound-ing! O sol-dier, e-quip for the fight!
2. North, east, south and west new oppresions Of sin are revealed ev-'ry day;
3. The le-gions of Sa-tan ad-vanc-ing With boldness our val-or de-fy;
4. A-rise, in the name of Je-ho-vah, And go to the front at His word!
The slo-gan of love is re-sound-ing, A-rouse ye for God and the right!
Then, Christian, why yet will you slum-ber? To arms! and to du-ty a-way!
Entrenchments they dai-ly are build-ing! Oh, why will we stand i-dly by!
Be loy-al and true and cou-ra-geous To die, if you must, for the Lord.
CHORUS.
Slum-ber no lon-ger, O sol-dier, Go forth at our
Sol-dier, a-wake!
Lead-er's com-mand;
go forth;
There's a fight to be fought And a
work to be wrought, And the king-dom of God is at hand.

No. 80. Loyalty to Christ.

Dr. E. T. Cassel.

Flora H. Cassel.

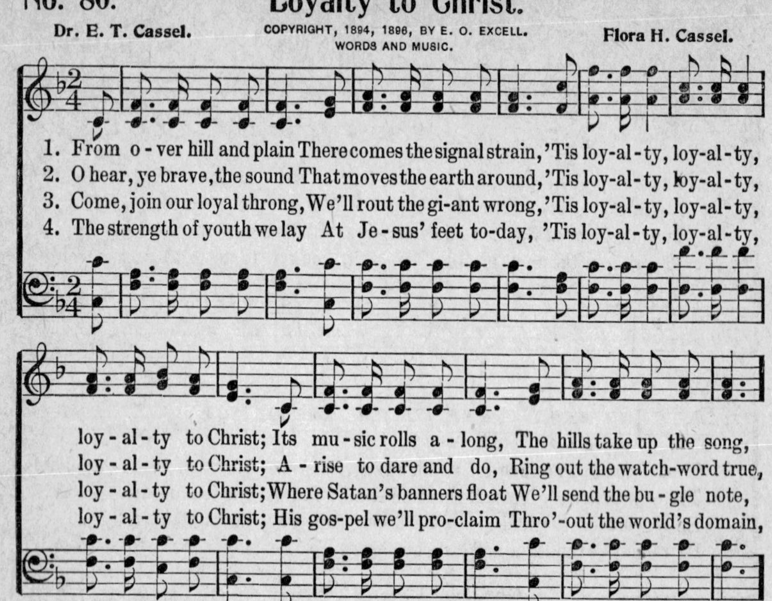
1. From o - ver hill and plain There comes the signal strain, 'Tis loy-al - ty, loy-al - ty,
2. O hear, ye brave, the sound That moves the earth around, 'Tis loy-al - ty, loy-al - ty,
3. Come, join our loyal throng, We'll rout the gi-ant wrong, 'Tis loy-al - ty, loy-al - ty,
4. The strength of youth we lay At Je - sus' feet to-day, 'Tis loy-al - ty, loy-al - ty,
loy - al - ty to Christ; Its mu - sic rolls a - long, The hills take up the song,
loy - al - ty to Christ; A - rise to dare and do, Ring out the watch-word true,
loy - al - ty to Christ; Where Satan's banners float We'll send the bu - gle note,
loy - al - ty to Christ; His gos-pel we'll pro-claim Thro'-out the world's domain,

CHORUS.
Of loy-al-ty, loy-al-ty, Yes, loy - al-ty to Christ. "On to vic - to-ry! On to
vic-to-ry!" Cries our great Commander; "On!". . . . We'll move at His command,
great Commander; "On!"

We'll soon pos-sess the land, Thro' loy-al-ty, loy-al-ty, Yes, loy-al-ty to Christ.

No. 81. A Happy Day.

Rev. Neal A. McAulay.

Chas. H. Gabriel.

1. When I gave my heart to Je-sus, When I chose the nar-row way,
When I vowed to do His bid-ding, 'Twas for me a hap-py day.

2. When I saw His cross up-lift-ed, Where His life-blood ebbed a-way,
When I knelt in deep con-tri-tion, 'Twas for me a hap-py day.

3. When I saw Him rise vic-to-rious, From the tomb where-in He lay,
And be-held Him pass to glo-ry, 'Twas for me a hap-py day.

4. When I felt the Ho-ly Spir-it Wash my ev-'ry sin a-way,
When He filled my soul with rapture, 'Twas for me a hap-py day.

CHORUS.

I am hap-py, ... I am hap-py, ... For He
oh, so hap-py, oh, so hap-py,
keeps me, oh, so happy day by day; I am hap-py, ...
keeps me, oh, so hap-py, oh, so hap-py, day by day; oh, so hap-py,
I am hap-py, ... I am hap-py in the liv-ing way.
oh, so hap-py.

No. 82. The Hope Set Before You.
Fanny J. Crosby.
COPYRIGHT, 1910, BY E. O. EXCELL.
WORDS AND MUSIC.
E. O. Excell.
1. Lay hold on the hope set before you, And let not a moment be lost,
2. Lay hold on the hope set before you, Of life that you now may receive,
3. Lay hold on the hope set before you, Of joy that no mortal can speak;
4. Lay hold on the hope set before you, A hope that is steadfast and sure;
The Sav-ior has purchased your ransom, But think what a price it hath cost!
If, glad - ly His mer-cy ac - cept-ing, You tru - ly re-pent and be-lieve.
It tell - eth of rest for the wear-y, Thro' Je - sus, the low-ly and meek.
O haste to the bless-ed Re-deem-er, The lov - ing, the perfect and pure.
CHORUS.
Lay hold...... on e - ter-nal sal-va - - tion, Lay
Lay hold, lay hold............ on e - ter - nal sal - va - tion, Lay
hold.... on the gift of God's on - ly Son; Lay hold.... on His in-
hold, lay hold......... on God's on - ly Son; Lay hold, lay hold........
fi - nite mer - cy, Lay hold..... on the Might - y One!
on His mer - cy, Lay hold, lay hold on the Might - y One!

No. 83. Growing Dearer Each Day.
C. H. G.
COPYRIGHT, 1907, BY CHAS. H. GABRIEL.
E. O. EXCELL, OWNER.
Chas. H. Gabriel.
1. How sweet is the love of my Savior! 'Tis bound-less and deep as the sea; And
2. I know He is ev - er be-side me! E - ter - ni - ty on - ly will prove The
3. Wher-ev - er He leads I will fol-low, Thro' sor - row, or shadow, or sun; And
4. Some day face to face I shall see Him, And oh, what a joy it will be To
best of it all, it is dai - ly Grow-ing sweet - er and sweeter to me.
height and the depth of His mercy, And the breadth of His in - fi - nite love.
tho' I be tried in the fur-nace, I can say, "Lord, Thy will be it done."
know that His love, now so precious, Will for-ev - er grow sweeter to me!
CHORUS.
Sweet - er and sweeter to me, ... Dear - er and
Sweet-er to me, grow - ing sweet-er to me, Dear - er each day,
dear - er each day; . . . Oh, won - der - ful love of my
grow - ing dear - er each day; Oh, won - der - ful love, love of my
Sav - ior, Grow - ing dear - - er each step of my way!
Sav - ior, Grow - ing dear - er and dear - er each step of my way!

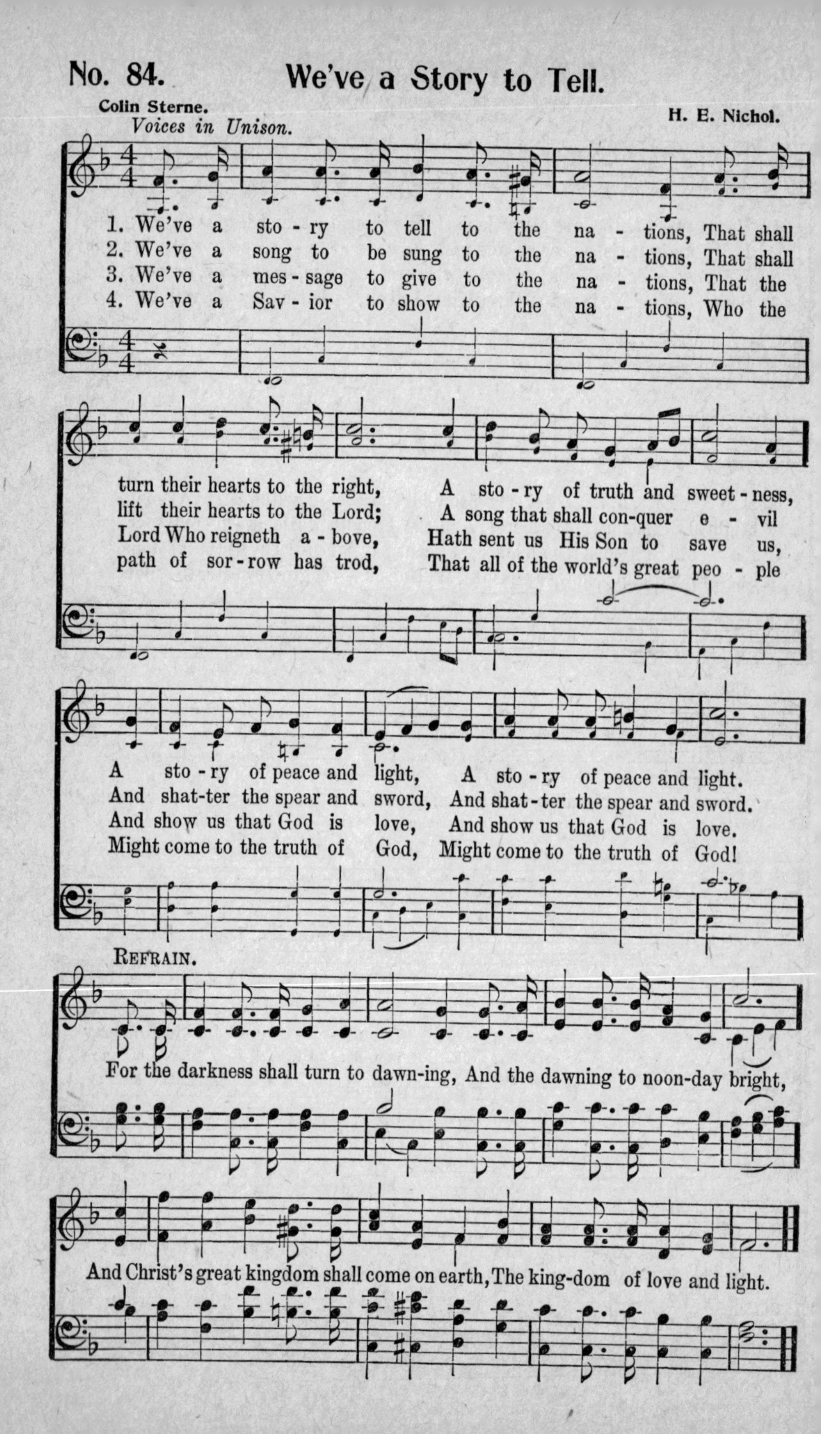
No. 84. We've a Story to Tell.
Colin Sterne.
H. E. Nichol.
Voices in Unison.
1. We've a sto - ry to tell to the na - tions, That shall turn their hearts to the right, A sto - ry of truth and sweet - ness, A sto - ry of peace and light, A sto - ry of peace and light.
2. We've a song to be sung to the na - tions, That shall lift their hearts to the Lord; A song that shall con-quer e - vil And shat-ter the spear and sword, And shat - ter the spear and sword.
3. We've a mes - sage to give to the na - tions, That the Lord Who reigneth a - bove, Hath sent us His Son to save us, And show us that God is love, And show us that God is love.
4. We've a Sav - ior to show to the na - tions, Who the path of sor - row has trod, That all of the world's great peo - ple Might come to the truth of God, Might come to the truth of God!
Refrain.
For the darkness shall turn to dawn-ing, And the dawning to noon-day bright,
And Christ's great kingdom shall come on earth, The king-dom of love and light.

No. 85. Servant of God, Awake.

Charlotte G. Homer.

Chas. H. Gabriel.

1. Serv - ant of God, a - wake un - to thy du - ty; Why will ye
2. Wide are the plains that glimm'ring lie be - fore thee Ripe un - to
3. Up! in the name of Him who died to save you; Seek for the
4. "He that en - dur - eth," is the word re - cord - ed, Shall joy and
doubt, why fal - ter, why de - lay? Look on the fields that wave in gold - en
har - vest; thrust the sick - le in! High in the heav'ns the sun is burn - ing
err - ing as He sought for you! Al - ways re - mem - ber what in love He
ev - er - last - ing life ob - tain; To him a crown at last shall be a-
beau - ty, While thou art dream - ing pre - cious hours a - way.
o'er thee,—Still thou art i - dle! Now the work be - gin.
gave you, And be a serv - ant loy - al, brave, and true.
ward - ed, Thro' Christ the Lord, who was for sin - ners slain.
CHORUS.
Serv - ant of God, a - rouse ye, a - wake! Je - sus is call - ing! Go,
la - bor for His sake! Je - sus is call - ing! Go, la - bor for His sake!

No. 86. True to My Savior.

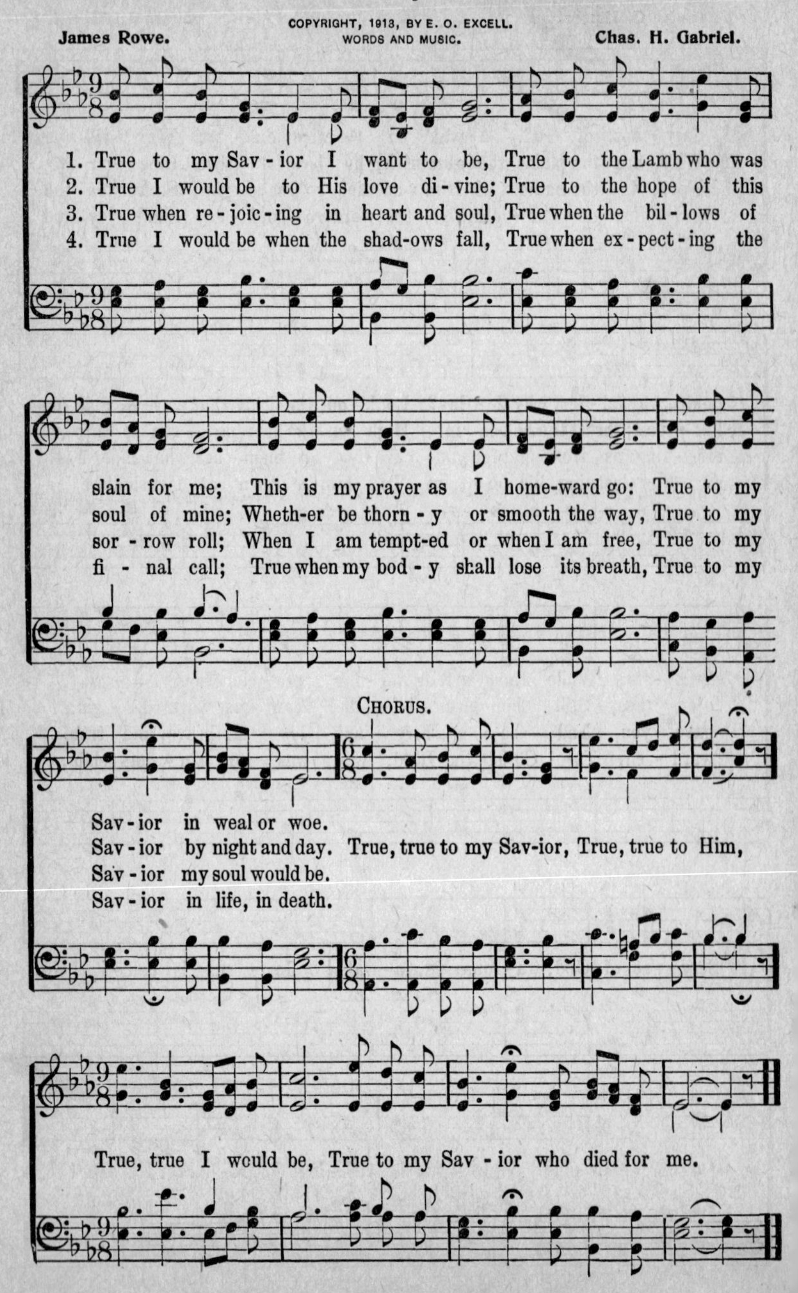
COPYRIGHT, 1913, BY E. O. EXCELL.
WORDS AND MUSIC.
James Rowe.
Chas. H. Gabriel.
1. True to my Sav-ior I want to be, True to the Lamb who was slain for me; This is my prayer as I home-ward go: True to my Sav-ior in weal or woe.
2. True I would be to His love di-vine; True to the hope of this soul of mine; Wheth-er be thorn-y or smooth the way, True to my Sav-ior by night and day.
3. True when re-joic-ing in heart and soul, True when the bil-lows of sor-row roll; When I am tempt-ed or when I am free, True to my Sav-ior my soul would be.
4. True I would be when the shad-ows fall, True when ex-pect-ing the fi-nal call; True when my bod-y shall lose its breath, True to my Sav-ior in life, in death.
CHORUS.
True, true to my Sav-ior, True, true to Him, True, true I would be, True to my Sav-ior who died for me.

No. 87. It Is Well With My Soul.

H. G. Spafford. P. P. Bliss.

1. When peace, like a river, attendeth my way, When sorrows like sea-billows roll; Whatever my lot, Thou hast taught me to say, It is well, it is well with my soul.
2. Tho' Satan should buffet, tho' trials should come, Let this blest assurance control, That Christ has regarded my helpless estate, And hath shed His own blood for my soul.
3. My sin—oh, the bliss of this glorious tho't—My sin—not in part, but the whole, Is nailed to the cross and I bear it no more, Praise the Lord, praise the Lord, O my soul!
4. And, Lord, haste the day when the faith shall be sight, The clouds be rolled back as a scroll, The trump shall resound and the Lord shall descend, "Even so"—it is well with my soul.
CHORUS.
It is well . . . with my soul, . . . It is well, it is well with my soul.
It is well, with my soul,

No. 88. The Unclouded Day.
Words and Melody by
Rev. J. K. Alwood.
Arr. by
E. O. E.
1. O they tell me of a home far be-yond the skies, O they tell me of a home far a-way; O they tell me of a home where no storm-clouds rise, O they tell me of an un-cloud-ed day.
2. O they tell me of a home where my friends have gone, O they tell me of that land far a-way; Where the tree of life in e-ter-nal bloom Sheds its fragrance thro' the un-cloud-ed day.
3. O they tell me of the King in His beau-ty there, And they tell me that mine eyes shall be-hold, Where He sits on the throne that is whit-er than snow, In the cit-y that is made of gold.
4. O they tell me that He smiles on His chil-dren there, And His smile drives their sor-rows all a-way; And they tell me that no tears ev-er come a-gain, In that love-ly land of un-cloud-ed day.
D. S.—O they tell me of a home where no storm-clouds rise, O they tell me of an un-cloud-ed day.
Fine.
Chorus.
O the land of cloud-less day, O the land of an un-cloud-ed sky;
D. S.

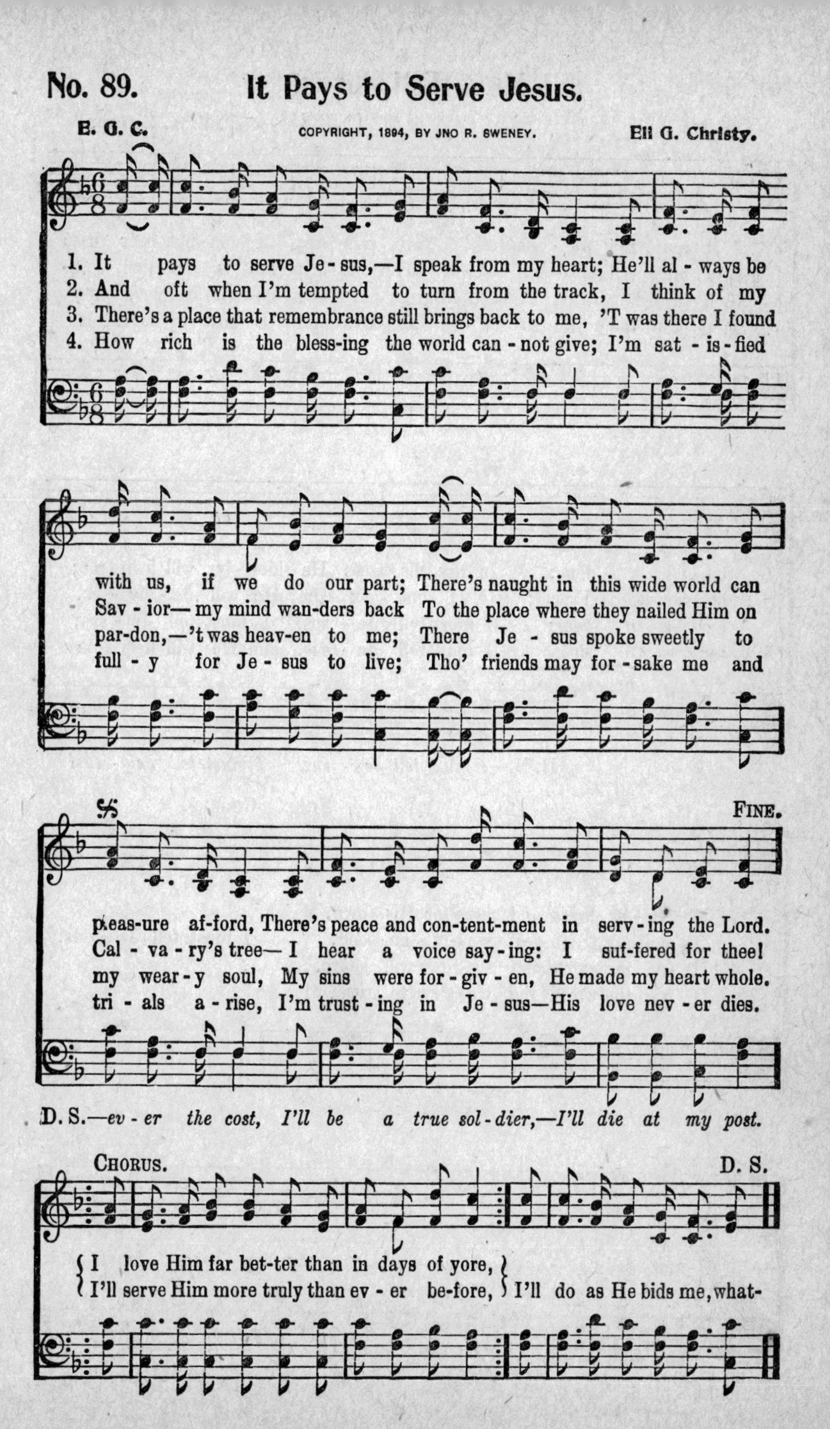
No. 89. It Pays to Serve Jesus.
E. G. C.
COPYRIGHT, 1894, BY JNO R. SWENEY.
Eli G. Christy.
1. It pays to serve Je - sus,—I speak from my heart; He'll al - ways be
2. And oft when I'm tempted to turn from the track, I think of my
3. There's a place that remembrance still brings back to me, 'T was there I found
4. How rich is the bless-ing the world can - not give; I'm sat - is - fied
with us, if we do our part; There's naught in this wide world can
Sav - ior— my mind wan-ders back To the place where they nailed Him on
par-don,—'t was heav-en to me; There Je - sus spoke sweetly to
full - y for Je - sus to live; Tho' friends may for - sake me and
pleas-ure af-ford, There's peace and con-tent-ment in serv - ing the Lord.
Cal - va - ry's tree— I hear a voice say - ing: I suf-fered for thee!
my wear - y soul, My sins were for - giv - en, He made my heart whole.
tri - als a - rise, I'm trust - ing in Je - sus—His love nev - er dies.
FINE.
D. S.—ev - er the cost, I'll be a true sol - dier,—I'll die at my post.
CHORUS.
D. S.
I love Him far bet-ter than in days of yore,
I'll serve Him more truly than ev - er be-fore,
I'll do as He bids me, what-

No. 90.
I Must Tell Jesus.
E. A. H.
COPYRIGHT, 1893, BY THE HOFFMAN MUSIC CO.
Rev. E. A. Hoffman.
1. I must tell Je - sus all of my tri - als; I can - not bear these burdens a - lone; In my dis - tress He kind - ly will help me; He ev - er loves and cares for His own.
2. I must tell Je - sus all of my troub - les; He is a kind, compas-sion-ate Friend; If I but ask Him, He will de - liv - er, Make of my troub - les quick - ly an end.
3. Tempted and tried I need a great Sav - ior, One who can help my bur-dens to bear; I must tell Je - sus, I must tell Je - sus; He all my cares and sor - rows will share.
4. O how the world to e - vil al - lures me! O how my heart is tempted to sin! I must tell Je - sus, and He will help me O - ver the world the vic - t'ry to win.
D. S.—I must tell Je - sus! I must tell Je - sus!
FINE. CHORUS.
I must tell Je - sus!
Je - sus can help me, Je - sus a - lone.
D. S.
I must tell Je - sus! I can - not bear my bur - dens a - lone;

No. 91. Have You Made the World Better?

Nella F. Ford. COPYRIGHT, 1913, BY CHAS. H. GABRIEL. E. O. EXCELL, OWNER. Chas. H. Gabriel.

1. When the last rays of sun-set are low in the west, When the toil-ers come
2. Did a storm-beat-en pilgrim, cast down in the race, See the Christ that you
3. Did the stran-ger who traveled with you all day long Feel the touch of your
4. When my life-day is o-ver, and sun-set has come, When the work is all
home, and the world is at rest, To the ques-tion my an-swer must
love when he looked in your face? Did you pray for the friend who has
faith in your word, in your song? Has your heart felt the bur-den for
done and the toil-ers go home, May I know that for which I will
D. S.—Have you done what you could in all
Fine.
be yea or nay—"Have you made the world bet-ter by liv-ing to-day?"
drift-ed a-way—Have you made the world bet-ter by liv-ing to-day?
souls gone astray—Have you made the world bet-ter by liv-ing to-day?
con-stant-ly pray—I have made the world bet-ter by liv-ing to-day!
things, as you should—Have you made the world better by liv-ing to-day?
Chorus.
D. S.
Have you made it better, Have you made the world bet-ter by liv-ing to-day?

No. 92. As a Volunteer.

W. S. Brown.

Chas. H. Gabriel.

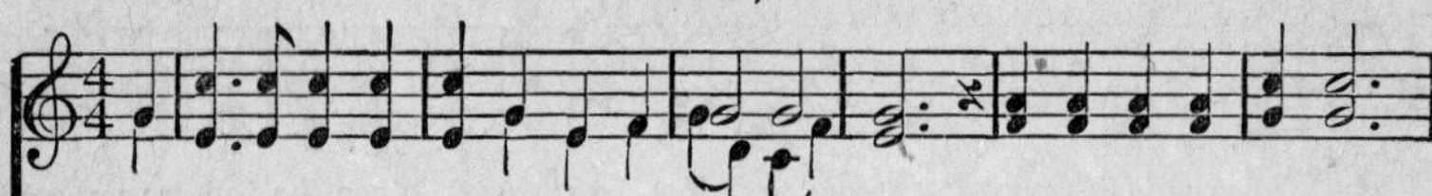

1. A call for loy-al soldiers Comes to one and all; Sol-diers for the con-flict,
2. Yes, Jesus calls for soldiers Who are filled with pow'r, Soldiers who will serve Him
3. He calls you, for He loves you With a heart most kind, He whose heart was broken,
4. And when the war is o-ver, And the vic-t'ry won, When the true and faith-ful

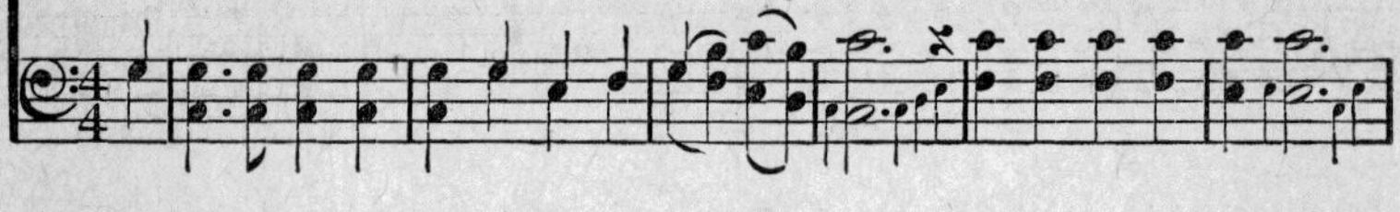

Will you heed the call? Will you an-swer quick-ly, With a read-y cheer,
Ev-'ry day and hour; He will not for-sake you, He is ev-er near;
Bro-ken for man-kind; Now, just now He calls you, Calls in ac-cents clear,
Gath-er one by one, He will crown with glo-ry All who there ap-pear;

D. S.—*Je-sus is the Cap-tain, We will nev-er fear;*

FINE. CHORUS.

Will you be en-list-ed As a vol-un-teer? A vol-un-teer for Je-sus,

Will you be en-list-ed As a vol-un-teer?

D. S.

A sol-dier true! Oth-ers have en-list-ed, Why not you?

Oh, why not?

No. 93. He Supplieth All of My Need.

T. O. Chisholm. Chas. H. Gabriel.

1. All of my need He free-ly sup-pli-eth, Day aft-er day His good-ness I prove; Mer-cies un-fail-ing, new ev-'ry morn-ing, Tell me of God's un-change-a-ble love.
2. All of my need He free-ly sup-pli-eth, Wis-dom and guid-ance, strength as my day; Grace for each tri-al, com-fort in sor-row, Bless-ed com-mun-ion all of the way.
3. All of my need He free-ly sup-pli-eth, There's not a void that He can-not feel; Nev-er a bur-den He can-not light-en, Nev-er a heart-ache He can-not heal.
4. All of my need He free-ly sup-pli-eth, I shall not want, what-ev-er be-tide; He that de-liv-ered Christ for my ran-som, With Him will all things sure-ly pro-vide.
D. S.—Noth-ing have I, yet I am con-tent-ed, For He sup-pli-eth all of my need.
FINE.
CHORUS.
God hath laid help on One that is might-y, One who is Friend and Broth-er in-deed;
D. S.

No. 94. When I Go Home.

Jennie Ree. Chas. H. Gabriel.

1. A lit - tle while and then the sum - mer Day, When I go Home;
2. Work ceas-es not in sun-shine or in show'r, Till I go Home;
3. All will be well, and all be hap - pi - ness, When I go Home;
4. I'll meet the loved ones I have lost a - while, When I go Home;
'T is lone-some win - ter now, but 't will be May, When I go Home; Be-
But in the still - ness of the twi - light hour, I dream of Home; And
The wan - der - ings all o'er, and lone - li - ness, When I go Home; There
And, best of all, I'll see my Sav - ior smile, When I go Home; Oh,
yond the gloom of moor and fen I see The wel - come warm of
when the night-wind moans a - cross the wold I feel no dread of
will be light at e - ven - tide for me, The light that nev - er
what a joy thro' all e - ter - ni - ty, To sing the praise of
those who wait for me, When I go Home, when I go Home.
dark, or chill of cold— I dream of Home, I dream of Home.
was on land or sea, When I go Home, when I go Home.
Him who died for me, When I go Home, when I go Home.

No. 95. Spend One Hour With Jesus.
WORDS AND MUSIC COPYRIGHT, 1912, BY E. O. EXCELL.
Katharine A. Grimes.
INTERNATIONAL COPYRIGHT SECURED.
E. O. Excell.
1. Wear - y soul by sin op-pressed, Spend one hour with Je - sus;
2. Do you fear the gath-'ring gloom? Spend one hour with Je - sus;
3. Ev - 'ry need He will sup - ply, Spend one hour with Je - sus;
4. All a - long life's storm-y way, Spend one hour with Je - sus;
He will give your spir - it rest, Spend one hour with Je - sus:
In the si - lent in - ner room, Spend one hour with Je - sus:
He a - lone can sat - is - fy, Spend one hour with Je - sus:
Call up - on Him day by day, Spend one hour with Je - sus:
He has felt your grief be - fore, Num-bered all your sor - rows o'er,
He will speak un - to your soul, Make your ev - 'ry heart-ache whole,
Oh, the mer - cy He will show, Oh, the grace He will be - stow,
Tell Him all— He is your Friend, He will count-less bless - ings send.
He will ev - 'ry joy re - store; Spend one hour with Je - sus.
Point you to the Heav'n-ly Goal; Spend one hour with Je - sus.
Grace to con - quer ev - 'ry foe; Spend one hour with Je - sus.
He will keep you to the end; Spend one hour with Je - sus.

No. 96. Jesus, Friend of Sinners.

Charles Irvin Junkin.
COPYRIGHT, 1909, BY CHARLES IRVIN JUNKIN.
USED BY PERMISSION.
Geo. C. Stebbins.
1. Je - sus, Friend of sin - ners, Hast Thou love for me?
2. Je - sus, Friend of sin - ners, Thou hast read my heart,
3. Je - sus, Friend of sin - ners, Thou hast touched my soul,
4. Je - sus, Friend of sin - ners, Bid me fol - low Thee,
5. Je - sus, Friend of sin - ners, Hold me by Thy side,
Son of God the Ho - ly, Man of mys - ter - y,
Searching its re - cess - es, With a lov - er's art;
Not with scorn - ful pit - y, Not with beg - gar's dole;
O'er the rug - ged high - ways, E'en to Cal - va - ry;
Till the shad - ows deep - en Tow'rd the e - ven - tide:
Lov - er of the chil - dren, Teach - er of the wise,
Naught have I with - hold - en, Noth - ing hid from Thee,
Thou hast not de - spis - ed Men that faint or fall,
Let me know Thy Spir - it, Sweet, and strong, and wise;
To Thy strength and beau - ty I would ev - er bend,
Let me read the se - cret In Thy friend - ly eyes.
Waste, or want, or fol - ly, Things that should not be.
Ten - der - er than broth - er, For Thou know - est all.
I would win the friend - ship In Thy lov - ing eyes.
Till, in dawn e - ter - nal, Friend shall be as Friend!

No. 97.
Let Him In.
Rev. J. B. Atchinson.
COPYRIGHT, 1909, BY E. O. EXCELL.
RENEWAL.
E. O. Excell.
1. There's a Stran-ger at the door, Let Him in;
2. O - pen now to Him your heart, Let Him in;
3. Hear you now His lov-ing voice? Let Him in;
4. Now ad-mit the heav'n-ly Guest, Let Him in;
Let the Sav-ior in, Let the Sav-ior in;
He has been there oft be-fore, Let Him in;
If you wait He will de-part, Let Him in;
Now, oh, now make Him your choice, Let Him in;
He will make for you a feast, Let Him in;
Let the Sav-ior in, Let the Sav-ior in;
Let Him in, ere He is gone, Let Him in, the Ho-ly One,
Let Him in, He is your Friend, He your soul will sure de-fend,
He is stand-ing at your door, Joy to you He will re-store,
He will speak your sins for-giv'n, And when earth-ties all are riv'n,
Je-sus Christ, the Fa-ther's Son, Let Him in.
He will keep you to the end, Let Him in.
And His name you will a-dore, Let Him in.
He will take you home to heav'n, Let Him in.
Let the Sav-ior in, Let the Sav-ior in.

No. 98. Jesus is All the World to Me.

W. L. T. — Will L. Thompson.

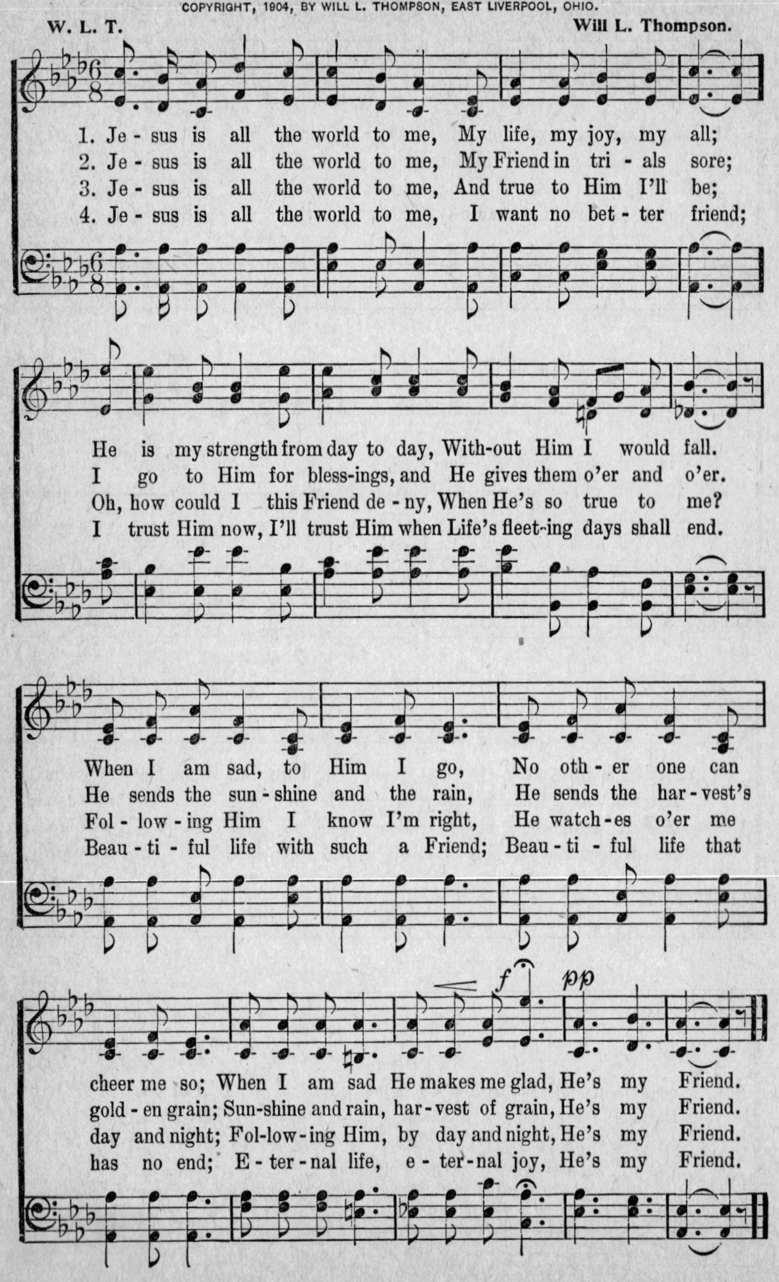
1. Je - sus is all the world to me, My life, my joy, my all;
2. Je - sus is all the world to me, My Friend in tri - als sore;
3. Je - sus is all the world to me, And true to Him I'll be;
4. Je - sus is all the world to me, I want no bet - ter friend;
He is my strength from day to day, With-out Him I would fall.
I go to Him for bless-ings, and He gives them o'er and o'er.
Oh, how could I this Friend de - ny, When He's so true to me?
I trust Him now, I'll trust Him when Life's fleet-ing days shall end.
When I am sad, to Him I go, No oth - er one can
He sends the sun - shine and the rain, He sends the har - vest's
Fol - low - ing Him I know I'm right, He watch - es o'er me
Beau - ti - ful life with such a Friend; Beau - ti - ful life that
cheer me so; When I am sad He makes me glad, He's my Friend.
gold - en grain; Sun-shine and rain, har - vest of grain, He's my Friend.
day and night; Fol-low - ing Him, by day and night, He's my Friend.
has no end; E - ter - nal life, e - ter-nal joy, He's my Friend.
f
pp

No. 99. A Little Bit of Love.

To my Friend, Marion Lawrance.

E. O. E. — E. O. Excell.

1. Do you know the world is dy-ing For a lit-tle bit of love? Ev-'ry-
2. From the poor of ev-'ry cit-y, For a lit-tle bit of love, Hands are
3. Down be-fore their i-dols fall-ing, For a lit-tle bit of love, Man-y
4. While the souls of men are dy-ing For a lit-tle bit of love, While the

where we hear the sigh-ing For a lit-tle bit of love; For the love that rights a
reach-ing out in pit-y For a lit-tle bit of love; Some have burdens hard to
souls in vain are call-ing For a lit-tle bit of love; If they die in sin and
chil-dren, too, are cry-ing For a lit-tle bit of love, Stand no lon-ger i-dly

wrong, Fills the heart with hope and song; They have waited, oh, so long, For a
bear, Some have sorrows we should share; Shall they falter and de-spair For a
shame, Some one sure-ly is to blame For not go-ing in His name, With a
by, You can help them if you try; Go, then, saying, "Here am I," With a

D. S. each verse.

FINE. REFRAIN.

lit-tle bit of love. For a lit-tle bit of love, For a lit-tle bit of love.
lit-tle bit of love? For a lit-tle bit of love, For a lit-tle bit of love.
lit-tle bit of love. With a lit-tle bit of love, With a lit-tle bit of love.
lit-tle bit of love. With a lit-tle bit of love, With a lit-tle bit of love.

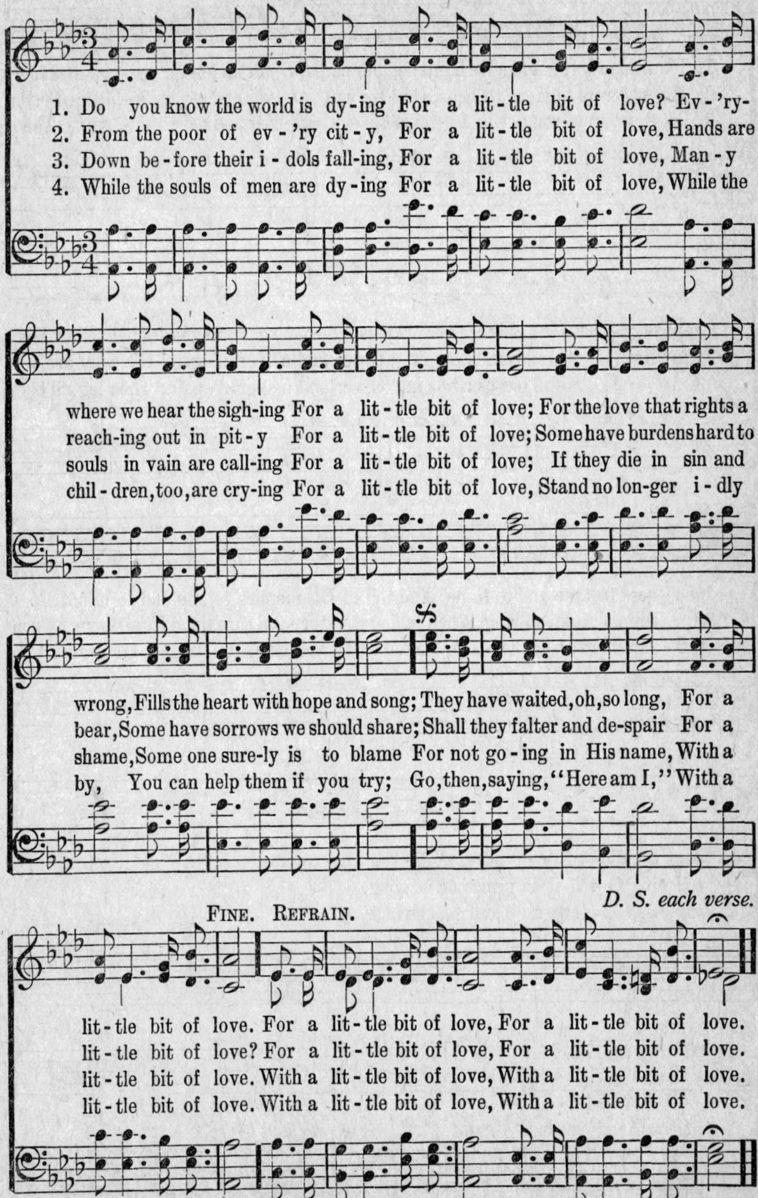

No. 100. Over and Over Again.

Floy S. Armstrong

Chas. H. Gabriel.

1. How man-y times has He lightened our cares, O-ver and o-ver a - gain! How
2. He ne'er re - fus-es to hear, tho' we call O - ver and o-ver a - gain, Sends
3. Tho' we may wander in by-ways of sin, O - ver and o-ver a - gain, The
many times has He answered our prayers, Over and over a - gain! Then tell of His
show'rs of blessings so freely on all, O-ver and o - ver a - gain; Oh, why are you
heart of Je-sus will bid us come in, O-ver and o - ver a - gain; Then let us be
good-ness to thee and to thine, And tell of His mercies to me and to mine, Re-
si - lent so often, so long, When telling the story will turn them from wrong? Then
will - ing, wher-ev-er the place, To tell of His kindness, His pardon, His grace, And
peat the old sto-ry of par-don di - vine, O - ver and o-ver a - gain. . . . .
tell it, O tell it in praise or in song,
some day in glory we'll look on His face, O - - ver and o - ver a - gain.
CHORUS.
O - ver and o-ver a - gain, . . . O - ver and o-ver a - gain, ...
and o - ver a - gain, and o - ver a - gain,

Over and Over Again.
O what a won-der-ful sto-ry to tell, O-ver and o-ver a-gain.
No. 101. A Word and a Smile.
Florence Hadley.
COPYRIGHT, 1913, BY E. O. EXCELL. WORDS AND MUSIC.
Chas. H. Gabriel.
1. Do you know what a cheerful word will do? It will drive away ev'ry doubt for you,
2. Do you know what a cheerful smile will do? It will change the sky to a tender blue;
3. Give us then words of cheer and smile the while; It will shorten many a weary mile,
It will bring the sun-shine day by day And set you singing a-long your way.
It will drive despair from the troubled heart And joy and hope to the soul impart.
It will help some soul as the days go by To find his way to that Home on High.
CHORUS.
Then let us be cheer-ful, you and I, Helping weary ones who are passing by;
For a lov-ing word and a cheerful smile Will bring us joy in the aft-er-while.

No. 102. O Where Are the Reapers?

Eben E. Rexford. George F. Root.

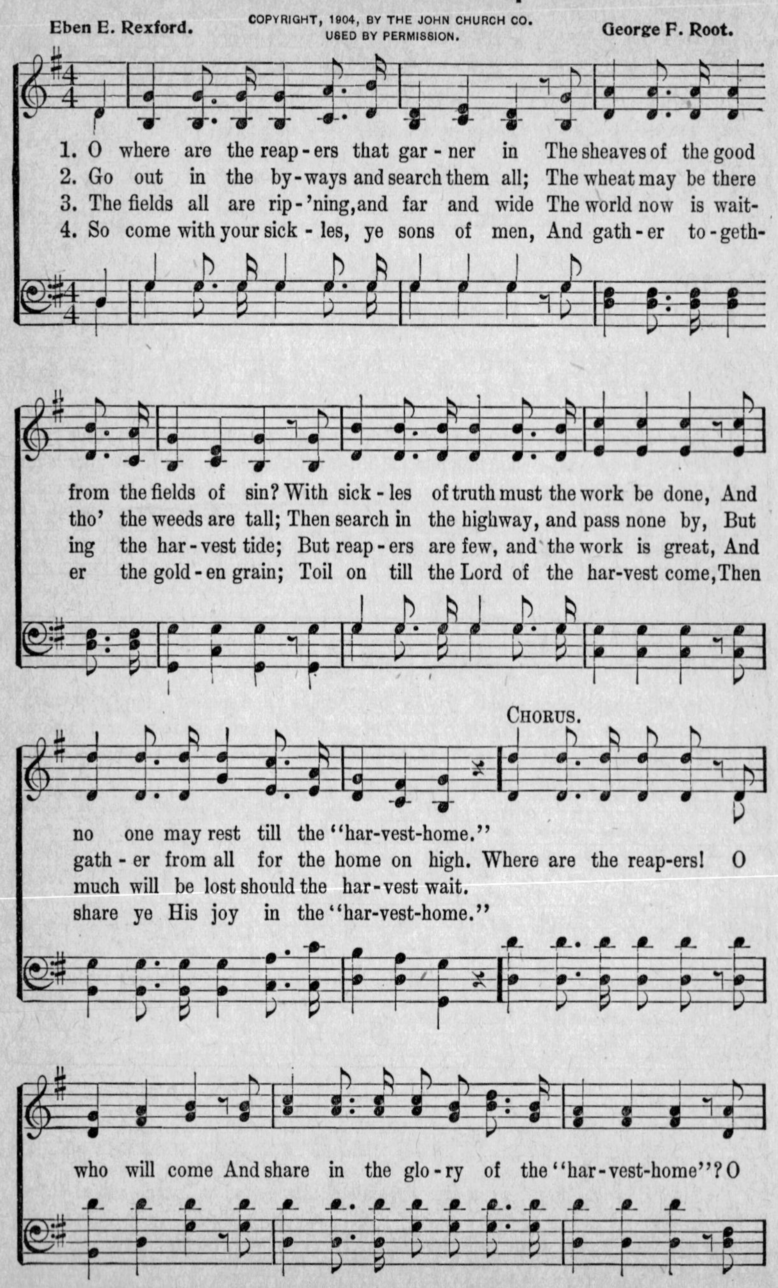
1. O where are the reap-ers that gar-ner in The sheaves of the good
2. Go out in the by-ways and search them all; The wheat may be there
3. The fields all are rip-'ning, and far and wide The world now is wait-
4. So come with your sick-les, ye sons of men, And gath-er to-geth-
from the fields of sin? With sick-les of truth must the work be done, And
tho' the weeds are tall; Then search in the highway, and pass none by, But
ing the har-vest tide; But reap-ers are few, and the work is great, And
er the gold-en grain; Toil on till the Lord of the har-vest come, Then
CHORUS.
no one may rest till the "har-vest-home."
gath-er from all for the home on high. Where are the reap-ers! O
much will be lost should the har-vest wait.
share ye His joy in the "har-vest-home."
who will come And share in the glo-ry of the "har-vest-home"? O

O Where Are the Reapers?
who will help us to gar-ner in The sheaves of good from the fields of sin?
No. 103. The Song-Land of My Soul.
Jesse Brown Pounds.
COPYRIGHT, 1902, BY E. O. EXCELL. WORDS AND MUSIC.
Victor H. Benke.
1. There are storms the world o'er-sweeping, I can hear their thun-d'ring roll;
2. There is war the world o'er-spreading; I can hear its cries of dole;
3. I can hear the glad E-van-gels Of a bet-ter day to be;
But my God His calm is keep-ing, In the song-land of my soul.
But no strife I need be dread-ing, In the song-land of my soul.
In my song-land with the an-gels, There my Fa-ther dwells with me.
CHORUS.
In the song-land, bless-ed song-land! In the song-land of my soul;
In the song-land, bless-ed song-land! In the song-land of my soul;
God His ho-ly calm is keep-ing, In the song-land of my soul.
rit.
In the song-land of my soul.

No. 104. Follow All the Way.
W. A. Ogden. COPYRIGHT, 1889, BY E. O. EXCELL. W. A. Ogden.
1. Oh, I love to think of Je-sus, As He journeyed to and fro, O'er the
2. Oh, I love to think of Je-sus, And His prais-es I would tell; How He
3. Oh, I love to think of Je-sus, As He walked up-on the wave; How the
bar-ren hills of Ju-dah, In the a-ges long a-go; How He healed the wayside
gave the liv-ing wa-ter To the wom-an at the well, How He filled the emp-ty
elements obeyed Him When the mighty word He gave. Speak the word now to my
beg-gar, How He made the lep-er whole, How in love He lit the al-tar
ves-sels At the mar-riage feast that day, How He spake the word of comfort
spir-it, Lord, Thy blessed "Peace, be still"; I would fol-low where Thou leadest,
On the sin-pol-lu-ted soul.
To the poor who thronged this way.
I would mag-ni-fy Thy will.
CHORUS.
I will fol - - - low where He
I will fol-low where He lead-eth,
lead - eth, I will pas - - ture where He feed - eth,
fol-low where He lead-eth, Pas-ture where He feed-eth, pasture where He feedeth,

Follow All the Way.

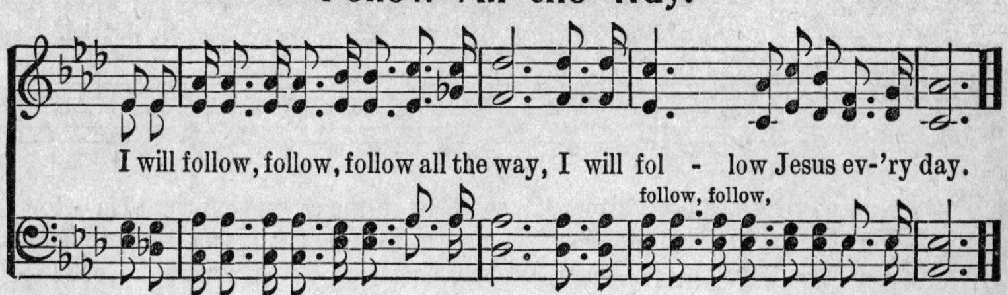

I will follow, follow, follow all the way, I will fol - low Jesus ev-'ry day.
follow, follow,

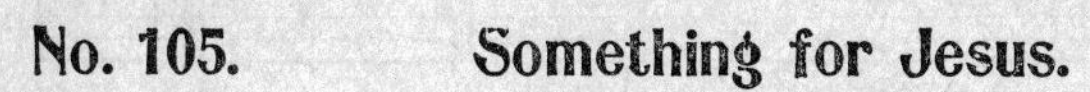

No. 105. Something for Jesus.

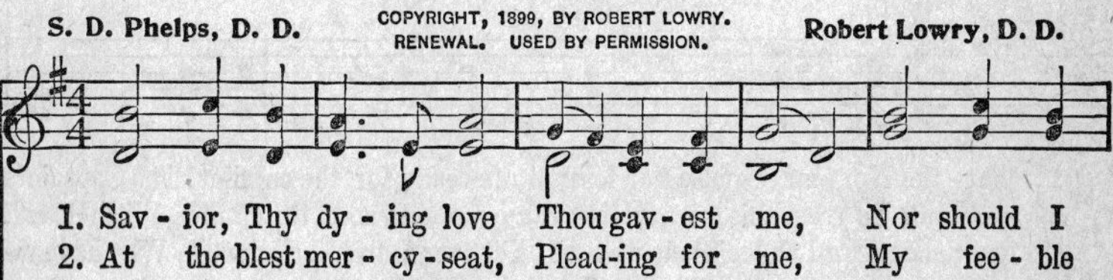

S. D. Phelps, D. D.
COPYRIGHT, 1899, BY ROBERT LOWRY.
RENEWAL. USED BY PERMISSION.
Robert Lowry, D. D.

1. Sav - ior, Thy dy - ing love Thou gav - est me, Nor should I
2. At the blest mer - cy - seat, Plead-ing for me, My fee - ble
3. Give me a faith - ful heart,—Like-ness to Thee,— That each de-
4. All that I am and have,—Thy gifts so free,— In joy, in

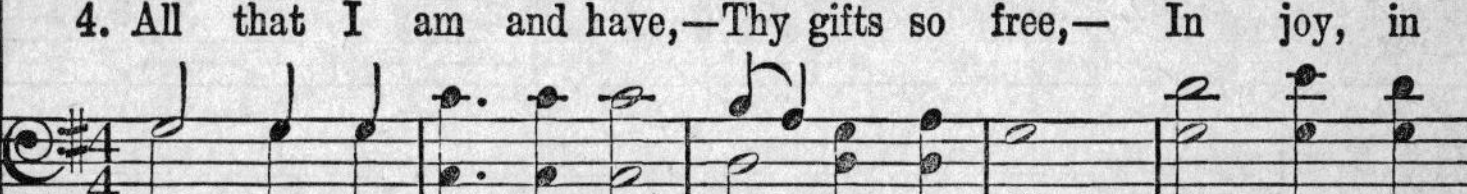

aught with-hold, Dear Lord, from Thee: In love my soul would bow,
faith looks up, Je - sus, to Thee: Help me the cross to bear,
part - ing day Henceforth may see Some work of love be - gun,
grief, thro' life, Dear Lord, for Thee! And when Thy face I see,

My heart ful - fil its vow, Some off'ring bring Thee now, Something for Thee.
Thy wondrous love de-clare, Some song to raise, or prayer, Something for Thee.
Some deed of kindness done, Some wand'rer sought and won, Something for Thee.
My ransomed soul shall be, Thro' all e - ter - ni - ty, Something for Thee.

No. 106. The Banner of the Cross.
E. M. Bangs.
COPYRIGHT, 1913, BY CHAS. H. GABRIEL.
E. O. EXCELL, OWNER.
Chas. H. Gabriel.
1. Gird on your stead-fast armor, O sol-diers of the cross, Go forward in - to bat-tle, Nor fear re-pulse nor loss; Make ready for the conflict, The Captain's call o - bey; Then ral-ly and march onward, The trumpet sounds to-day.
2. The Gi-ant of Temp-ta-tion Will meet us as we go; We need our strongest ar - mor To greet this mighty foe; But our good sword, Resistance, Will hold and bind him fast, And with our Cap-tain lead-ing, We'll conquer him at last.
3. The en - e-mies ap-proaching Are Selfishness, and Greed, Vain-glory, and Im-pa-tience: Our Leader's help we need. Yet ever march-ing onward, Why have we fear of loss, When o-ver us is float-ing The Ban-ner of the Cross?
CHORUS.
Then onward to the battle, We're marching in our might, We're pressing tow'rd the vic-to-ry, We're fighting for the right; Upon the breeze resplendent Our col-ors

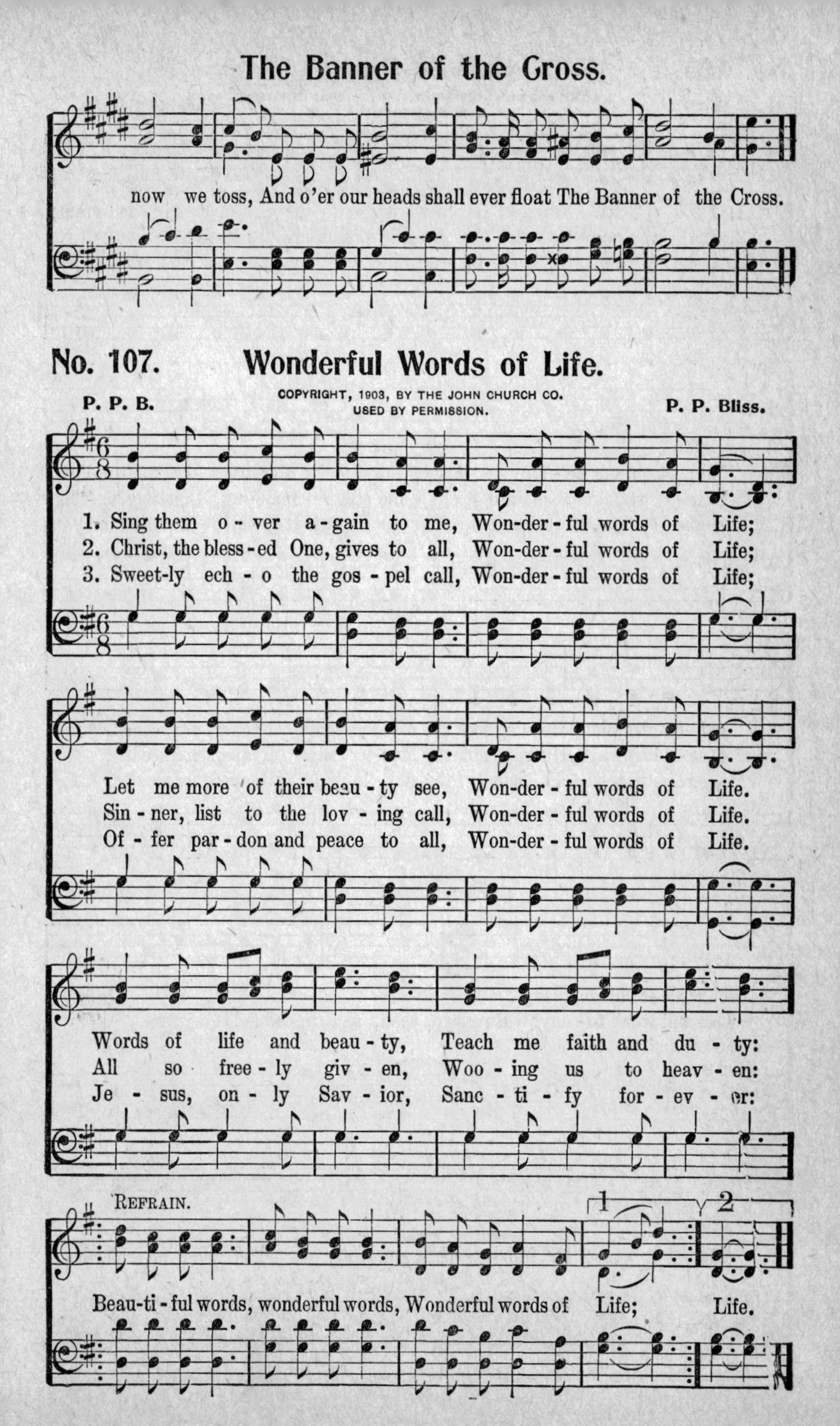
The Banner of the Cross.
now we toss, And o'er our heads shall ever float The Banner of the Cross.
No. 107. Wonderful Words of Life.
COPYRIGHT, 1903, BY THE JOHN CHURCH CO.
USED BY PERMISSION.
P. P. B.
P. P. Bliss.
1. Sing them o - ver a - gain to me, Won-der - ful words of Life;
2. Christ, the bless - ed One, gives to all, Won-der - ful words of Life;
3. Sweet-ly ech - o the gos - pel call, Won-der - ful words of Life;
Let me more of their beau - ty see, Won-der - ful words of Life.
Sin - ner, list to the lov - ing call, Won-der - ful words of Life.
Of - fer par - don and peace to all, Won-der - ful words of Life.
Words of life and beau - ty, Teach me faith and du - ty:
All so free - ly giv - en, Woo - ing us to heav - en:
Je - sus, on - ly Sav - ior, Sanc - ti - fy for - ev - er:
REFRAIN.
Beau-ti - ful words, wonderful words, Wonderful words of Life; Life.

No. 108. Harvest Song.
C. H. G.
WORDS AND MUSIC COPYRIGHT, 1907, BY CHAS. H. GABRIEL.
E. O. EXCELL, OWNER.
Chas. H. Gabriel.
1. Look, the har-vest-field is teem-ing With the rich and ri-pened grain;
2. In the mar-kets and the by-ways, Whil-ing pre-cious hours a-way,
3. Hear ye not the faith-ful sing-ing Of the la-bor and the yield?
Wide it spreads be-fore us, Bright the sky is o'er us; In the sun-light,
Man-y stand com-plain-ing, I-dle still re-main-ing, Loit'ring in the
Rouse ye, then, O sleep-ers, Join the hap-py reap-ers; To the wind your
gold-en gleaming, Heaving like the rest-less main, "Reapers are needed," re-
dust-y highways, Hearing not the Mas-ter say: "Reapers are needed, O
sor-rows fling-ing, Pa-tient-ly the sick-le wield: "Reapers are needed, A-
CHORUS.
sounds o'er hill and plain.
who will work to-day?" Rouse ye, then, and to the fields a-way, Go
wake, and to the field!" to the fields a-way,
la-bor for the Mas-ter while you may; Lo! He is call-ing,
Mas-ter while you may;

Harvest Song.
night is fall-ing, Has - ten to o - bey, For reap-ers are need-ed to - day.
No. 109. Close to Thee.
Fanny J. Crosby.
Silas J. Vail.
1. Thou, my ev - er-last - ing por - tion, More than friend or life to me;
2. Not for ease or world - ly pleas - ure, Nor for fame my prayer shall be;
3. Lead me thro' the vale of shad - ows, Bear me o'er life's fit - ful sea;
All a - long my pil - grim jour - ney, Sav - ior, let me walk with Thee.
Glad - ly will I toil and suf - fer, On - ly let me walk with Thee.
Then the gate of life e - ter - nal May I en - ter, Lord, with Thee.
Refrain.
Close to Thee, close to Thee, Close to Thee, close to Thee;
Close to Thee, close to Thee, Close to Thee, close to Thee;
Close to Thee, close to Thee, Close to Thee, close to Thee;
All a - long my pil - grim jour - ney, Sav - ior, let me walk with Thee.
Glad - ly will I toil and suf - fer, On - ly let me walk with Thee.
Then the gate of life e - ter - nal May I en - ter, Lord, with Thee.

E. O. Excell's Favorite -
No. 110. More Like the Master.
C. H. G.
COPYRIGHT, 1906, BY CHAS. H. GABRIEL.
E. O. EXCELL, OWNER.
Chas. H. Gabriel.
1. More like the Mas - ter I would ev - er be, More of His meek-ness,
2. More like the Mas - ter is my dai - ly prayer; More strength to car-ry
3. More like the Mas - ter I would live and grow; More of His love to
more hu - mil - i - ty; More zeal to la - bor, more cour-age to be
cross - es I must bear; More earn-est ef - fort to bring His king-dom
oth - ers I would show; More self - de - ni - al, like His in Gal - i-
rit.
true, More con - se - cra - tion for work He bids me do.
in; More of His Spir - it, the wan-der - er to win.
lee, More like the Mas - ter I long to ev - er be.
CHORUS.
Take Thou my heart, . . I would be Thine a - lone; . . Take Thou my
Take my heart, O take my heart, I would be Thine a - lone; Take my heart, O
heart . . and make it all Thine own; . . Purge me from sin, . . O
take my heart and make it all Thine own; Purge Thou me from ev - 'ry sin, O

More Like the Master.

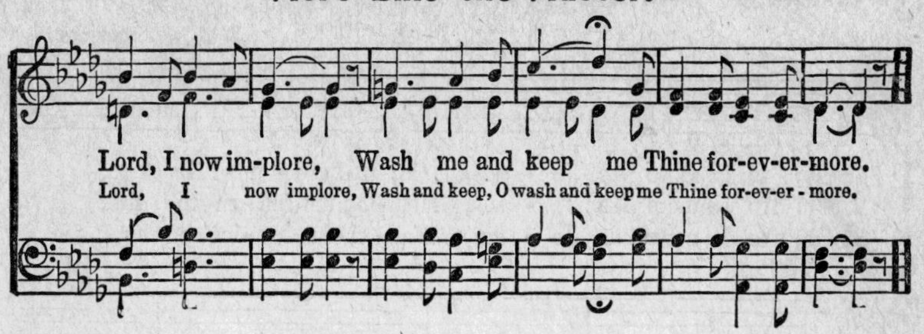
Lord, I now im-plore, Wash me and keep me Thine for-ev-er-more.
Lord, I now implore, Wash and keep, O wash and keep me Thine for-ev-er - more.

No. 111. Anywhere With Jesus.

John R. Clements.

E. O. Excell.

1. I'll go an - y-where, my Sav - ior, If Thou wilt make it clear; I will tell sal - va-tion's sto - ry To lost ones far and near.
2. I'll do an - y-thing, my Sav - ior, That hon-or brings to Thee; I will fol - low close Thy lead - ing, Wher-e'er it tak - eth me.
3. I'll be an - y-thing, my Sav - ior, In sta-tion high or low; I will toil, or wait, or suf - fer, If Thou dost will it so.
4. I'll hold ev-'ry-thing, my Sav - ior, A sa-cred trust of Thine; And the tal - ents to me giv - en, I'll count them not as mine.
CHORUS.
An - y-where, my

Sav-ior, Anywhere with Thee, Anywhere and ev'rywhere, As Thou leadest me.

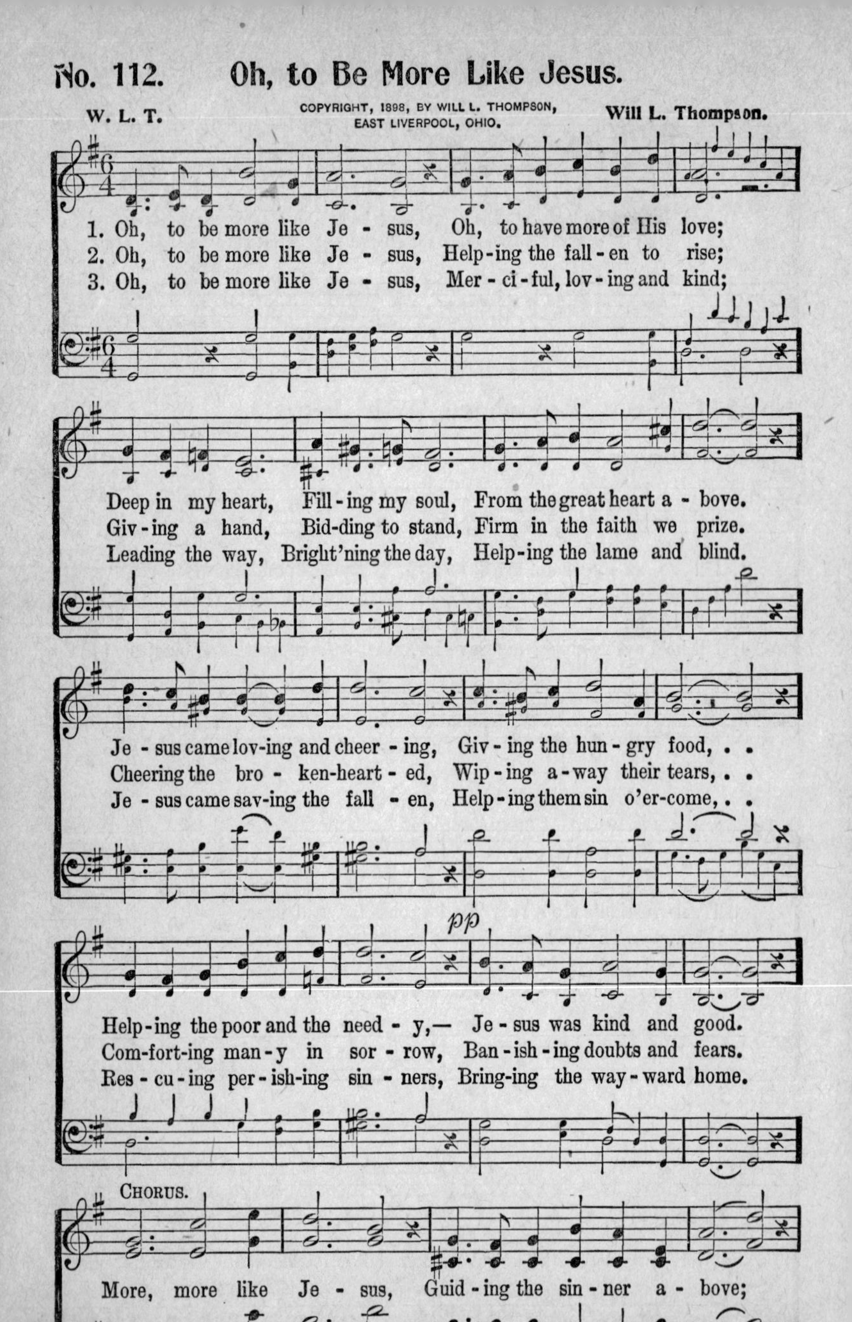
No. 112. Oh, to Be More Like Jesus.
W. L. T.
COPYRIGHT, 1898, BY WILL L. THOMPSON, EAST LIVERPOOL, OHIO.
Will L. Thompson.
1. Oh, to be more like Je - sus, Oh, to have more of His love;
2. Oh, to be more like Je - sus, Help-ing the fall-en to rise;
3. Oh, to be more like Je - sus, Mer - ci - ful, lov - ing and kind;
Deep in my heart, Fill-ing my soul, From the great heart a - bove.
Giv-ing a hand, Bid-ding to stand, Firm in the faith we prize.
Leading the way, Bright'ning the day, Help-ing the lame and blind.
Je - sus came lov-ing and cheer - ing, Giv - ing the hun - gry food, . .
Cheering the bro - ken-heart - ed, Wip - ing a - way their tears, . .
Je - sus came sav-ing the fall - en, Help - ing them sin o'er-come, . .
pp
Help-ing the poor and the need - y,— Je - sus was kind and good.
Com-fort-ing man-y in sor - row, Ban - ish - ing doubts and fears.
Res - cu - ing per - ish-ing sin - ners, Bring-ing the way - ward home.
CHORUS.
More, more like Je - sus, Guid - ing the sin - ner a - bove;

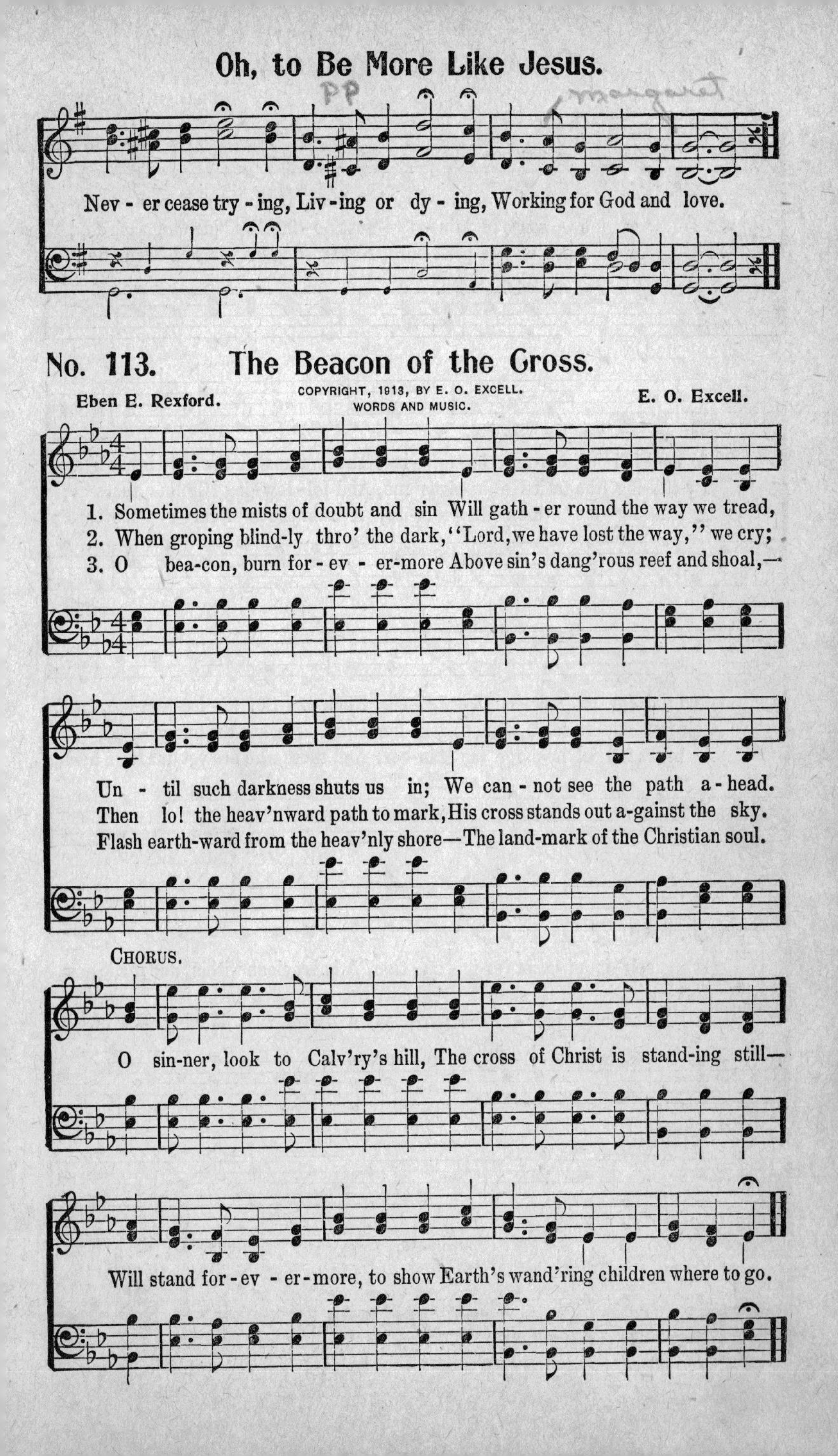

Oh, to Be More Like Jesus.
Nev - er cease try - ing, Liv - ing or dy - ing, Working for God and love.
No. 113. The Beacon of the Cross.
Eben E. Rexford.
COPYRIGHT, 1913, BY E. O. EXCELL.
WORDS AND MUSIC.
E. O. Excell.
1. Sometimes the mists of doubt and sin Will gath - er round the way we tread,
2. When groping blind-ly thro' the dark, "Lord, we have lost the way," we cry;
3. O bea-con, burn for - ev - er-more Above sin's dang'rous reef and shoal,—
Un - til such darkness shuts us in; We can - not see the path a - head.
Then lo! the heav'nward path to mark, His cross stands out a-gainst the sky.
Flash earth-ward from the heav'nly shore—The land-mark of the Christian soul.
CHORUS.
O sin-ner, look to Calv'ry's hill, The cross of Christ is stand-ing still—
Will stand for - ev - er-more, to show Earth's wand'ring children where to go.

No. 114. Oh, For a Clean Heart.
E. Hoening.
COPYRIGHT, 1897, BY CHAS. H. GABRIEL. E. O. EXCELL, OWNER.
Chas. H. Gabriel.
1. Oh, for a heart of de - vo - tion, A spir - it that wor-ships a - right,
2. Oh, for a deep sense of du - ty—Just do - ing His bid - ding each day,
3. Oh, for a sense of de-pend-ence, Not trusting to what I can do;
A soul full of ear-nest be - liev - ing, That walks with the Lord in the light;
By tak-ing the task He as-signs me, And fol - low - ing Him in the way;
A lean-ing by faith on His prom-ise, A zeal that will car - ry me thro';
And oh, for a spir - it like Je - sus, Kind, gen-tle, af - fec-tion-ate, true,
Con-tent-ed to serve, without ask - ing Him just what the har-vest will be,
A heart full of love for the Mas-ter, And those who are yet far from home;
A spir-it of sweet res-ig - na - tion, A heart clean within, and made new.
But wait-ing till He shall re - veal it, Con-tent then the blessing to see.
A mind full of sanc - ti-fied pur-pose, A heart that is ful-ly His own.
CHORUS.
Oh, . . . for a clean heart, Je - - - sus, I pray Thee,
Oh, for a clean heart, a clean heart, Je - sus, my Sav - ior, I pray Thee,

Oh, For a Clean Heart.

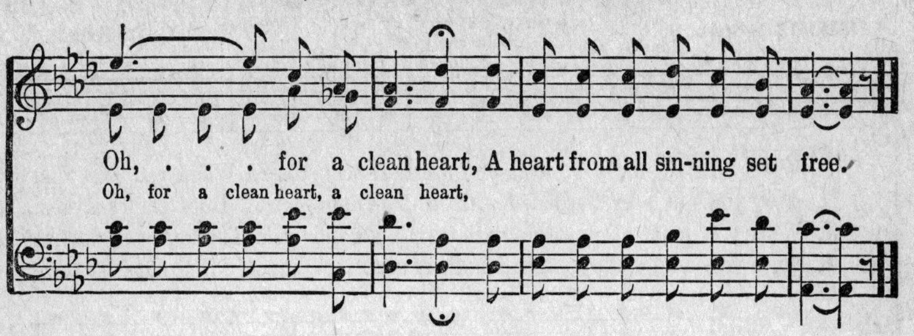
Oh, . . . for a clean heart, A heart from all sin-ning set free.
Oh, for a clean heart, a clean heart,

No. 115. Let the Lower Lights Be Burning.

P. P. B.

P. P. Bliss.

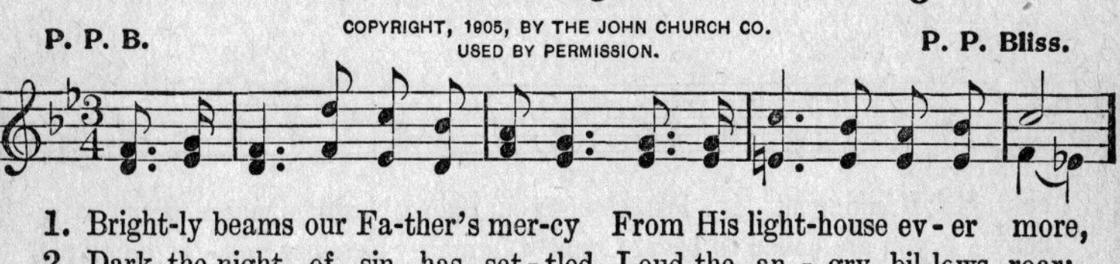

1. Bright-ly beams our Fa-ther's mer-cy From His light-house ev-er more,
2. Dark the night of sin has set-tled, Loud the an-gry bil-lows roar;
3. Trim your fee-ble lamp, my brother: Some poor sail-or tem-pest tossed,

FINE.

But to us He gives the keep-ing Of the lights a-long the shore.
Ea-ger eyes are watch-ing, long-ing, For the lights a-long the shore.
Try-ing now to make the har-bor, In the dark-ness may be lost.

D. S.—*Some poor fainting, struggling sea-man You may res-cue, you may save.*

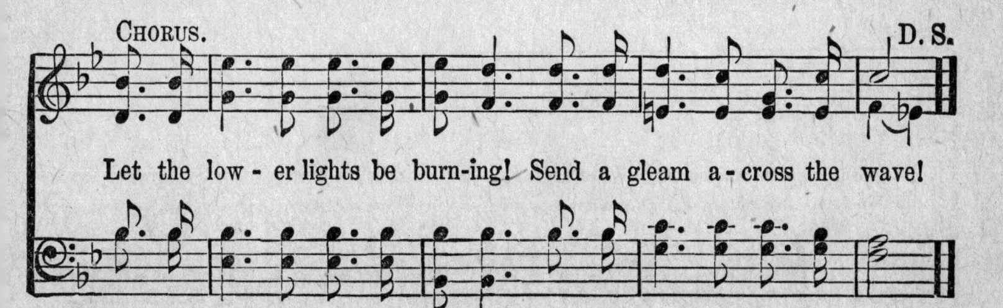
CHORUS.
D. S.
Let the low-er lights be burn-ing! Send a gleam a-cross the wave!

No. 116. Count Your Blessings.

Rev. J. Oatman, Jr. | E. O. Excell.

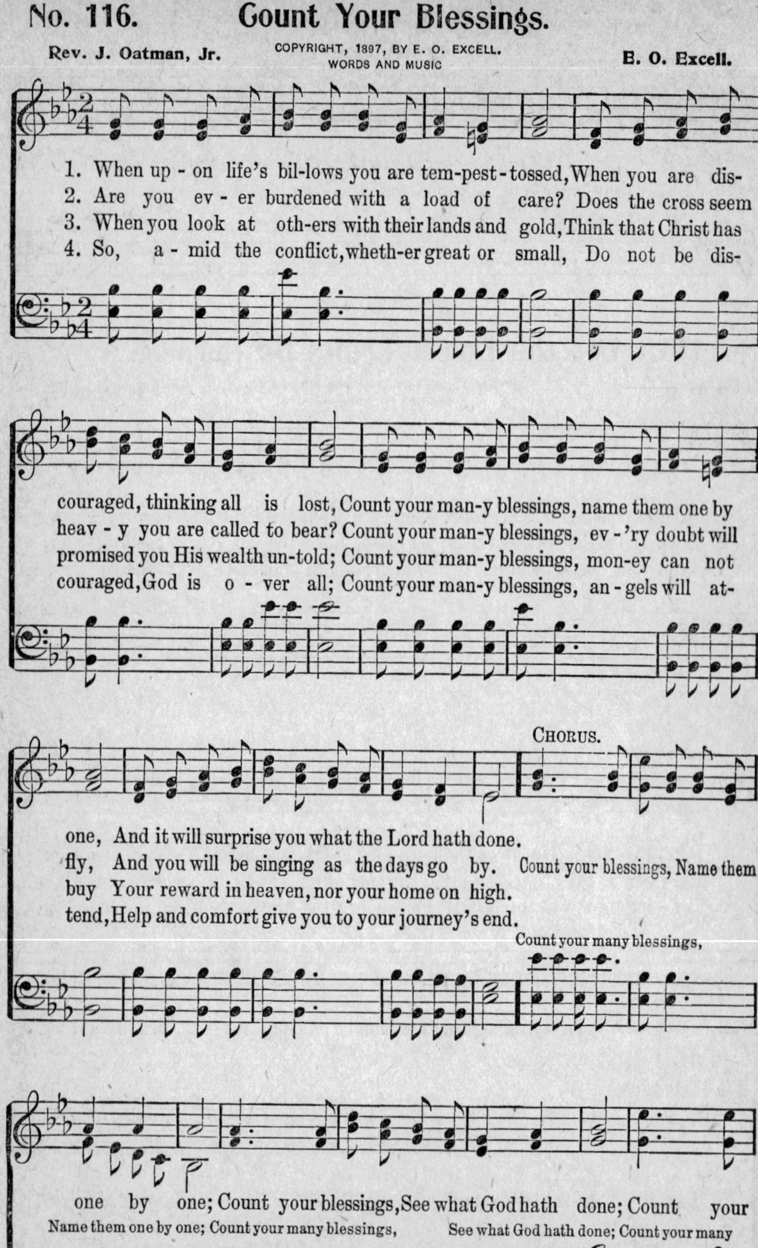
1. When up - on life's bil-lows you are tem-pest-tossed, When you are dis-couraged, thinking all is lost, Count your man-y blessings, name them one by one, And it will surprise you what the Lord hath done.
2. Are you ev - er burdened with a load of care? Does the cross seem heav - y you are called to bear? Count your man-y blessings, ev - 'ry doubt will fly, And you will be singing as the days go by.
3. When you look at oth-ers with their lands and gold, Think that Christ has promised you His wealth un-told; Count your man-y blessings, mon-ey can not buy Your reward in heaven, nor your home on high.
4. So, a - mid the conflict, wheth-er great or small, Do not be dis-couraged, God is o - ver all; Count your man-y blessings, an - gels will at-tend, Help and comfort give you to your journey's end.
CHORUS.
Count your blessings, Name them one by one; Count your blessings, See what God hath done; Count your
Count your many blessings, Name them one by one; Count your many blessings, See what God hath done; Count your many

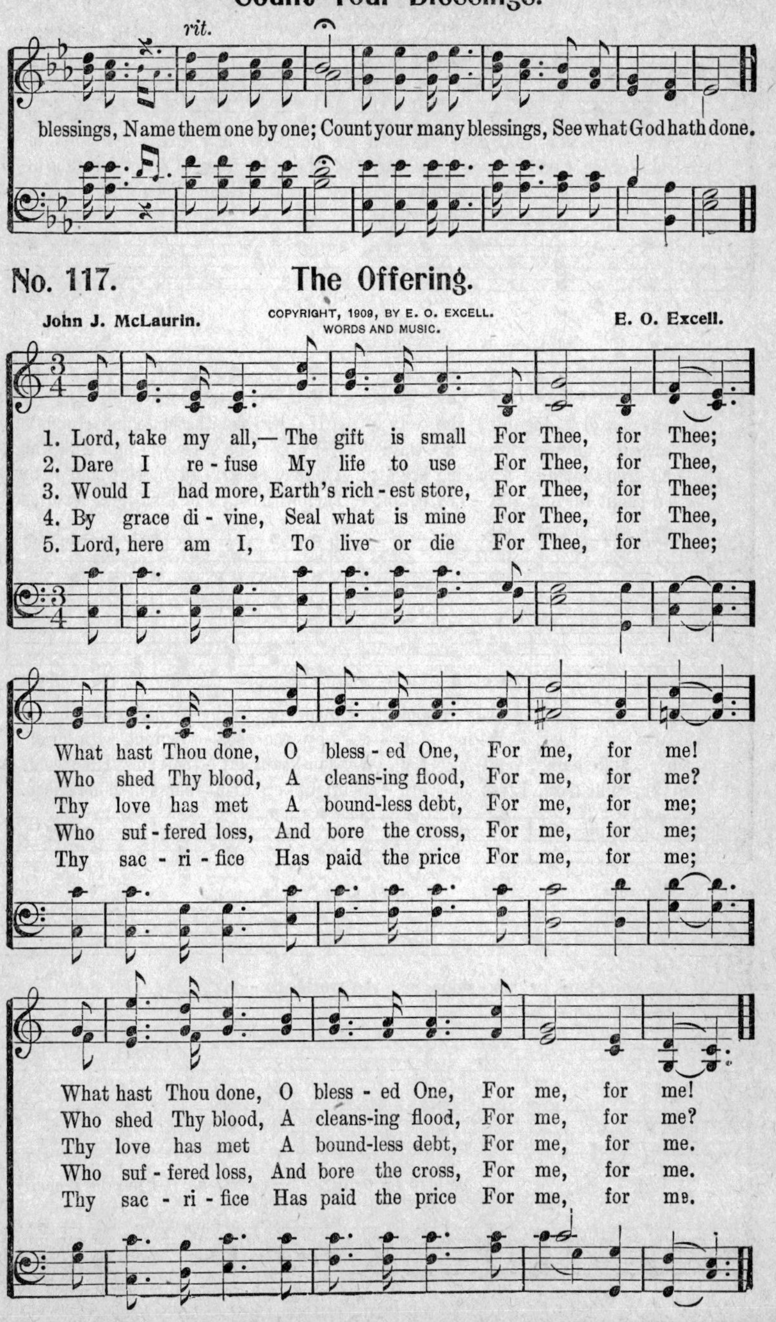
Count Your Blessings.
rit.
blessings, Name them one by one; Count your many blessings, See what God hath done.
No. 117. The Offering.
John J. McLaurin.
COPYRIGHT, 1909, BY E. O. EXCELL. WORDS AND MUSIC.
E. O. Excell.
1. Lord, take my all,— The gift is small For Thee, for Thee;
2. Dare I re - fuse My life to use For Thee, for Thee,
3. Would I had more, Earth's rich - est store, For Thee, for Thee;
4. By grace di - vine, Seal what is mine For Thee, for Thee,
5. Lord, here am I, To live or die For Thee, for Thee;
What hast Thou done, O bless - ed One, For me, for me!
Who shed Thy blood, A cleans-ing flood, For me, for me?
Thy love has met A bound-less debt, For me, for me;
Who suf - fered loss, And bore the cross, For me, for me;
Thy sac - ri - fice Has paid the price For me, for me;
What hast Thou done, O bless - ed One, For me, for me!
Who shed Thy blood, A cleans-ing flood, For me, for me?
Thy love has met A bound-less debt, For me, for me.
Who suf - fered loss, And bore the cross, For me, for me.
Thy sac - ri - fice Has paid the price For me, for me.

No. 118. Cloud or Sunshine.
Rev. M. S. Brown.
COPYRIGHT, 1908, BY CHAS. H. GABRIEL.
E. O. EXCELL, OWNER.
Chas. H. Gabriel.
1. Ev - 'ry sky that glis - tens with the gold - en day, Has its cloud of
2. Sun - shine would be bright-er for us day by day, If the clouds of
3. There are souls in dark-ness, long-ing for the light; We who are God's
4. Let us then look up - ward for a gold - en gleam Out of Heav-en's
sor - row drift - ing o'er the way; If we are the sun-shine, clouds will
dark-ness all were swept a - way; Why not be the sun - light, fill - ing
chil-dren should be shin - ing bright; There are hearts all shad-owed o'er by
sun - light till our fa - ces beam; Then with hearts of kind-ness let us
quick - ly flee, And the souls that meet us will be light and free.
hearts with cheer, Driv - ing far a - way the sor - row met with here.
sin and shame, Wait-ing for a sun-beam giv - en in His name.
make, while here, Lives of oth - ers bright - er with our sun-shine cheer.
CHORUS.
Are you cloud or sun - shine in the world to - day? Are you spread-ing
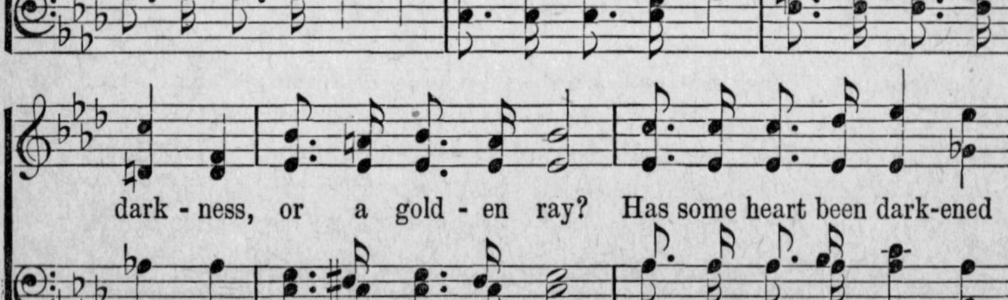
dark - ness, or a gold - en ray? Has some heart been dark-ened

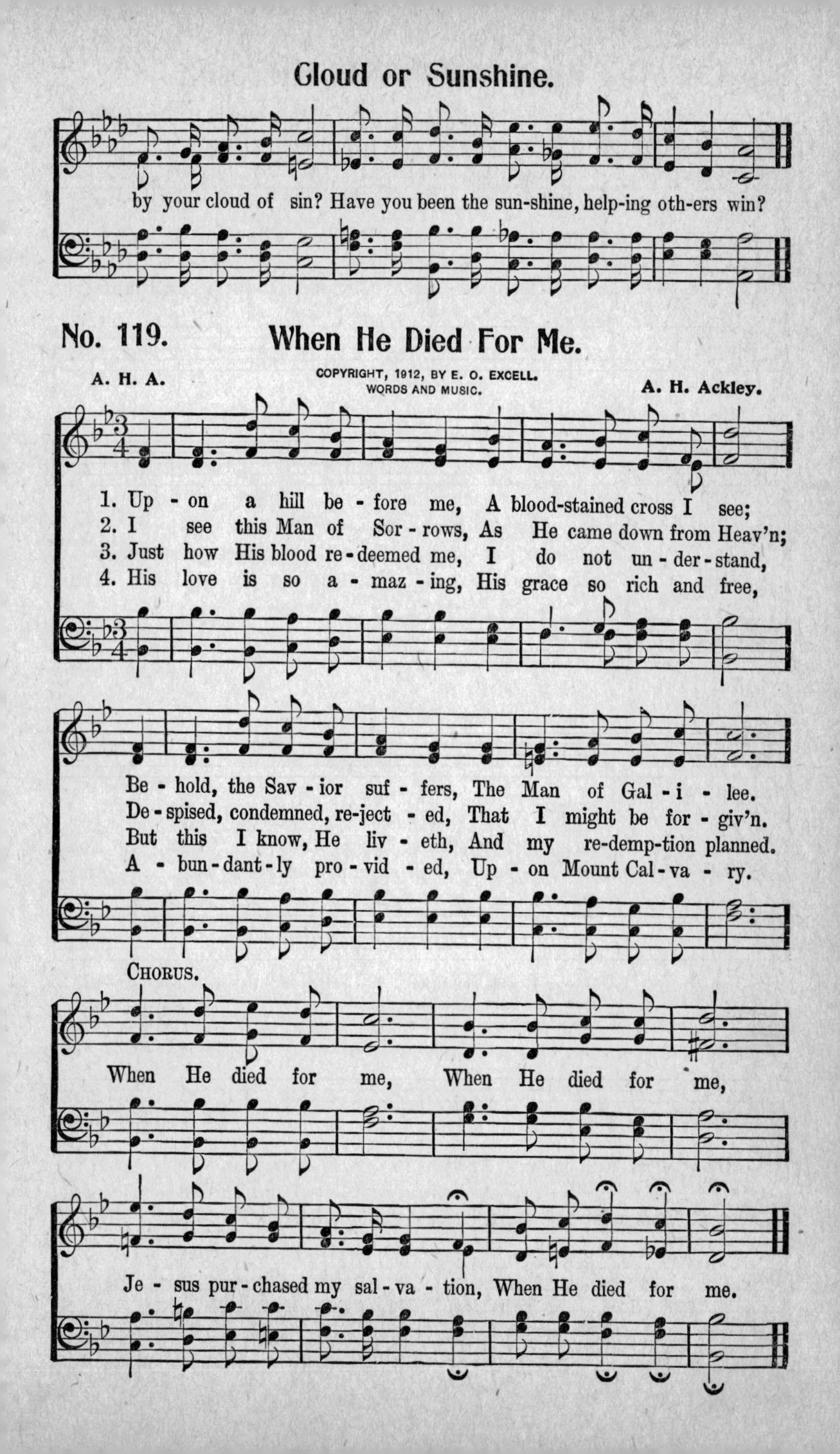
Cloud or Sunshine.
by your cloud of sin? Have you been the sun-shine, help-ing oth-ers win?
No. 119.
When He Died For Me.
A. H. A.
COPYRIGHT, 1912, BY E. O. EXCELL.
WORDS AND MUSIC.
A. H. Ackley.
1. Up - on a hill be - fore me, A blood-stained cross I see;
2. I see this Man of Sor - rows, As He came down from Heav'n;
3. Just how His blood re - deemed me, I do not un - der - stand,
4. His love is so a - maz - ing, His grace so rich and free,
Be - hold, the Sav - ior suf - fers, The Man of Gal - i - lee.
De - spised, condemned, re-ject - ed, That I might be for - giv'n.
But this I know, He liv - eth, And my re-demp-tion planned.
A - bun-dant-ly pro-vid - ed, Up - on Mount Cal - va - ry.
CHORUS.
When He died for me, When He died for me,
Je - sus pur-chased my sal - va - tion, When He died for me.

No. 120. The Whole Wide World for Jesus.
COPYRIGHT, 1908, BY WILL L. THOMPSON,
EAST LIVERPOOL, OHIO.
Will L. Thompson.
1. The whole wide world for Je - sus! Once more, be - fore we part,
2. The whole wide world for Je - sus! From out the Gold - en Gate,
3. The whole wide world for Je - sus! Its hearts, and homes, and thrones;
Ring out the joy - ful watch-word From ev - 'ry grate - ful heart; The
Thro' all the South Sea Is - lands, To Chi - na's prince-ly state; From
Ring out a - gain the watch-word In loud and joy - ous tones: The
whole wide world for Je - sus! Be this our bat - tle cry; . . The
In - dia's vales and moun-tains, Thro' Per-sia's land of bloom, . To
whole wide world for Je - sus! With prayer the song we'll wing, . . And
The whole wide world for Je - sus! Be this our bat - tle
From In - dia's vales and moun-tains, Thro' Per - sia's land of
The whole wide world for Je - sus! With prayer the song we'll
CHORUS.
Cru - ci - fied shall con-quer, And vic - to - ry is nigh.
sto - ried Pal - es - ti - na, And Af-ric's des - ert gloom. This whole wide world
speed the prayer with la-bor, Till earth shall crown Him King.
cry; . . shall con - quer,
bloom, Pal - es - ti - na,
wing, . . with la - bor,

The Whole Wide World for Jesus.
For Je-sus! for Je-sus! This whole wide world For Je-sus Christ, our Lord!
No. 121.
Jesus is Calling.
Fanny J. Crosby.
COPYRIGHT, 1911, BY GEO. C. STEBBINS, RENEWAL.
Geo. C. Stebbins.
1. Je-sus is ten-der-ly call-ing thee home—Call-ing to-day, call-ing to-day;
2. Je-sus is call-ing the wear-y to rest—Call-ing to-day, call-ing to-day;
3. Je-sus is waiting, oh, come to Him now—Waiting to-day, waiting to-day;
4. Je-sus is pleading, oh, list to His voice—Hear Him to-day, hear Him to-day;
Why from the sun-shine of love wilt thou roam Far-ther and far-ther a-way?
Bring Him thy bur-den, and thou shalt be blest; He will not turn Thee a-way.
Come with thy sins, at His feet low-ly bow; Come, and no lon-ger de-lay.
They who be-lieve on His name shall re-joice; Quickly a-rise and a-way.
CHORUS.
Call - ing to-day! Call - ing to-day!
Call-ing, call-ing to-day, to-day! Call-ing, call-ing to-day, to-day!
Je - sus is call - ing, is ten-der-ly call-ing to-day.
Je-sus is ten-der-ly call-ing to-day,

No. 122. Where Hast Thou Gleaned To-Day?

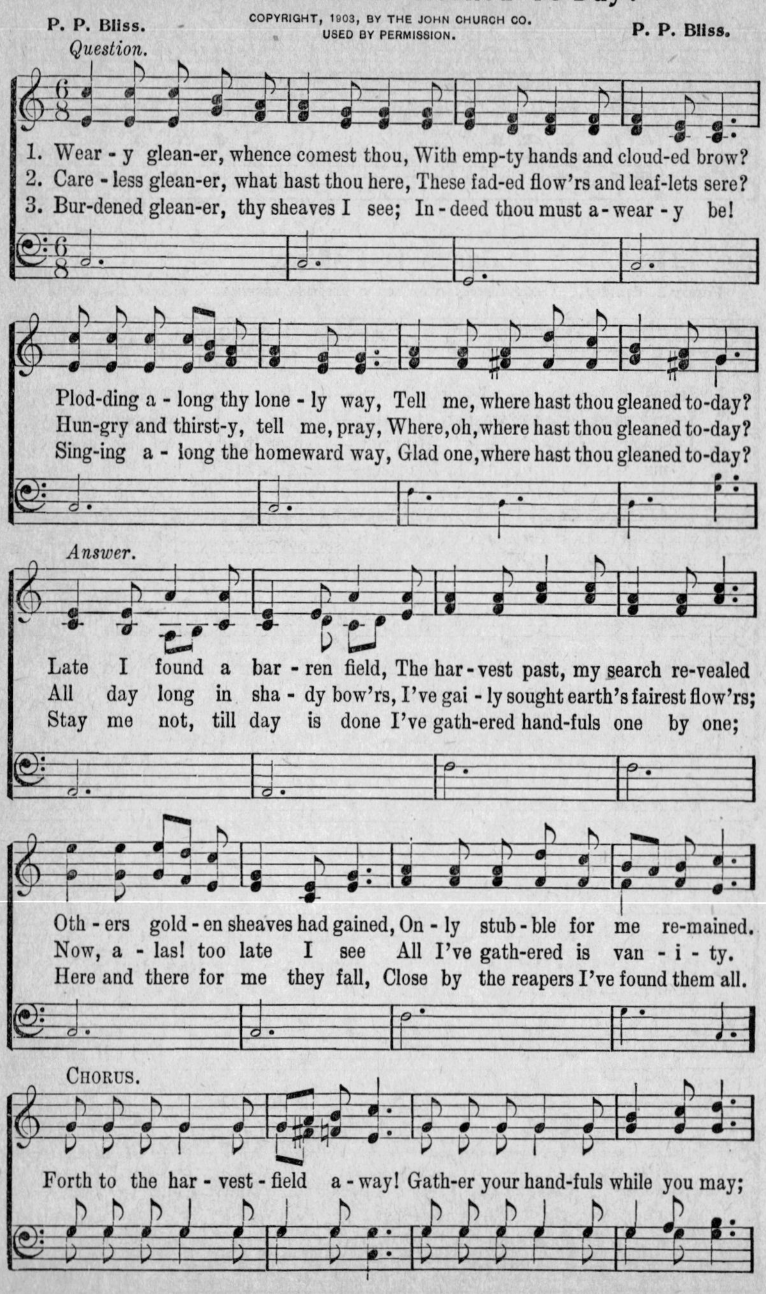
P. P. Bliss.
COPYRIGHT, 1903, BY THE JOHN CHURCH CO.
USED BY PERMISSION.
P. P. Bliss.
Question.
1. Wear - y glean-er, whence comest thou, With emp-ty hands and cloud-ed brow?
2. Care - less glean-er, what hast thou here, These fad-ed flow'rs and leaf-lets sere?
3. Bur-dened glean-er, thy sheaves I see; In - deed thou must a - wear - y be!
Plod-ding a - long thy lone - ly way, Tell me, where hast thou gleaned to-day?
Hun-gry and thirst-y, tell me, pray, Where, oh, where hast thou gleaned to-day?
Sing-ing a - long the homeward way, Glad one, where hast thou gleaned to-day?
Answer.
Late I found a bar - ren field, The har - vest past, my search re-vealed
All day long in sha - dy bow'rs, I've gai - ly sought earth's fairest flow'rs;
Stay me not, till day is done I've gath-ered hand-fuls one by one;
Oth - ers gold - en sheaves had gained, On - ly stub - ble for me re-mained.
Now, a - las! too late I see All I've gath-ered is van - i - ty.
Here and there for me they fall, Close by the reapers I've found them all.
Chorus.
Forth to the har - vest - field a - way! Gath-er your hand-fuls while you may;

Where Hast Thou Gleaned To-Day?

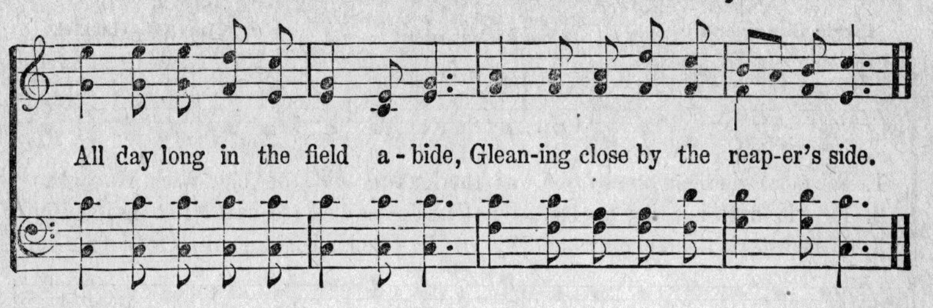
All day long in the field a-bide, Glean-ing close by the reap-er's side.

No. 123. Look and Live.

W. A. O. | COPYRIGHT, 1887, BY E. O. EXCELL. WORDS AND MUSIC. | W. A. Ogden.

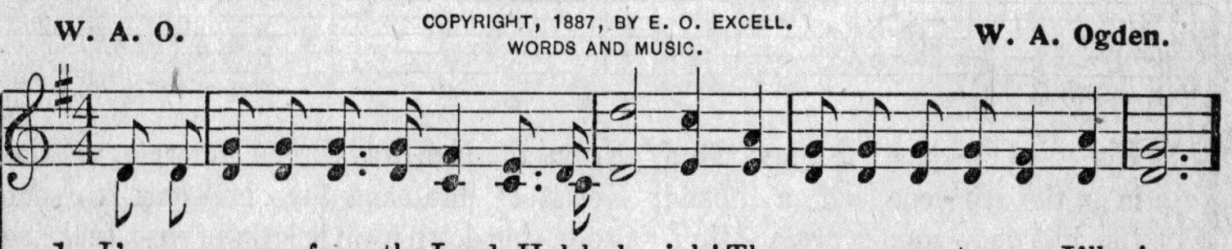

1. I've a message from the Lord, Hal-le-lu-jah! The message un-to you I'll give;
2. I've a message full of love, Hal-le-lu-jah! A message, O my friend, for you;
3. Life is of-fered un-to you, Hal-le-lu-jah! E-ter-nal life thy soul shall have,
4. I will tell you how I came, Hal-le-lu-jah! To Je-sus when He made me whole:

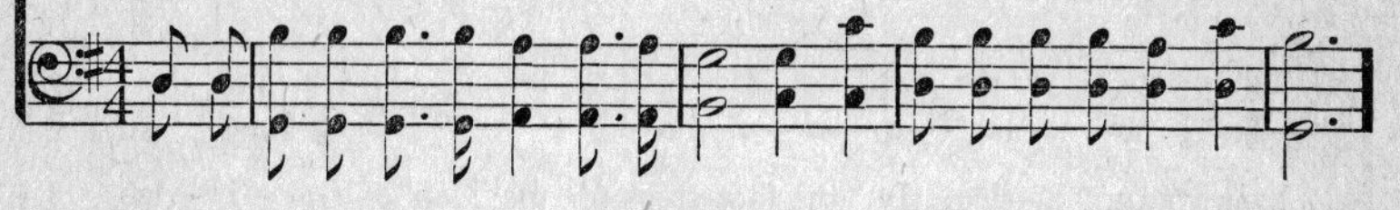

FINE.

'T is re-cord-ed in His word, Hal-le-lu-jah! It is on-ly that you "look and live."
'T is a message from above, Hal-le-lu-jah! Je-sus said it, and I know 't is true.
If you'll on-ly look to Him, Hal-le-lu-jah! Look to Je-sus, who a-lone can save.
'T was believing on His name, Hal-le-lu-jah! I trust-ed, and He saved my soul.

D. S.—*'T is recorded in His word, Hal-le-lu-jah! It is only that you "look and live."*

CHORUS. D. S.

"Look and live,". . . . my brother, live, Look to Je-sus now and live;
"Look and live," my brother, live, "Look and live."

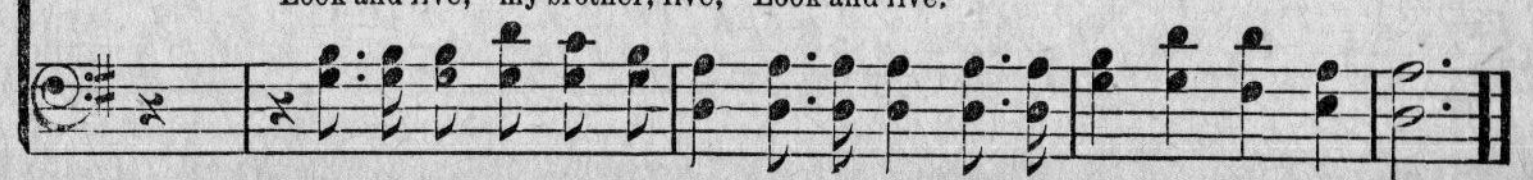

No. 124. Win Them One By One.
Lizzie DeArmond.
COPYRIGHT, 1912, BY E. O. EXCELL. WORDS AND MUSIC.
Chas. H. Gabriel.
1. We must win them one by one as the Mas-ter did of old, When He said to His dis-ci-ples "Fol-low Me;" From the high-ways broad and wide, to the by-ways turn a-side, In the foot-steps of the Man of Gal-i-lee.
2. Is it noth-ing they are lost, souls that Je-sus died to save? Let us glad-ly in the res-cue lend a hand; News of life and love im-part to some wear-y, sin-ful heart, Help some broth-er in the glo-ry light to stand.
3. We must win them one by one by a lit-tle kind-ness shown, Or a gen-tle touch of hu-man sym-pa-thy; Stoop-ing down from heigths of ease, seek-ing on-ly God to please, Pointing ev-er to the Christ of Cal-va-ry.
CHORUS.
One by one, yes, one by one, We must win them for Je-sus one by one; In the nar-row ways of life, a-mid the tu-mult

Win Them One By One. Very Slow.
and the strife, We must win them for Je - sus one by one.
No. 125. The Song of My Heart.
Rev. A. H. Ackley.
COPYRIGHT, 1914, BY E. O. EXCELL.
WORDS AND MUSIC.
B. D. Ackley.
1. There's a song in my heart, 'tis Je - sus, Its mel - o - dy came frow a - bove;
2. Its mu - sic dis - pels the mid-night, And scatters the foes that op - press;
3. When I sing with the saints in glo - ry, No mel - o - dy sweet-er can be
No mor - tal can meas-ure its full - ness, No an - gel can fath-om its love.
'T is sun-light to all who can sing it, A joy to the soul in dis - tress.
Than Je - sus the King of the a - ges, The Sav - ior who suf-fered for me.
CHORUS.
The song of my heart is Je - sus, No friend is so dear to me;
He par-doned my soul for - ev - er, When He died on mount Cal-va - ry.

No. 126. We Walk Together.

(To Bethany.)
Maggie E. Gregory.
COPYRIGHT, 1907, BY CHAS. H. GABRIEL.
E. O. EXCELL, OWNER.
Chas. H. Gabriel.
1. We walk to-geth-er, my Lord and I, A-long the King's high-way;
2. We walk to-geth-er, thro' joy or pain, In fel-low-ship com-plete;
He leads me gen-tly, no fear have I, He guards me night and day.
To live is Christ and to die is gain, And work for Him is sweet.
We walk to-geth-er, He leads the way, No e-vil can I fear,
We walk to-geth-er, my Lord and I, Oh, praise His ten-der love;
rit.
But fol-low Je-sus from day to day, Con-tent while He is near.
He'll guide me safe to my home on high, In realms of bliss a-bove.
CHORUS.
Thro' days of sun-shine or cloud-ed sky, We walk to-geth-er, my Lord and

We Walk Together.
rit.
I, We walk to-geth - er, my Lord and I. a tempo.
No. 127. Softly and Tenderly.
W. L. T.
USED BY PER. WILL L. THOMPSON ESTATE, EAST LIVERPOOL, O.
Will L. Thompson.
1. Soft - ly and ten-der-ly Je - sus is call-ing, Call-ing for you and for me;
2. Why should we tar-ry when Jesus is pleading, Pleading for you and for me?
3. Time is now fleeting, the moments are passing, Passing from you and from me;
4. Oh! for the wonderful love He has promised, Promised for you and for me;
FINE.
See, on the portals He's waiting and watching, Watching for you and for me.
Why should we lin-ger and heed not His mercies, Mer-cies for you and for me?
Shadows are gath-er-ing, death beds are coming, Coming for you and for me.
Tho' we have sinned, He has mercy and pardon, Pardon for you and for me.
D. S.—Ear-nest-ly, ten - der - ly, Je - sus is call-ing, Call-ing, O sin-ner, come home!
CHORUS.
Come home, come home, Ye who are wear-y, come home,
Come home, come home,
D.S.

No. 128. His Wondrous Gifts To Me.
COPYRIGHT, 1913, BY E. O. EXCELL.
WORDS AND MUSIC.
Rev. T. O. Chisholm.
Samuel W. Beazley.
1. Years I spent in sin and fol - ly, Wand'ring far, so far from God,
2. Joy have I that nev - er fail - eth, Joy this world could ne'er af - ford,
3. Wondrous love my heart is fill - ing, Love for Him who first loved me,
Led by Satan's fair al - lure-ments Down the broad and e - vil road;
Pure and sweet and sat - is - fy - ing— Pre-cious gift from Christ my Lord!
Love for all for whom He suf-fered On the cross of Cal - va - ry;
rit.
But at last my feet grew wear - y, Guilt and fear my soul pos - sessed,
E'en when trib - u - la-tion com - eth, Thro' the clouds I can-not see,
Love that yields my rich-est treas-ure— E - ven life not counting dear—
a tempo.
rit.
Then I turned and came to Je - sus And He gave me peace and rest.
I re-joice in calm as - sur - ance Of the glo - ry yet to be.
To complete my course with glad-ness, And my Lord's "Well done" to hear.
CHORUS.

I have "peace that passeth understanding," I have joy, a deep, un-fail-ing spring,

His Wondrous Gifts To Me.
rit.
I have love, abounding, overflowing–Wondrous gifts from Christ, my Lord and King.
No. 129. I've Found a Friend.
Rev J. G. Small.
COPYRIGHT, 1903, BY E. O. EXCELL.
INTERNATIONAL COPYRIGHT SECURED.
Aug. Halter.
1. I've found a Friend, O such a Friend! He loved me ere I knew Him;
2. I've found a Friend, O such a Friend! He bled, He died to save me;
3. I've found a Friend, O such a Friend! So kind, and true, and ten-der,
He drew me with the cords of love, And thus He bound me to Him.
And not a-lone the gift of love, But His own life He gave me.
So wise a Coun-sel-or and Guide, So might-y a De-fend-er.
CHORUS.
I love to sing of such a Friend, Whose love no pow'r can sev-er;
rit.
My heart, my strength, my life, my all, Are His, and His for-ev-er.

No. 130.

Hold Up the Cross.

Mrs. Frank A. Breck. COPYRIGHT, 1914, BY E. O. EXCELL. WORDS AND MUSIC. Chas. H. Gabriel.

1. Hold up the cross! there the Sav-ior of men Be-came our re-demp-tion from sin; Then her-ald the sto-ry a-gain and a-gain, Of all that dear Sav-ior has been.
2. Hold up the cross! 't is the sig-net of peace, The prom-ise of a-ges ful-filled; It means a do-min-ion that nev-er shall cease, The bless-ing our Fa-ther has willed.
3. Hold up the cross! let the peo-ple be-hold, And know that sal-va-tion may be A-bun-dant and free, to the young and the old, Yea, all who are will-ing to see.
4. Hold up the cross! there is no oth-er way For sin-ners, by sin-ning en-slaved, To come from the bondage of dark-ness to day, And be ev-er-last-ing-ly saved.

CHORUS.

Hold up the cross!
Hold up the cross! Hold up the cross!
Hold up the cross of Je-sus!

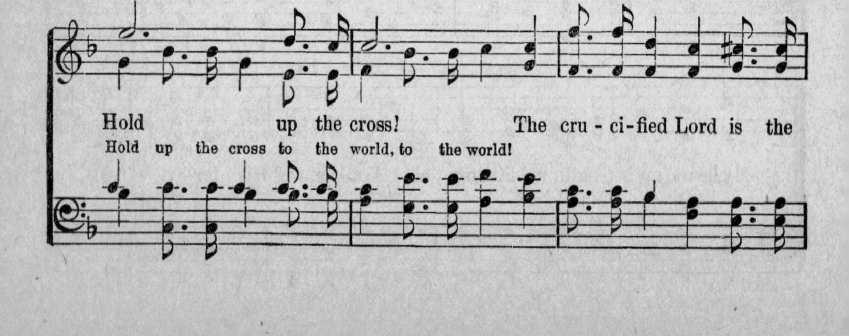

Hold up the cross! The cru-ci-fied Lord is the
Hold up the cross to the world, to the world!

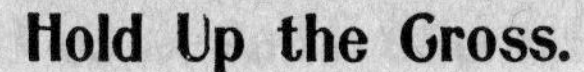

Hold Up the Cross.

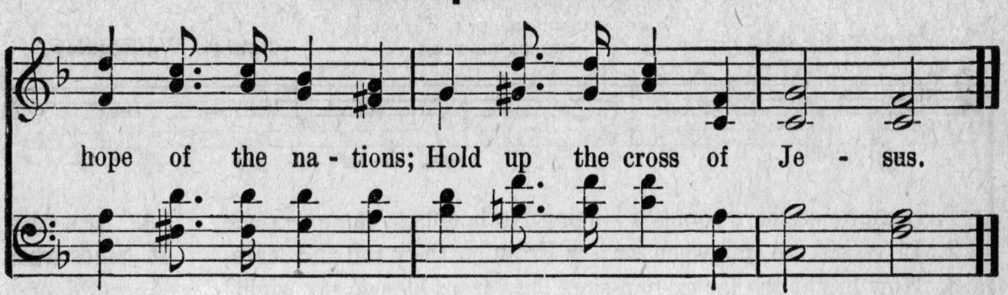
hope of the na - tions; Hold up the cross of Je - sus.

No. 131. More Like Jesus.

J. M. S.

J. M. Stillman.

1. I want to be more like Je - sus, And fol-low Him day by day;
2. I want to be kind and gen - tle To those who are in dis - tress;
3. I want to be meek and low - ly, Like Je - sus, our Friend and King;
4. I want to be pure and ho - ly, As pure as the crys - tal snow;

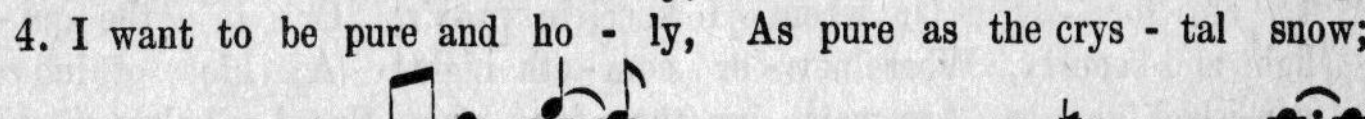

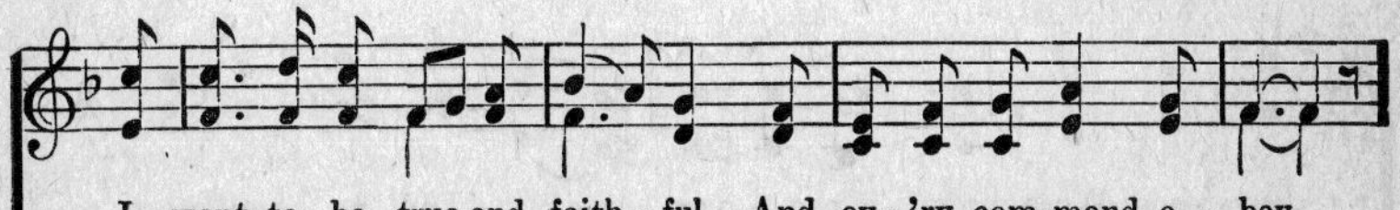

I want to be true and faith - ful, And ev - 'ry com-mand o - bey.
To com-fort the bro - ken-heart - ed With sweet words of ten - der - ness.
I want to be strong and ear - nest, And souls to the Sav - ior bring.
I want to love Je - sus dear - ly, For Je - sus loves me, I know.

REFRAIN.

1
2

More and more like Jesus, I would ever be; . . . My Sav-ior who died for me.
I . . . . ever would be;

No. 132. The Life That is to Be.

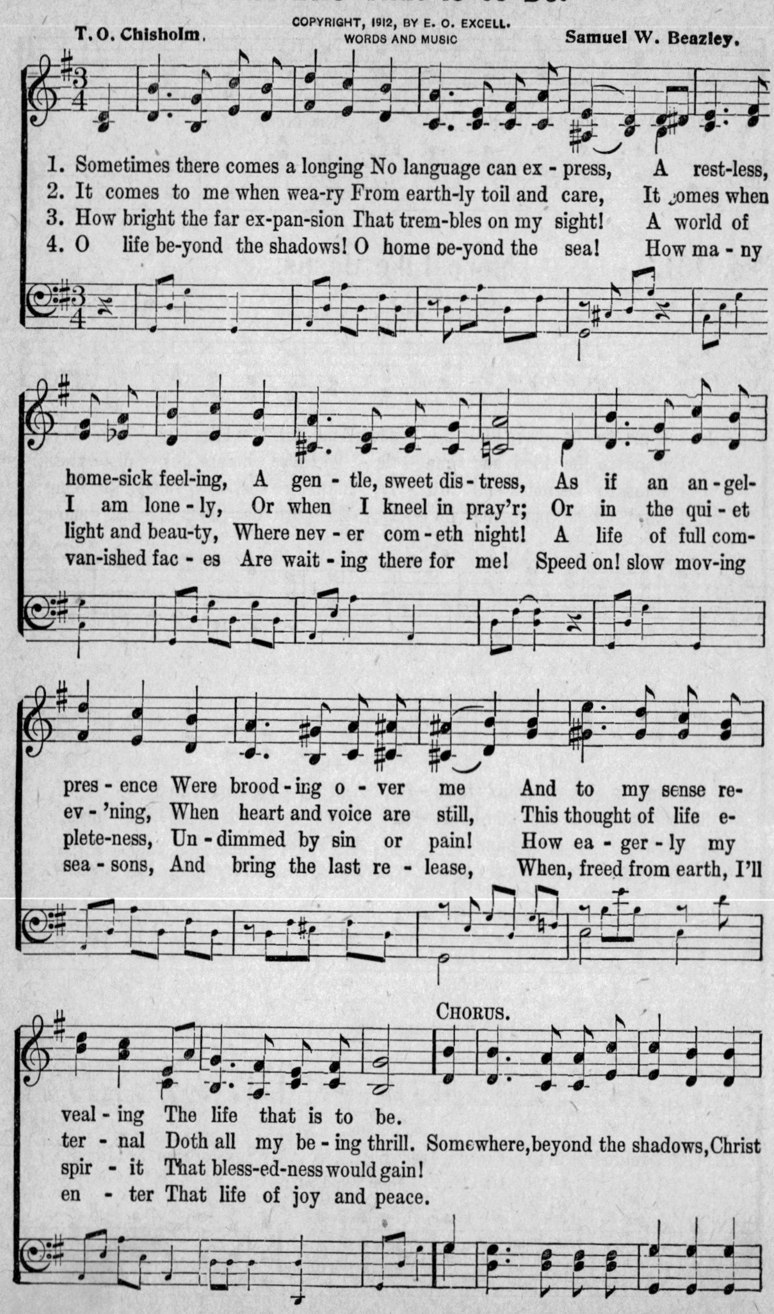
T. O. Chisholm.
COPYRIGHT, 1912, BY E. O. EXCELL. WORDS AND MUSIC
Samuel W. Beazley.
1. Sometimes there comes a longing No language can ex - press, A rest-less,
2. It comes to me when wea-ry From earth-ly toil and care, It comes when
3. How bright the far ex-pan-sion That trem-bles on my sight! A world of
4. O life be-yond the shadows! O home be-yond the sea! How ma - ny
home-sick feel-ing, A gen - tle, sweet dis - tress, As if an an - gel-
I am lone - ly, Or when I kneel in pray'r; Or in the qui - et
light and beau-ty, Where nev - er com - eth night! A life of full com-
van-ished fac - es Are wait - ing there for me! Speed on! slow mov-ing
pres - ence Were brood - ing o - ver me And to my sense re-
ev - 'ning, When heart and voice are still, This thought of life e-
plete-ness, Un - dimmed by sin or pain! How ea - ger - ly my
sea - sons, And bring the last re - lease, When, freed from earth, I'll
veal - ing The life that is to be.
ter - nal Doth all my be - ing thrill.
spir - it That bless-ed-ness would gain!
en - ter That life of joy and peace.
CHORUS.
Somewhere, beyond the shadows, Christ

The Life That Is to be.
has a home for me, Each pass-ing day brings nearer The life that is to be.
No. 133.
Beautiful Isle.
Jessie B. Pounds.
COPYRIGHT, 1897, BY E. O. EXCELL.
WORDS AND MUSIC.
J. S. Fearis.
1. Some-where the sun is shin - ing, Some-where the song - birds dwell;
2. Some-where the day is lon - ger, Some-where the task is done;
3. Some-where the load is lift - ed, Close by an o - pen gate;
Hush, then, thy sad re - pin - ing, God lives, and all is well.
Some-where the heart is stron - ger, Some-where the guer - don won.
Some-where the clouds are rift - ed, Some-where the an - gels wait.
CHORUS.
Some - where, Some - where, Beau-ti - ful Isle of Some-where!
Some-where, beau-ti - ful, beau - ti - ful Isle,
Land of the true, where we live a - new,—Beau-ti-ful Isle of Some-where!

No. 134. Ashamed of Jesus.
Joseph Grigg.
COPYRIGHT, 1914, BY E. O. EXCELL.
E. O. Excell.
1. Je - sus, and shall it ev - er be, A mor - tal man ashamed of Thee? A - shamed of Thee, whom an-gels praise, Whose glories shine thro' end-less days? A - shamed of Je - sus! soon - er far Let eve-ning blush to own a star; He sheds the beams of light di - vine O'er this be-night - ed soul of mine.
2. A-shamed of Jesus! that dear Friend On whom my hopes of Heav'n depend? No; when I blush, be this my shame, That I no more re - vere His name. A - shamed of Je - sus! yes, I may When I've no guilt to wash a - way; No tear to wipe, no good to crave, No fears to quell, no soul to save.
Ashamed of Je - sus! just as soon Let midnight be ashamed of noon; . . . . . .
Let mid-night be ashamed of noon;
Till then—nor is my boasting vain—Till then I boast a Sav - ior slain; . . . .
Till then I boast a Sav-ior slain;

Ashamed of Jesus.

'Tis mid-night with my soul till He, Bright Morning Star, bid dark-ness flee.
And oh, may this my glo - ry be, That Christ is not a-shamed of me!
No. 135.
All Thine Own.
Maggie E. Gregory.
COPYRIGHT, 1914, BY E. O. EXCELL.
WORDS AND MUSIC.
Chas. H. Gabriel.
1. Sav - ior, our hearts shall be Thy throne, Our love shall be Thy crown;
2. Sav - ior, our hearts shall be Thy throne, Our lives shall be Thy praise;
3. Hum-bly we make the of - fer - ing, Come, reign up - on Thy throne;
Here at Thy sa - cred, pierc - ed feet Our of - f'rings lay we down.
And for Thy glo - ry we will live Thro' all our fu - ture days.
Kneeling be - fore the mer - cy - seat, Lord, seal us all Thine own.
CHORUS.
All Thine own, all Thine own, Take us, dear Lord, to be Thine own;
All Thine own, all Thine own, Our hearts to be Thy throne.

No. 136. My Ever Faithful Friend.

Rev. T. O. Chisholm.

Chas. H. Gabriel.

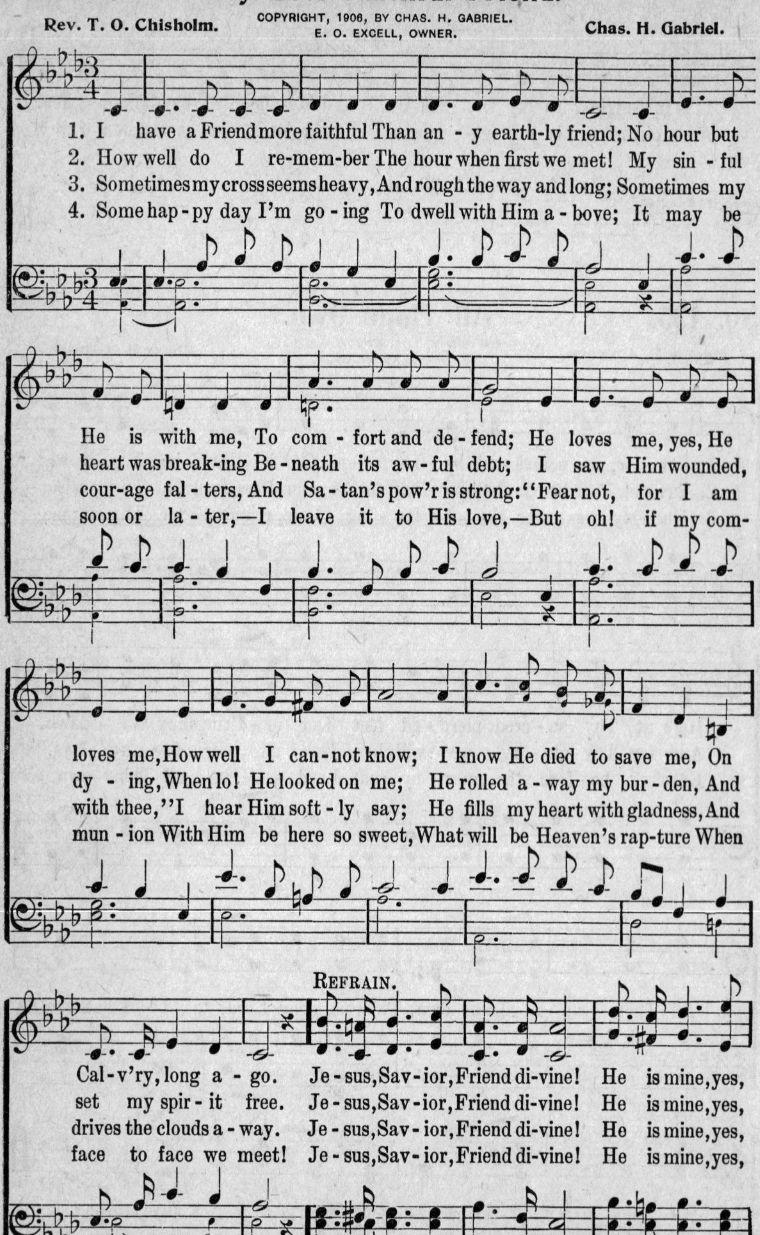
1. I have a Friend more faithful Than an - y earth-ly friend; No hour but
2. How well do I re-mem-ber The hour when first we met! My sin - ful
3. Sometimes my cross seems heavy, And rough the way and long; Sometimes my
4. Some hap - py day I'm go - ing To dwell with Him a - bove; It may be
He is with me, To com - fort and de - fend; He loves me, yes, He
heart was break-ing Be - neath its aw - ful debt; I saw Him wounded,
cour-age fal - ters, And Sa - tan's pow'r is strong: "Fear not, for I am
soon or la - ter,—I leave it to His love,—But oh! if my com-
loves me, How well I can-not know; I know He died to save me, On
dy - ing, When lo! He looked on me; He rolled a - way my bur - den, And
with thee," I hear Him soft - ly say; He fills my heart with gladness, And
mun - ion With Him be here so sweet, What will be Heaven's rap-ture When
REFRAIN.
Cal-v'ry, long a - go. Je - sus, Sav - ior, Friend di-vine! He is mine, yes,
set my spir - it free. Je - sus, Sav - ior, Friend di-vine! He is mine, yes,
drives the clouds a - way. Je - sus, Sav - ior, Friend di-vine! He is mine, yes,
face to face we meet! Je - sus, Sav - ior, Friend di-vine! He is mine, yes,

My Ever Faithful Friend.
He is mine! I know He died to save me, On Cal-v'ry, long a - go.
He is mine! He rolled a - way my bur-den, And set my spir - it free.
He is mine! He fills my heart with gladness, And drives the clouds a - way.
He is mine! What will be Heaven's rap-ture When face to face we meet!
No. 137. I Need Thee Every Hour.
Mrs. Annie S. Hawks.
COPYRIGHT, 1900, BY MARY RUNYON LOWRY. RENEWAL. USED BY PERMISSION.
Rev. Robert Lowry.
1. I need Thee ev-'ry hour, Most gra - cious Lord; No ten - der voice like Thine Can peace af - ford.
2. I need Thee ev-'ry hour, Stay Thou near by; Temp-ta-tions lose their pow'r When Thou art nigh.
3. I need Thee ev-'ry hour, In joy or pain; Come quick-ly and a - bide, Or life is vain.
4. I need Thee ev-'ry hour, Most Ho - ly One; O make me Thine in - deed, Thou bless - ed Son!
CHORUS.
I need Thee, O I need Thee; Ev-'ry hour I need Thee! O bless me now, my Sav - ior, I come to Thee!

No. 138. Holy Twilight Hour.

(The Winona Bethany Hymn.)

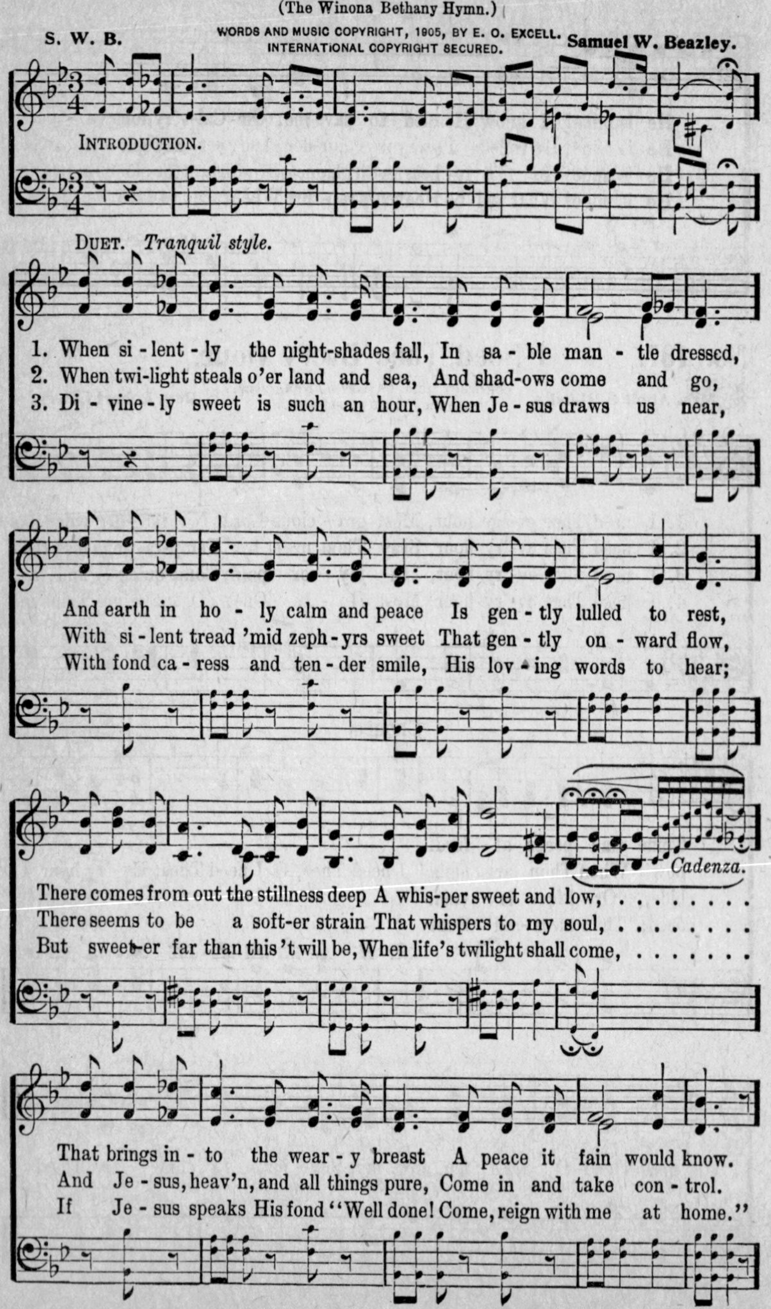
S. W. B.
WORDS AND MUSIC COPYRIGHT, 1905, BY E. O. EXCELL.
INTERNATIONAL COPYRIGHT SECURED.
Samuel W. Beazley.
INTRODUCTION.
DUET. Tranquil style.
1. When si - lent - ly the night-shades fall, In sa - ble man - tle dressed,
2. When twi-light steals o'er land and sea, And shad-ows come and go,
3. Di - vine - ly sweet is such an hour, When Je - sus draws us near,
And earth in ho - ly calm and peace Is gen - tly lulled to rest,
With si - lent tread 'mid zeph - yrs sweet That gen - tly on - ward flow,
With fond ca - ress and ten - der smile, His lov - ing words to hear;
Cadenza.
There comes from out the stillness deep A whis-per sweet and low, ...
There seems to be a soft-er strain That whispers to my soul, ...
But sweet-er far than this 't will be, When life's twilight shall come, ...
That brings in - to the wear - y breast A peace it fain would know.
And Je - sus, heav'n, and all things pure, Come in and take con - trol.
If Je - sus speaks His fond "Well done! Come, reign with me at home."

Holy Twilight Hour.
QUARTET.
Ho - ly twi-light hour, bless-ed twi-light hour, Thro' thy wooing, Jesus speaks and bids us "Come"!
Ho - ly twi-light hour, bless-ed twi-light hour, Thro' thy tranquil dream the [Omit . . . . .] heart sings Home, sweet home. . .
Twi-light hour, twi-light hour,
sweet home.
rit.
No. 139. Twilight Is Falling.
A. S. Kieffer.
USED BY PERMISSION.
B. C. Unseld.
1. Twi-light is fall-ing o-ver the sea, Shad-ows are steal-ing dark on the lea; Borne on the night-winds, voi-ces of yore Come from the far-off shore.
2. Voi-ces of loved ones, songs of the past, Still lin-ger round me while life shall last; Lone-ly I wan-der, sad-ly I roam, Seek-ing that far-off home.
3. Come in the twi-light, come, come to me! Bring-ing some mes-sage o-ver the sea, Cheer-ing my path-way while here I roam, Seek-ing that far-off home.
FINE.
D. S.—Gleam-eth a man-sion, filled with de-light, Sweet hap-py home so bright!
f CHORUS.
Far a-way beyond the star-lit skies, Where the love-light never, never dies,
D. S.

No. 140. Saved! Saved!

J. P. S

J. P. Scholfield.

1. I've found a Friend who is all to me,... His love is ev - er true;........... I love to tell.. how He lift - ed me, ...And what His grace can do for you....
2. He saves me from ev - 'ry sin and harm,.. Se- cures my soul each day;........... I'm lean - ing strong on His might - y arm;.. I know He'll guide me all the way..
3. When poor and need - y, and all a - lone,... In love He said to me,........... "Come un - to Me... and I'll lead you home,.. To live with Me e - ter - nal - ly."...

Saved! Saved!

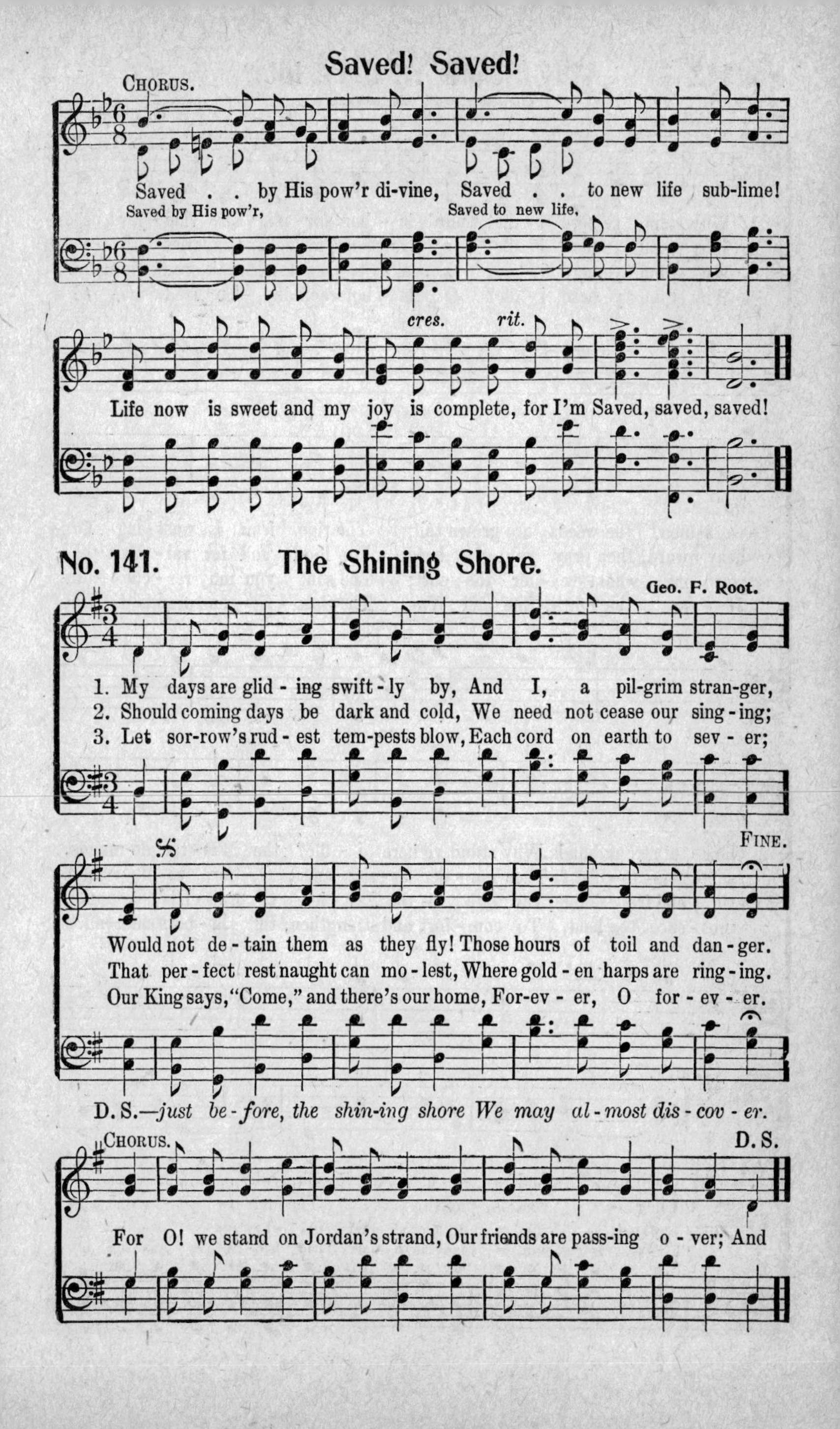

CHORUS.
Saved . . by His pow'r di-vine, Saved . . to new life sub-lime!
Saved by His pow'r, Saved to new life,
cres. rit.
Life now is sweet and my joy is complete, for I'm Saved, saved, saved!

No. 141. The Shining Shore.

Geo. F. Root.

1. My days are glid - ing swift - ly by, And I, a pil-grim stran-ger,
2. Should coming days be dark and cold, We need not cease our sing - ing;
3. Let sor-row's rud - est tem-pests blow, Each cord on earth to sev - er;
FINE.
Would not de - tain them as they fly! Those hours of toil and dan - ger.
That per - fect rest naught can mo - lest, Where gold - en harps are ring - ing.
Our King says, "Come," and there's our home, For-ev - er, O for - ev - er.
D. S.—just be - fore, the shin-ing shore We may al - most dis - cov - er.
CHORUS.
D. S.
For O! we stand on Jordan's strand, Our friends are pass-ing o - ver; And

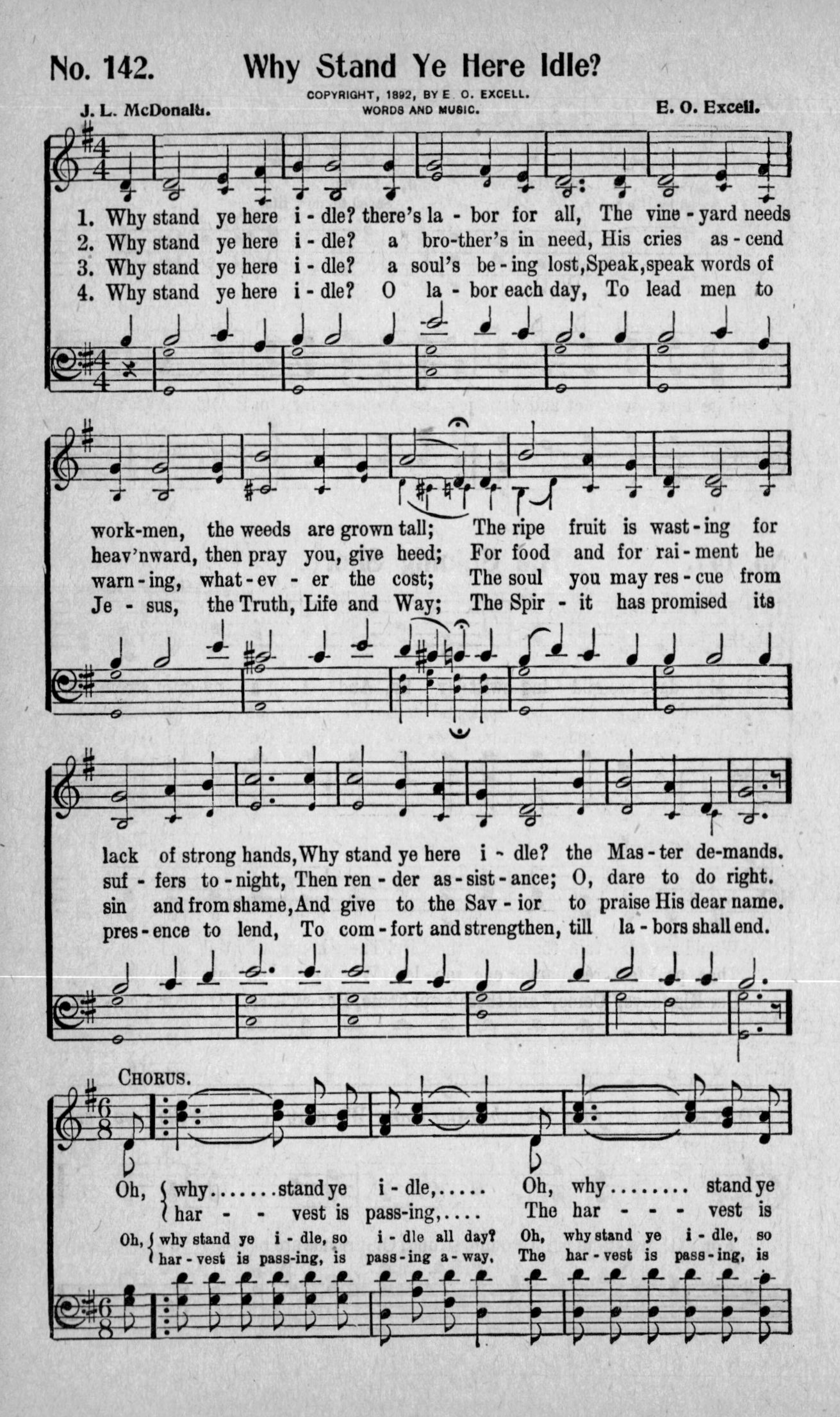
No. 142. Why Stand Ye Here Idle?
COPYRIGHT, 1892, BY E. O. EXCELL. WORDS AND MUSIC.
J. L. McDonald.
E. O. Excell.
1. Why stand ye here i - dle? there's la - bor for all, The vine - yard needs work-men, the weeds are grown tall; The ripe fruit is wast - ing for lack of strong hands, Why stand ye here i - dle? the Mas - ter de-mands.
2. Why stand ye here i - dle? a bro-ther's in need, His cries as - cend heav'nward, then pray you, give heed; For food and for rai - ment he suf - fers to - night, Then ren - der as - sist - ance; O, dare to do right.
3. Why stand ye here i - dle? a soul's be - ing lost, Speak, speak words of warn - ing, what - ev - er the cost; The soul you may res - cue from sin and from shame, And give to the Sav - ior to praise His dear name.
4. Why stand ye here i - dle? O la - bor each day, To lead men to Je - sus, the Truth, Life and Way; The Spir - it has promised its pres - ence to lend, To com - fort and strengthen, till la - bors shall end.
CHORUS.
Oh, why....... stand ye i - dle,..... Oh, why........ stand ye
har - - vest is pass-ing,.... The har - - - vest is
Oh, why stand ye i - dle, so i - dle all day? Oh, why stand ye i - dle, so
har - vest is pass-ing, is pass-ing a - way, The har - vest is pass - ing, is

Why Stand Ye Here Idle?

i - dle,....... Oh, why.......... stand ye i - dle,.......
pass - ing,...... The har - - - - vest is pass - ing,. .....
i - dle all day? Oh, why stand ye i - dle, so i - dle all day,
pass - ing a - way, The har - vest is pass - ing, is pass - ing a - way,
1
rit.
2
i - - - dle all day?..... The pass - - ing a - way.
i - dle all day, i - dle all day? The pass-ing a-way, passing a - way.
No. 143.
No Dying There.
F. A. B.
COPYRIGHT, 1892, BY W. A. PENN.
E. O. EXCELL, OWNER.
F. A. Blackmer.
1. A land by faith I see, Where saints shall ever be Free from mor-tal-i - ty,
2. There friends shall meet again, In happiness to reign, While thro' that blest domain,
3. There sorrow cannot stay; There tears are wiped away, One bright, e-ter-nal day,
D. S.—In that fair, heav'nly land,
FINE.
REFRAIN.
D.S.
No dy-ing there. No dying there, . . . No dying there; . . .
No dying there. No dy-ing there, No dy-ing there;

No. 144. The Church in the Wildwood.
W. S. P.
NEW ARRANGEMENT OF WORDS AND MUSIC
COPYRIGHT, 1910, BY E. O. EXCELL.
Dr. William S. Pitts.
1. There's a church in the val-ley by the wild-wood, No love-li-er
2. Oh, come to the church in the wild-wood, To the trees where the
3. How sweet on a clear, Sab-bath morn-ing To list to the
4. From the church in the val-ley by the wild-wood, When day fades a-
spot in the dale; No place is so dear to my child-hood As the
wild flow-ers bloom; Where the part-ing hymn will be chant-ed, We will
clear ring-ing bell; Its tones so sweet-ly are call-ing, Oh,
way in-to night, I would fain from this spot of my child-hood Wing my
D. S.—No spot is so dear to my child-hood As the
FINE. CHORUS.
lit-tle brown church in the vale. Come to the
weep by the side of the tomb.
come to the church in the vale.
way to the man-sions of light.
Oh, come, come, come, come, come, come,
lit-tle brown church in the vale.
D. S.
church in the wild-wood, Oh, come to the church in the vale;
come, come, come, come, come, come, come, come, come, come, come, come, come;

Children's Songs

No. 145. Dear Little Stranger.
C. H. G.
COPYRIGHT, 1900, BY E. O. EXCELL.
WORDS AND MUSIC.
Chas. H. Gabriel.
1. Low in a man - ger—dear lit - tle Stran - ger, Je - sus, the won - der - ful Savior, was born; There was none to receive Him, none to believe Him, None but the an - gels were watching that morn.
2. An - gels de - scend - ing, o - ver Him bend - ing, Chant - ed a ten - der and si - lent refrain; Then a won - der - ful sto - ry told of His glo - ry, Un - to the shepherds on Beth - le - hem's plain.
3. Dear lit - tle Stran - ger, born in a man - ger, Mak - er and Monarch, and Sav - ior of all; I will love Thee for - ev - er! grieve Thee? no, never! Thou didst for me make Thy bed in a stall.
CHORUS.
Dear lit - tle Stranger, slept in a man - ger,
No down - y pil - low un - der His head;
But with the poor He slumbered se - cure, The dear lit - tle Babe in His bed.
1
2

No. 146. I'll Be a Sunbeam.

To my grandson, Edwin O. Excell, Jr.

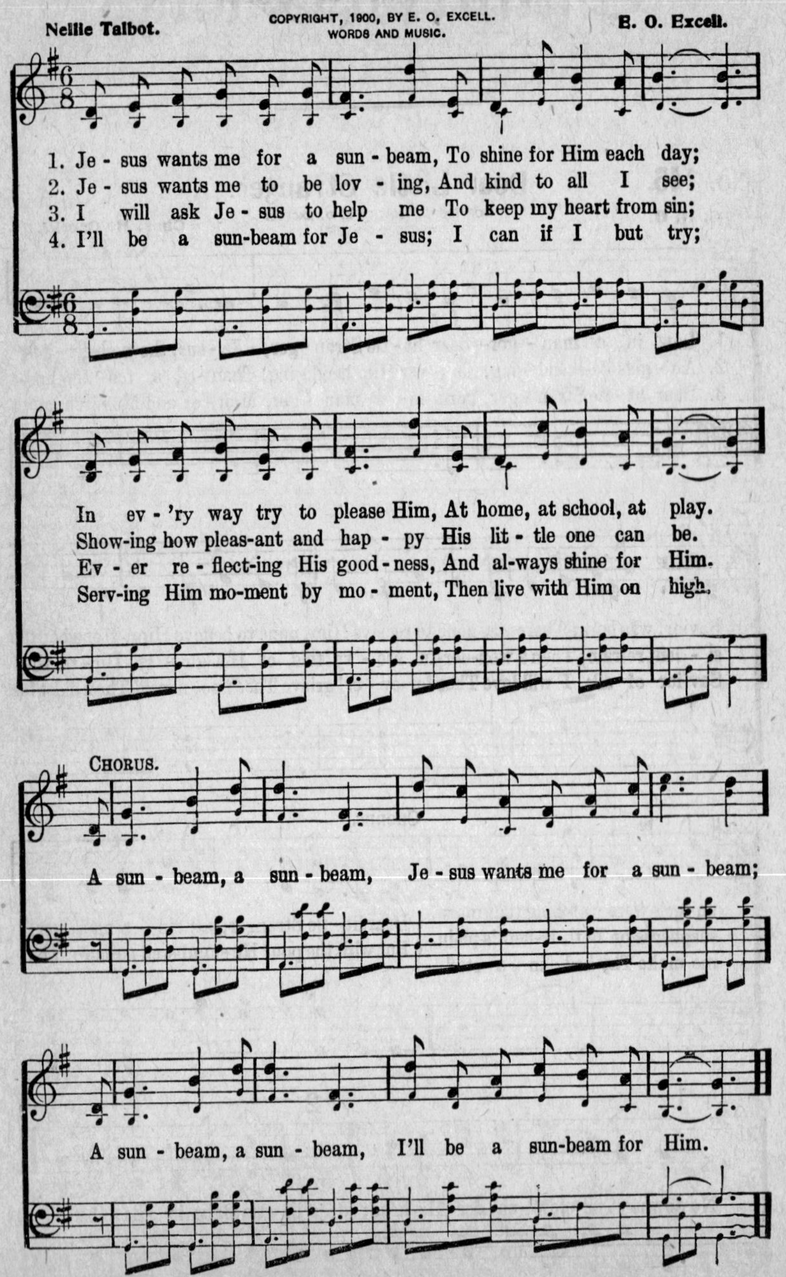
Nellie Talbot.
COPYRIGHT, 1900, BY E. O. EXCELL.
WORDS AND MUSIC.
E. O. Excell.
1. Je - sus wants me for a sun - beam, To shine for Him each day;
2. Je - sus wants me to be lov - ing, And kind to all I see;
3. I will ask Je - sus to help me To keep my heart from sin;
4. I'll be a sun-beam for Je - sus; I can if I but try;
In ev - 'ry way try to please Him, At home, at school, at play.
Show-ing how pleas-ant and hap - py His lit - tle one can be.
Ev - er re - flect-ing His good - ness, And al-ways shine for Him.
Serv-ing Him mo-ment by mo - ment, Then live with Him on high.
CHORUS.
A sun - beam, a sun - beam, Je - sus wants me for a sun - beam;
A sun - beam, a sun - beam, I'll be a sun-beam for Him.

No. 147. Let the Sunshine In.

Ada Blenkhorn. | Chas. H. Gabriel.

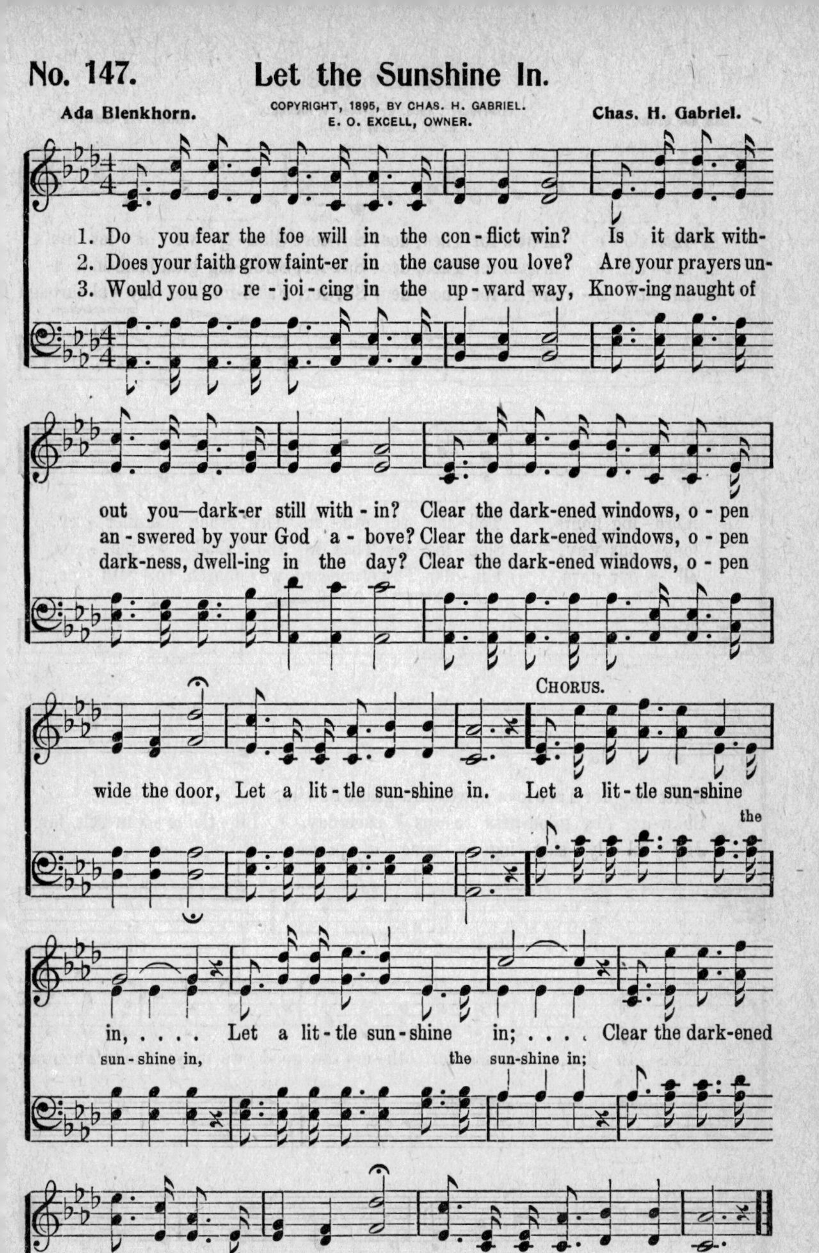
1. Do you fear the foe will in the con-flict win? Is it dark with-
2. Does your faith grow faint-er in the cause you love? Are your prayers un-
3. Would you go re-joi-cing in the up-ward way, Know-ing naught of
out you—dark-er still with-in? Clear the dark-ened windows, o-pen
an-swered by your God a-bove? Clear the dark-ened windows, o-pen
dark-ness, dwell-ing in the day? Clear the dark-ened windows, o-pen
wide the door, Let a lit-tle sun-shine in.
CHORUS.
Let a lit-tle sun-shine
the
in, ... Let a lit-tle sun-shine in; . . . . Clear the dark-ened
sun-shine in, the sun-shine in;

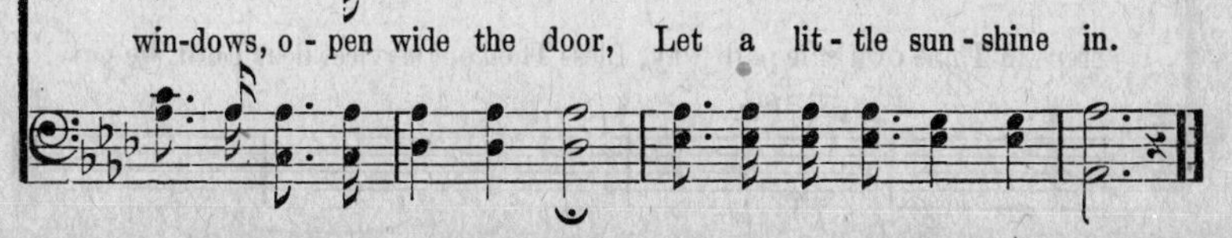
win-dows, o-pen wide the door, Let a lit-tle sun-shine in.

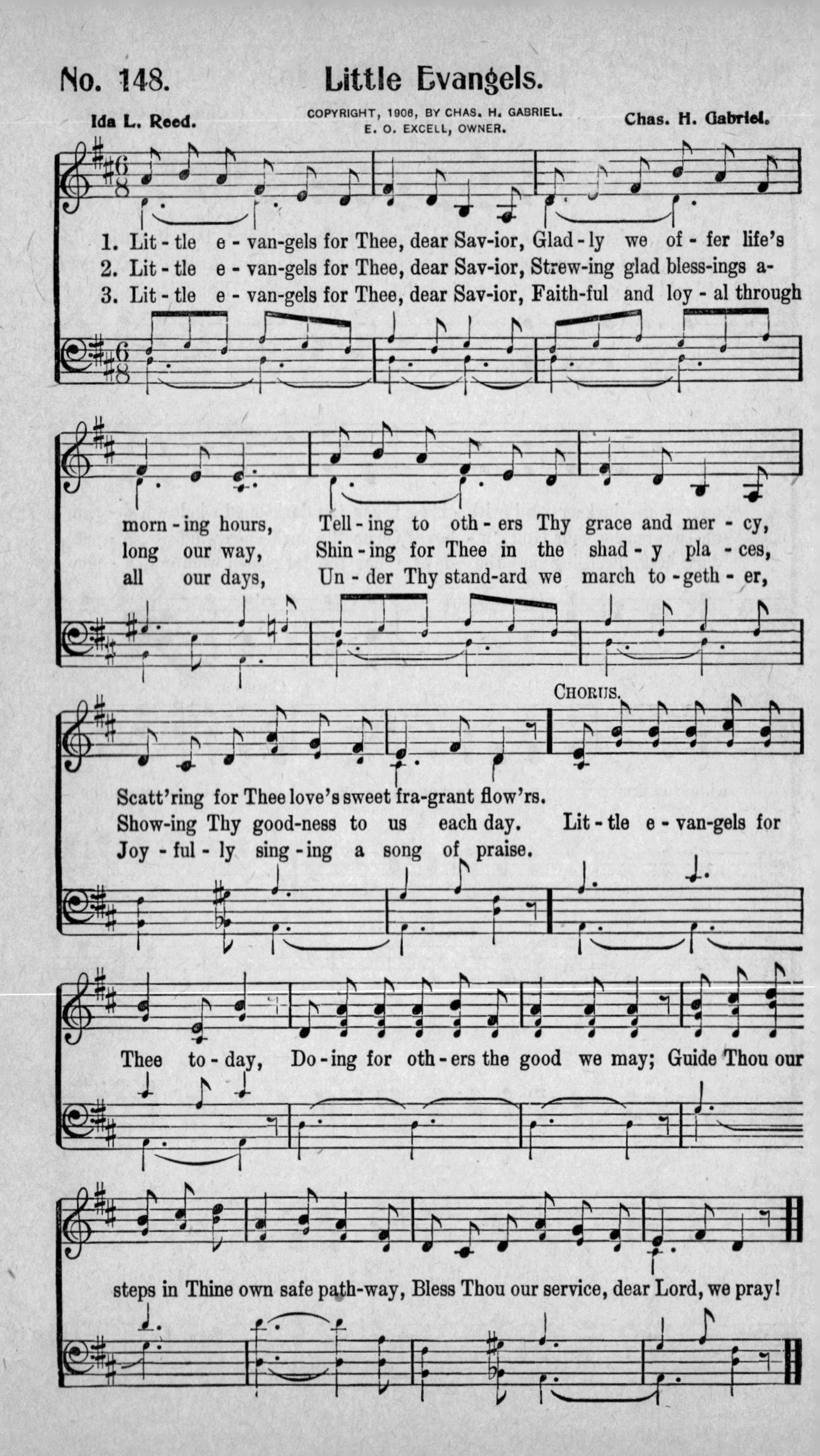
No. 148.
Little Evangels.
Ida L. Reed.
COPYRIGHT, 1906, BY CHAS. H. GABRIEL.
E. O. EXCELL, OWNER.
Chas. H. Gabriel.
1. Lit-tle e-van-gels for Thee, dear Sav-ior, Glad-ly we of-fer life's
2. Lit-tle e-van-gels for Thee, dear Sav-ior, Strew-ing glad bless-ings a-
3. Lit-tle e-van-gels for Thee, dear Sav-ior, Faith-ful and loy-al through
morn-ing hours, Tell-ing to oth-ers Thy grace and mer-cy,
long our way, Shin-ing for Thee in the shad-y pla-ces,
all our days, Un-der Thy stand-ard we march to-geth-er,
Scatt'ring for Thee love's sweet fra-grant flow'rs.
Show-ing Thy good-ness to us each day.
Joy-ful-ly sing-ing a song of praise.
CHORUS.
Lit-tle e-van-gels for Thee to-day, Do-ing for oth-ers the good we may; Guide Thou our
steps in Thine own safe path-way, Bless Thou our service, dear Lord, we pray!

No. 149.
Luther's Cradle Hymn.
Martin Luther.
COPYRIGHT, 1896, BY CHAS. H. GABRIEL.
E. O. EXCELL, OWNER.
Chas. H. Gabriel.
1. A - way in a man - ger, No crib for His bed, The lit - tle Lord
2. The cat - tle were low - ing—The poor Ba - by wakes; But lit - tle Lord
3. Be near me, Lord Je - sus, I ask Thee to stay Close by me for-
rit.
a tempo.
Je - sus Lay down His wee head; The stars in the heav - ens Looked
Je - sus, No cry - ing He makes: I love Thee, Lord Je - sus, Look
ev - er, And love me, I pray; Bless all the dear chil - dren In
down where He lay, The lit - tle Lord Je - sus, A - sleep on the hay.
down from the sky, And stay by my cra - dle, To watch lull - a - by.
Thy ten - der care, And take us to heav - en, To live with Thee there.
Chorus.
A - sleep, a - sleep, A - sleep, the Sav - ior in a stall!
A - sleep, a - sleep,
A - sleep, a - sleep, A - sleep, the Lord of all! . . .
A - sleep, a - sleep, the Lord of all!

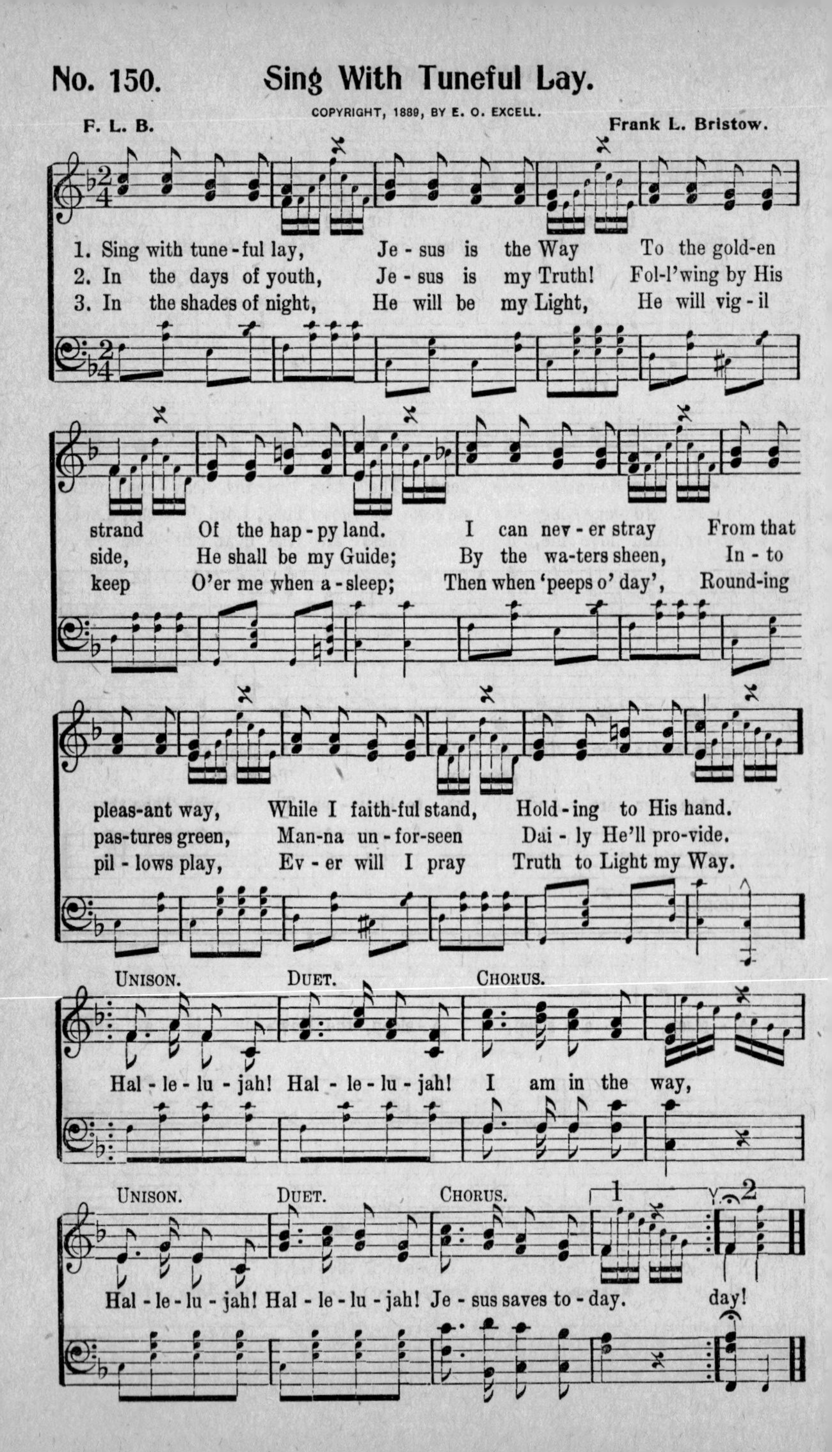
No. 150. Sing With Tuneful Lay.
COPYRIGHT, 1889, BY E. O. EXCELL.
F. L. B.
Frank L. Bristow.
1. Sing with tune-ful lay, Je-sus is the Way To the gold-en strand Of the hap-py land. I can nev-er stray From that pleas-ant way, While I faith-ful stand, Hold-ing to His hand.
2. In the days of youth, Je-sus is my Truth! Fol-l'wing by His side, He shall be my Guide; By the wa-ters sheen, In-to pas-tures green, Man-na un-for-seen Dai-ly He'll pro-vide.
3. In the shades of night, He will be my Light, He will vig-il keep O'er me when a-sleep; Then when 'peeps o' day', Round-ing pil-lows play, Ev-er will I pray Truth to Light my Way.
UNISON. DUET. CHORUS.
Hal-le-lu-jah! Hal-le-lu-jah! I am in the way,
UNISON. DUET. CHORUS.
Hal-le-lu-jah! Hal-le-lu-jah! Je-sus saves to-day. day!
1 2

No. 151. What They Seem to Say.

Eleanor Allen Schroll.
COPYRIGHT, 1908, BY CHAS. H. GABRIEL.
E. O. EXCELL, OWNER.
Chas. H. Gabriel.
1. Have you seen the sunbeams shin-ing, Shin-ing all a-long the way?
2. Have you heard the wild birds sing-ing, Sing-ing all a-long the way?
3. Have you seen the flow-ers grow-ing, Grow-ing all a-long the way?
Have you ev-er stopped to lis-ten What they al-ways seem to say?
Have you ev-er stopped to lis-ten What they al-ways seem to say?
Have you ev-er stopped to lis-ten What they al-ways seem to say?
Ev-'ry beam of beau-ty gives us Just a glimpse of heav'n a-bove;
Ev-'ry lit-tle song-ster gives us Just a glimpse of heav'n a-bove;
Ev-'ry pret-ty blos-som gives us Just a glimpse of heav'n a-bove;
FINE.
Ev-'ry lit-tle sunbeam whispers: God is wis-dom, God is love.
Ev-'ry lit-tle wild bird whispers: God is wis-dom, God is love.
Ev-'ry lit-tle flow-er whispers: God is wis-dom, God is love.
D. S.—May the children's hearts re-ech-o: God is wis-dom, God is love.
CHORUS.
D. S.
God is wis-dom, God is love; Read it in the stars a-bove;

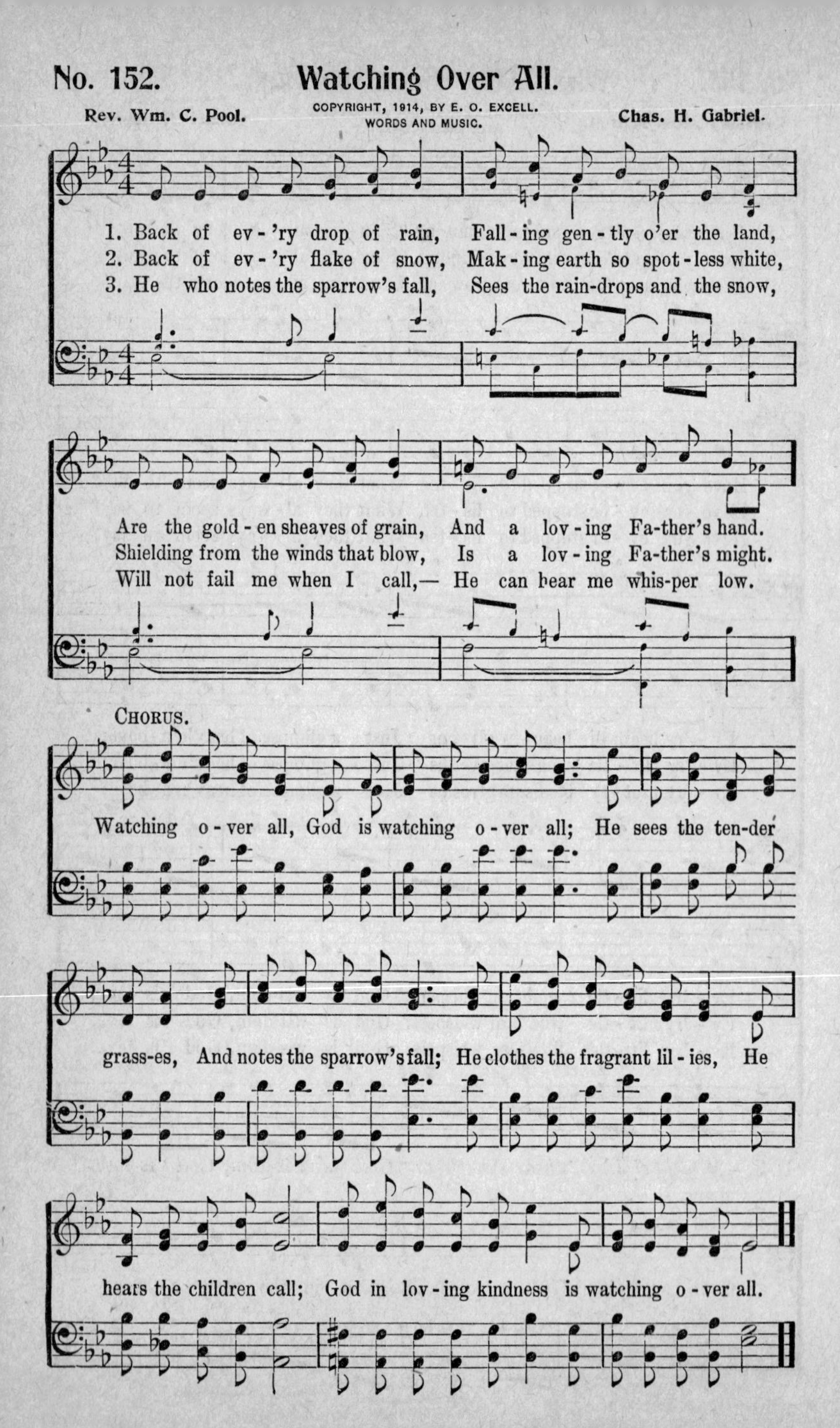
No. 152.
Watching Over All.
Rev. Wm. C. Pool.
COPYRIGHT, 1914, BY E. O. EXCELL.
WORDS AND MUSIC.
Chas. H. Gabriel.
1. Back of ev - 'ry drop of rain, Fall - ing gen - tly o'er the land,
2. Back of ev - 'ry flake of snow, Mak - ing earth so spot - less white,
3. He who notes the sparrow's fall, Sees the rain-drops and the snow,
Are the gold - en sheaves of grain, And a lov - ing Fa-ther's hand.
Shielding from the winds that blow, Is a lov - ing Fa-ther's might.
Will not fail me when I call,— He can hear me whis-per low.
CHORUS.
Watching o - ver all, God is watching o - ver all; He sees the ten-der
grass-es, And notes the sparrow's fall; He clothes the fragrant lil - ies, He
hears the children call; God in lov - ing kindness is watching o - ver all.

No. 153.
Little Sunbeams.
Eben E. Rexford.
COPYRIGHT, 1902, BY E. O. EXCELL. WORDS AND MUSIC.
Chas. H. Gabriel.
1. I think God gives the chil-dren, As thro' the land they go, The most de-light-ful mis-sion That an-y one can know; He wants us to be sun-beams Of love, and hope, and cheer, To bright-en up the shad-ows That oft-en gath-er here.
2. The clouds may hide the sun-shine Of heav-en from our sight, And life have much of sor-row To mar the heart's delight; But if like faith-ful sun-beams, We chil-dren do our part, We'll bring a ray of brightness To ev-'ry shadowed heart.
3. Then let us live our mis-sion Of sun-beams day by day, And scat-ter joy and brightness A-bout us all the way; Let's chase a-way life's shad-ows With lov-ing tho't and deed, And be the sun-shine-ma-kers Of which the world has need.
Chorus.
O we are lit-tle sun-beams, Sent down from God to man; In all life's sha-dy pla-ces We shine as best we can.

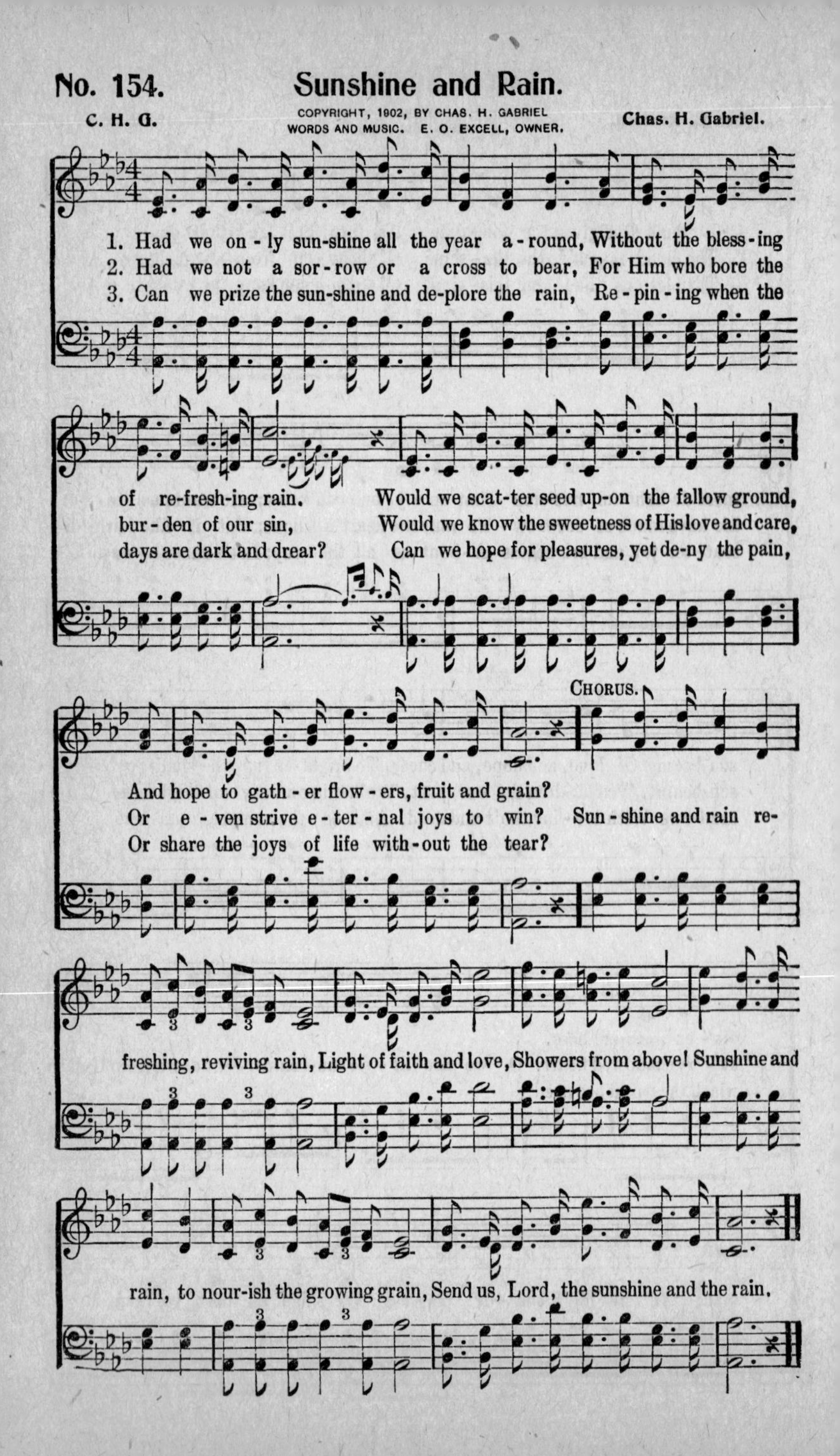
No. 154.
Sunshine and Rain.
C. H. G.
COPYRIGHT, 1902, BY CHAS. H. GABRIEL
WORDS AND MUSIC. E. O. EXCELL, OWNER.
Chas. H. Gabriel.
1. Had we on - ly sun-shine all the year a - round, Without the bless - ing
2. Had we not a sor - row or a cross to bear, For Him who bore the
3. Can we prize the sun-shine and de-plore the rain, Re - pin - ing when the
of re-fresh-ing rain. Would we scat-ter seed up-on the fallow ground,
bur - den of our sin, Would we know the sweetness of His love and care,
days are dark and drear? Can we hope for pleasures, yet de-ny the pain,
And hope to gath - er flow - ers, fruit and grain?
Or e - ven strive e - ter - nal joys to win?
Or share the joys of life with-out the tear?
CHORUS.
Sun - shine and rain re-
freshing, reviving rain, Light of faith and love, Showers from above! Sunshine and
rain, to nour-ish the growing grain, Send us, Lord, the sunshine and the rain.

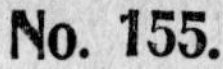

No. 155. Little Stars.

H. H. Pierson. J. S. Fearis.

1. Just as the stars are shin - ing, Mak - ing the dark - ness bright,
2. And as the stars are smil - ing Down on the earth be - low,
3. Each in his lit - tle cor - ner, Wheth-er at work or play,
4. How could they do with - out us? Dark would the world be then;
So we are shin - ing, shin - ing, Shed-ding our gold - en light.
We may re - flect the sun - light, Shin - ing wher - e'er we go.
We would be al - ways shin - ing, Turn - ing the night to day.
We are the Sav - ior's jew - els, Cheer - ing the hearts of men.
CHORUS.
Shin - ing, shin - ing, shin - ing, Just like the stars a - bove,
Mak - ing the world a - round us Hap - py with light and love.

No. 156. Keep Step in the March.
Jessie H. Brown.
COPYRIGHT, 1897, BY E. O. EXCELL. WORDS AND MUSIC.
Chas. H. Gabriel.
1. Keep step in the march for the truth and right—Keep step in the march, keep step! Be strong in the strength of the Lord, our might—
2. Keep step at the front of the mov-ing line—Keep step in the march, keep step! Keep step where the cross is the blaz-ing sign,—
3. Keep step with a tread that is firm and true—Keep step in the march, keep step! There's need in the ranks of the Lord for you—
Keep step in the march, keep step!
CHORUS.
Keep step! keep step!
Keep step for the right, by day and by night,
Keep step in the march, keep step! . . . Turn nev-er a-
keep step!
side, but with zeal and pride Keep step in the march, keep step!

No. 157. Be Careful.

C. H. G.

Chas. H. Gabriel.

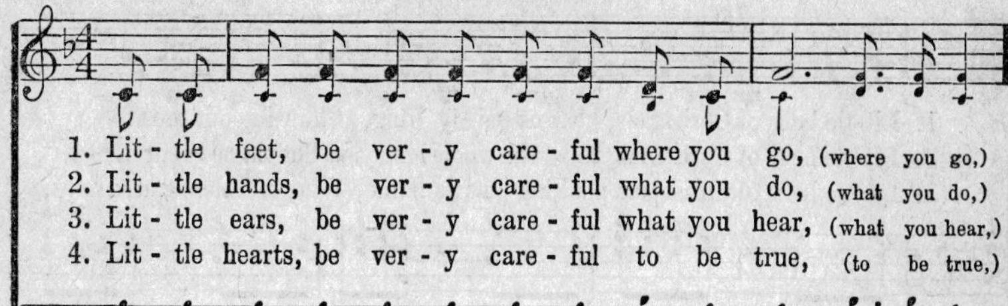

1. Lit - tle feet, be ver - y care - ful where you go, (where you go,)
2. Lit - tle hands, be ver - y care - ful what you do, (what you do,)
3. Lit - tle ears, be ver - y care - ful what you hear, (what you hear,)
4. Lit - tle hearts, be ver - y care - ful to be true, (to be true,)

As in life you dai - ly trav - el to and fro; (to and fro;)
Wrong or tho't-less ac - tions you will sure - ly rue; (you will rue;)
When the tempt - er whis - pers to you, dan - ger's near; (ver - y near;)
Love the Lord and He will sure - ly care for you; (care for you;)

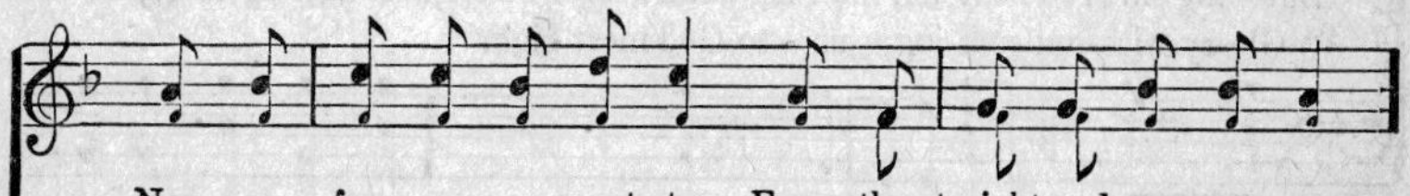

Nev - er for a mo-ment stray From the straight and nar - row way;
In - to mis-chief nev - er go, For 'tis ver - y wrong, you know;
Tho' he prom - ise ev - 'ry - thing, Ev - 'ry prom - ise is a sting!
Je - sus will not en - ter in Where there is the least of sin;

Oh, be care - ful, be care - ful, lit - tle feet.
Oh, be care - ful, be care - ful, lit - tle hands.
Oh, be care - ful, be care - ful, lit - tle ears.
Oh, be care - ful, be care - ful, lit - tle hearts.

No. 158. With Joy We Sing.

Lizzie DeArmond.

COPYRIGHT, 1907, BY CHAS. H. GABRIEL.
E. O. EXCELL, OWNER.

Chas. H. Gabriel.

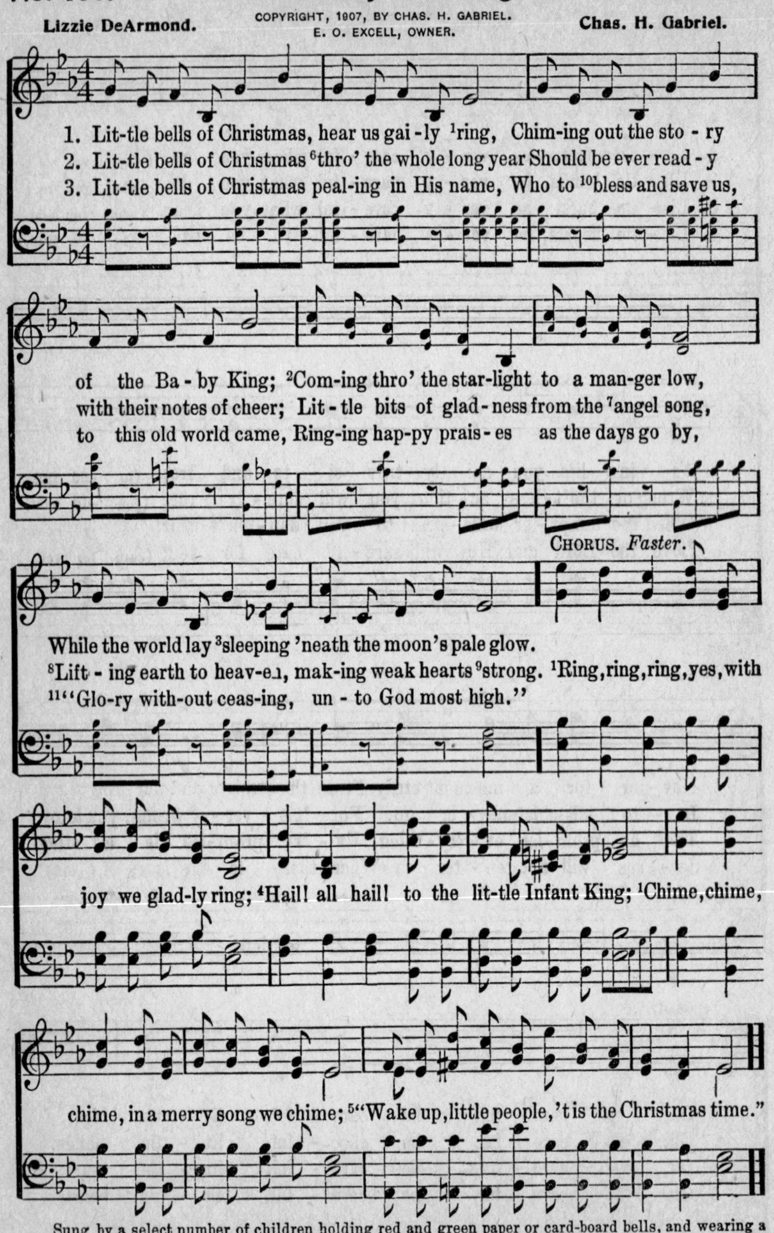

1. Lit-tle bells of Christmas, hear us gai - ly [1]ring, Chim-ing out the sto - ry
2. Lit-tle bells of Christmas [6]thro' the whole long year Should be ever read - y
3. Lit-tle bells of Christmas peal-ing in His name, Who to [10]bless and save us,
of the Ba - by King; [2]Com-ing thro' the star-light to a man-ger low,
with their notes of cheer; Lit - tle bits of glad - ness from the [7]angel song,
to this old world came, Ring-ing hap-py prais - es as the days go by,
While the world lay [3]sleeping 'neath the moon's pale glow.
[8]Lift - ing earth to heav-en, mak-ing weak hearts [9]strong.
[11]"Glo-ry with-out ceas-ing, un - to God most high."
CHORUS. Faster.
[1]Ring, ring, ring, yes, with joy we glad-ly ring; [4]Hail! all hail! to the lit-tle Infant King; [1]Chime, chime, chime, in a merry song we chime; [5]"Wake up, little people, 't is the Christmas time."

Sung by a select number of children holding red and green paper or card-board bells, and wearing a sprig of holly on breast. 1, make ringing motion with bells; 2, raise bells high, bring slowly downward; 3, close eyes, lay left cheek upon left hand; 4, wave bells held high; 5, turn bells outward and upward; 6, move bells in a semi-circle slowly from left to right; 7, point up with bells; 8, move bells slowly upward; 9, lay bells against heart; 10, fold hands across heart and look up; 11, hold bells high and make a ringing motion.

No. 159. Sunbeams Bright.

Lizzie DeArmond.
COPYRIGHT, 1906, BY CHAS. H. GABRIEL.
E. O. EXCELL, OWNER.
Chas. H. Gabriel.
1. Just a lit-tle sun-beam bright, Swift-ly [1]earth-ward wing-ing,
2. Just a lit-tle sun-beam bright, Down from [3]heav-en shin-ing,
3. Just a lit-tle sun-beam bright, Do-ing well its du-ty,
[2]Wa-king up the sleep-ing flow'rs, Joy and glad-ness bring-ing.
Giv-ing clouds that look so drear, Each a sil-ver [4]lin-ing.
Tell-ing of the [3]Fa-ther's love, [5]Fill-ing earth with beau-ty.
CHORUS.
Shin-ing bright-ly ev-'ry day, [6]Driv-ing gloom-y clouds a-way,
Lit-tle sun-beams we would be, [7]Point-ing ev-er, Lord, to Thee.

MOTIONS:—1. Raise right hand high, then bring it swiftly downward. 2. Stoop lightly, make motions as if lifting up flowers. 3. Point up. 4. Raise right hand and describe a semi-circle with it. 5. Hold arms out wide and bring them slowly together, till palms of hands touch. 6. Move right hand and arm with sweeping motion from left to right. 7. Pointing right hand slowly upwards.

No. 160. Our Colors So True.

Lizzie DeArmond. Chas. H. Gabriel.

1. [1]Three colors has the nation's flag Our [2]hearts delight to see,
The Red, and White, and starry Blue, Our pledge of liberty.

2. [3]Red speaks to us of Jesus' blood For all the [4]whole world shed,
That we might rise to life and light, Thro' Him who once was dead.

3. [5]White tells of those who, pure in heart, Shall see the Savior's face,
And in His likeness daily grow, In [6]heaven's holy place.

4. [7]Blue tells us of the faithful ones Who like the [8]stars shall be,
Bright jewels in the Victor's crown, Thro' all eternity.

CHORUS

O [1]Red, White, and Blue, our colors so true, An emblem fair of heav'nly things, to help us on our way;
O [1]Red, White, and Blue, the old and the new, Our [*Omit*..................] banner of gladness, we hail it today!

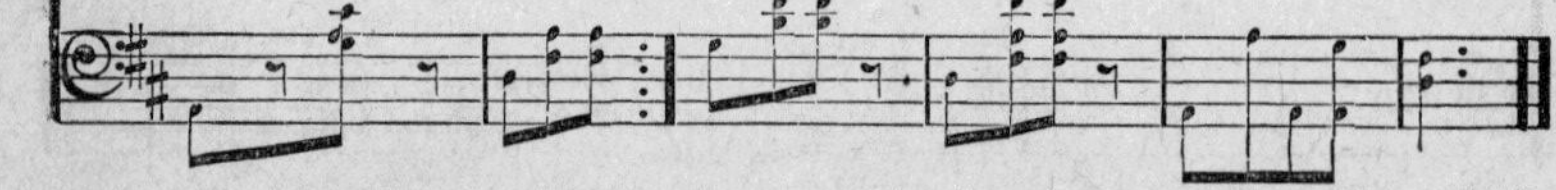

GESTURES:—1. Wave flags. 2. Lay flags across hearts. 3. Touch red stripe. 4. Describe semicircle outwards with flags. 5. Touch white stripe. 6. Hold flags up high. 7. Touch blue square. 8. Move flags held high, from left to right, shaking them slightly to give twinkling motion, like the stars.

All hold American flags.

No. 161. Little Star.

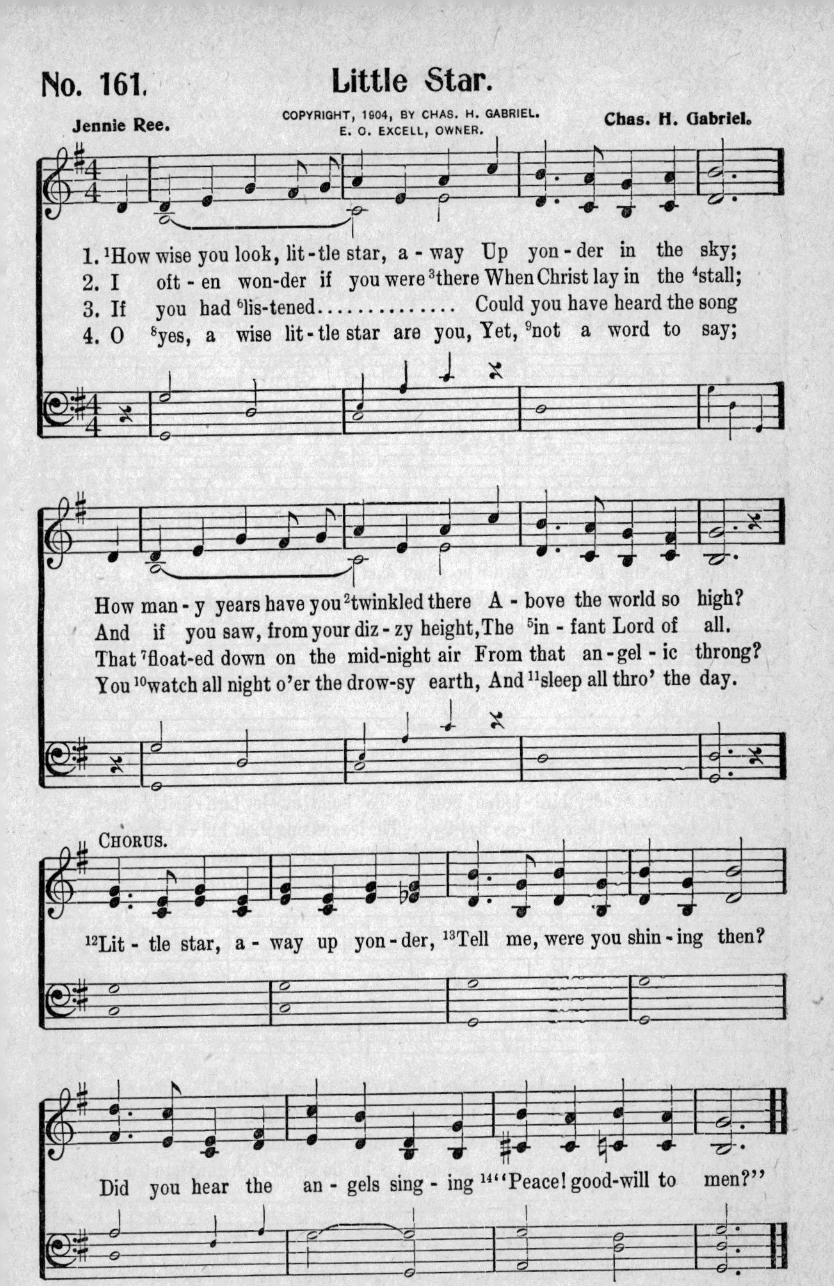

Jennie Ree.
COPYRIGHT, 1904, BY CHAS. H. GABRIEL.
E. O. EXCELL, OWNER.
Chas. H. Gabriel.
1. ¹How wise you look, lit-tle star, a-way Up yon-der in the sky;
2. I oft-en won-der if you were ³there When Christ lay in the ⁴stall;
3. If you had ⁶lis-tened.............. Could you have heard the song
4. O ⁸yes, a wise lit-tle star are you, Yet, ⁹not a word to say;
How man-y years have you ²twinkled there A-bove the world so high?
And if you saw, from your diz-zy height, The ⁵in-fant Lord of all.
That ⁷float-ed down on the mid-night air From that an-gel-ic throng?
You ¹⁰watch all night o'er the drow-sy earth, And ¹¹sleep all thro' the day.
CHORUS.
¹²Lit-tle star, a-way up yon-der, ¹³Tell me, were you shin-ing then?
Did you hear the an-gels sing-ing ¹⁴"Peace! good-will to men?"

1. Eyes upward. 2. Twinkling motion of fingers. 3. Pointing upward. 4. Pointing as toward a cradle or manger. 5. Bow heads reverently. 6. Listening attitude. 7. Raise arms and lower in a diagonal sweep. 8. Shake forefinger at supposed star. 9. Motion of lost faith. 10. Right elbow in left hand, right hand supporting chin, as if drowsy. 11. Ritard the music, close eyes as if going to sleep. 12. Eyes upward. 13. Both arms raised. 14. Hands clasped as in prayer.

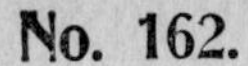

No. 162. The Birds' Nest.

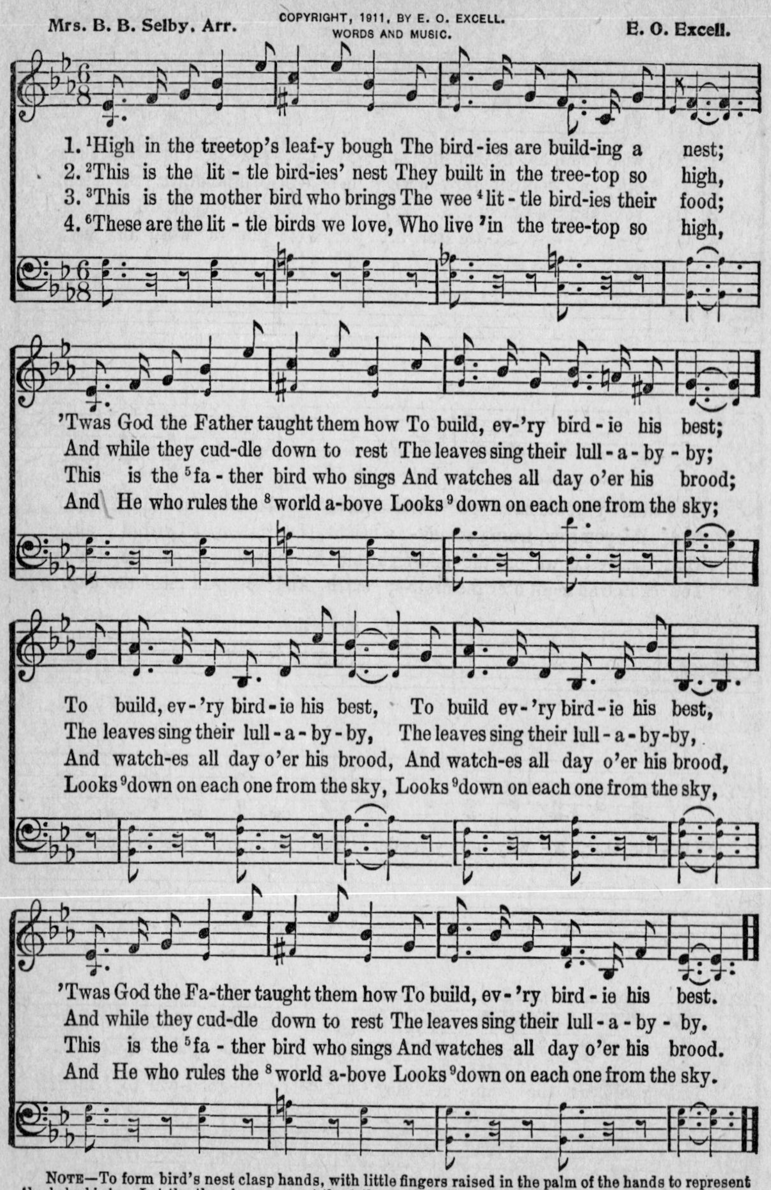
Mrs. B. B. Selby. Arr.
COPYRIGHT, 1911, BY E. O. EXCELL.
WORDS AND MUSIC.
E. O. Excell.
1. [1]High in the treetop's leaf-y bough The bird-ies are build-ing a nest;
2. [2]This is the lit - tle bird-ies' nest They built in the tree-top so high,
3. [3]This is the mother bird who brings The wee [4]lit - tle bird-ies their food;
4. [6]These are the lit - tle birds we love, Who live [7]in the tree-top so high,
'Twas God the Father taught them how To build, ev-'ry bird-ie his best;
And while they cud-dle down to rest The leaves sing their lull - a - by - by;
This is the [5]fa - ther bird who sings And watches all day o'er his brood;
And He who rules the [8]world a-bove Looks [9]down on each one from the sky;
To build, ev-'ry bird-ie his best, To build ev-'ry bird-ie his best,
The leaves sing their lull - a - by - by, The leaves sing their lull - a - by-by,
And watch-es all day o'er his brood, And watch-es all day o'er his brood,
Looks [9]down on each one from the sky, Looks [9]down on each one from the sky,
'Twas God the Fa-ther taught them how To build, ev-'ry bird-ie his best.
And while they cud-dle down to rest The leaves sing their lull - a - by - by.
This is the [5]fa - ther bird who sings And watches all day o'er his brood.
And He who rules the [8]world a-bove Looks [9]down on each one from the sky.

NOTE—To form bird's nest clasp hands, with little fingers raised in the palm of the hands to represent the baby birds. Let the thumbs represent the father and mother bird sitting on the forefingers which form the edge of the bird's nest.

MOTIONS—1, Point upward to treetop; 2, Hands clasped to form bird's nest; 3, Raise left hand thumb to represent the mother bird; 4, Raise little fingers representing the baby birds; 5, Raise right hand thumb representing the father bird; 6, Raise little fingers and thumbs representing the family of birds in the nest; 7, Point upward to treetop; 8, Look upward toward the sky; 9, Look down on the birds in the nest.

No. 163. Be a Little Sunbeam.

Rev. Thomas C. Harper.
COPYRIGHT, 1914, BY E. O. EXCELL.
WORDS AND MUSIC.
J. Owen Long.
1. Be a lit-tle sunbeam, Ra-di-ant and bright, Chasing all the darkness,
2. Be a lit-tle sunbeam, Warming with your glow, Hearts so cold and dreary,
3. Be a lit-tle sunbeam, Ra-di-ant and bright, Lift-ing drear-y shad-ows,
Flooding earth with light; Bright'ning ev'ry moment, Cheering hearts of woe,
In this world be-low. Car-ry hope and comfort, In your cheering ray,
Scat-ter-ing the night; In-to homes of sad-ness, En-ter with your cheer,
FINE.
CHORUS.
D.S.—Be a lit-tle sunbeam, Ev'rywhere you go.
Be a lit-tle sunbeam, Ev-'ry live-long day.
Be a lit-tle sunbeam, Shining all the year.
Sun-beam, sun-beam, Ra-di-ant and bright, Sun-beam, sun-beam, Flooding earth with light; Sun-beam, sun-beam, Cheering hearts of woe,
Be a lit-tle sun-beam, So bright, Be a lit-tle sun-beam, with light; Be a lit-tle sun-beam, of woe,
D. S.

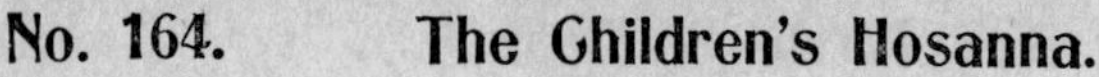
No. 164. The Children's Hosanna.

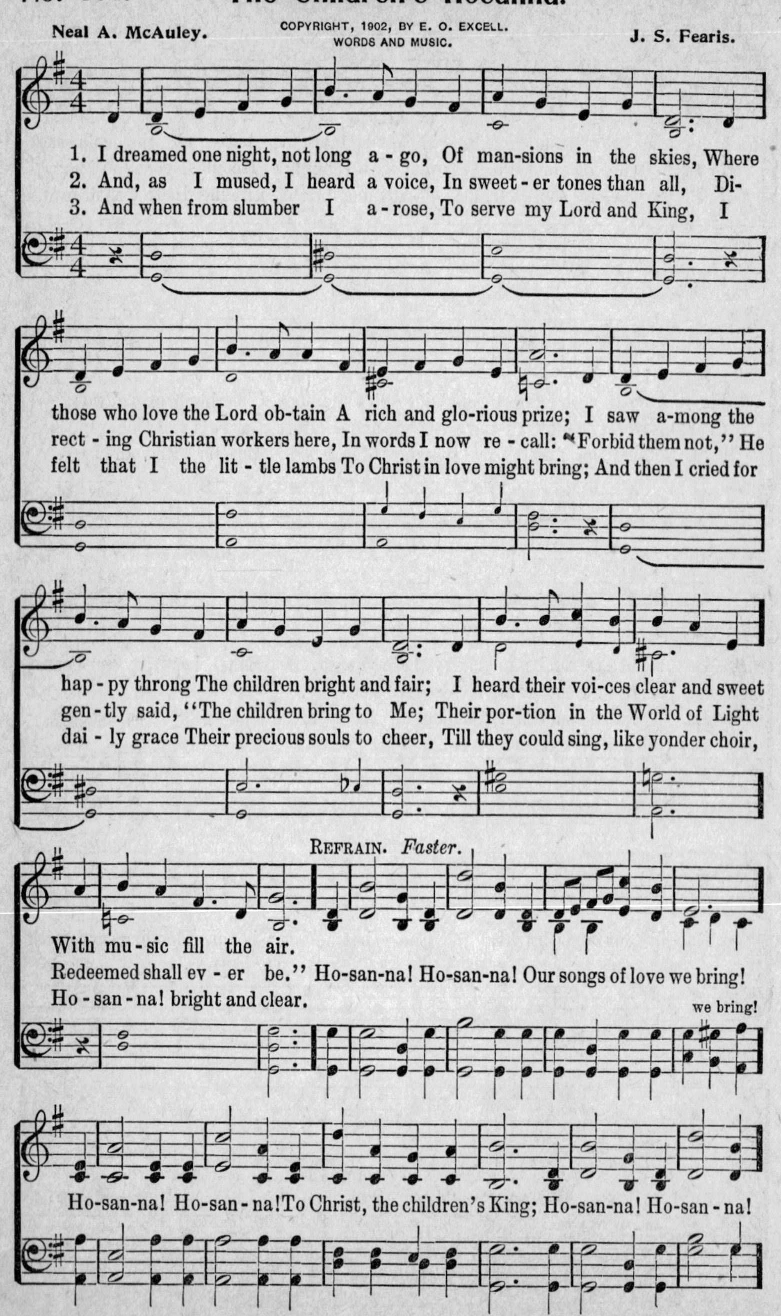
Neal A. McAuley.
COPYRIGHT, 1902, BY E. O. EXCELL.
WORDS AND MUSIC.
J. S. Fearis.
1. I dreamed one night, not long a - go, Of man-sions in the skies, Where
2. And, as I mused, I heard a voice, In sweet - er tones than all, Di-
3. And when from slumber I a - rose, To serve my Lord and King, I
those who love the Lord ob-tain A rich and glo-rious prize; I saw a-mong the
rect - ing Christian workers here, In words I now re - call: "Forbid them not," He
felt that I the lit - tle lambs To Christ in love might bring; And then I cried for
hap - py throng The children bright and fair; I heard their voi-ces clear and sweet
gen - tly said, "The children bring to Me; Their por-tion in the World of Light
dai - ly grace Their precious souls to cheer, Till they could sing, like yonder choir,
With mu - sic fill the air.
Redeemed shall ev - er be." Ho-san-na! Ho-san-na! Our songs of love we bring!
Ho - san - na! bright and clear.
REFRAIN. Faster.
we bring!
Ho-san-na! Ho-san - na! To Christ, the children's King; Ho-san-na! Ho-san - na!

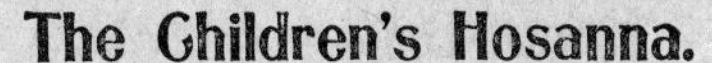
The Children's Hosanna.

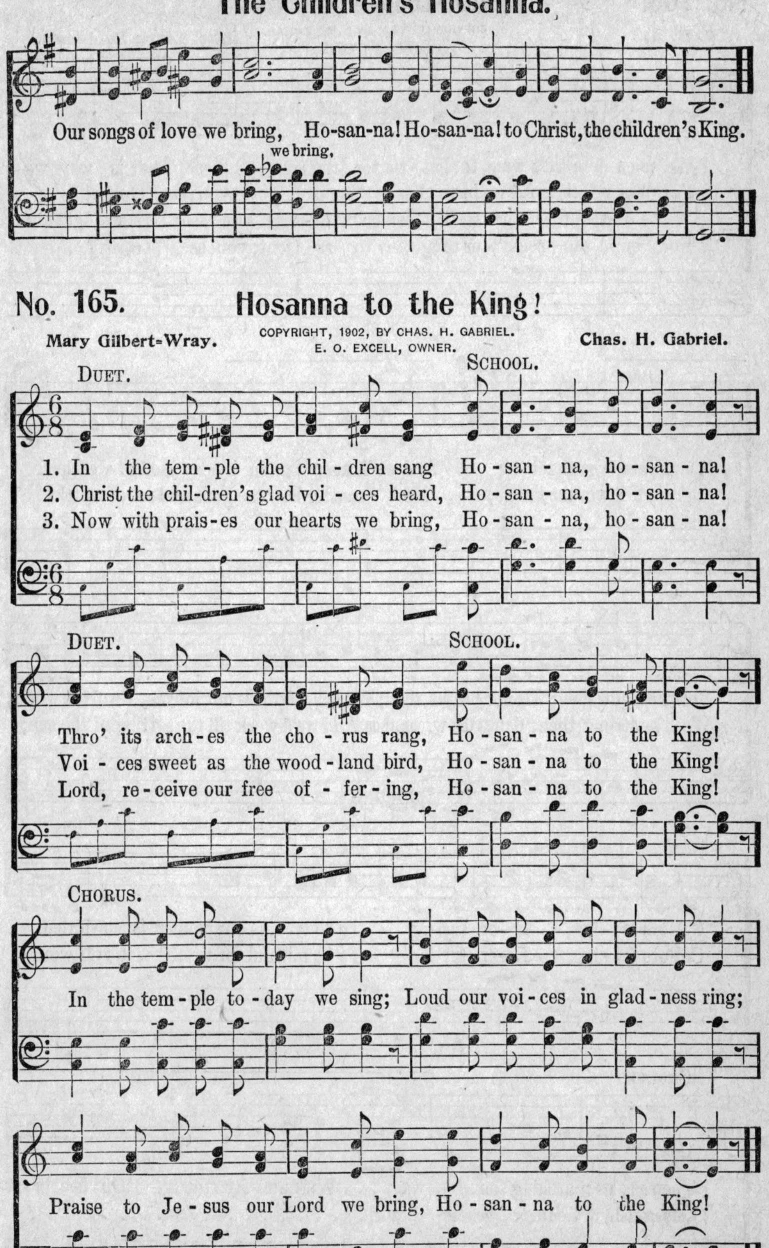
Our songs of love we bring, Ho-san-na! Ho-san-na! to Christ, the children's King.
we bring,
No. 165. Hosanna to the King!
Mary Gilbert-Wray.
COPYRIGHT, 1902, BY CHAS. H. GABRIEL.
E. O. EXCELL, OWNER.
Chas. H. Gabriel.
DUET.
SCHOOL.
1. In the tem-ple the chil-dren sang Ho-san-na, ho-san-na!
2. Christ the chil-dren's glad voi-ces heard, Ho-san-na, ho-san-na!
3. Now with prais-es our hearts we bring, Ho-san-na, ho-san-na!
DUET.
SCHOOL.
Thro' its arch-es the cho-rus rang, Ho-san-na to the King!
Voi-ces sweet as the wood-land bird, Ho-san-na to the King!
Lord, re-ceive our free of-fer-ing, Ho-san-na to the King!
CHORUS.
In the tem-ple to-day we sing; Loud our voi-ces in glad-ness ring;
Praise to Je-sus our Lord we bring, Ho-san-na to the King!

No. 166.
Honor-Bright Cadets.
C. B. A.
COPYRIGHT, 1802, BY E. O. EXCELL. WORDS AND MUSIC.
Mrs. Carrie B. Adams.
1
1. We're ca-dets that want to bat - tle for the right, you see; That is why we
For our watch-word we have chosen "Honor bright!" you see, [Omit.] . . . .
2. We're de-ter-mined that we'll never know de - feat, you see; If we fight for
For our Lead-er nev - er taught us to re - treat, you see, [Omit.] . . . .
2
band ourselves together; And we'll keep it up in ev-'ry kind of weather.
right, we'll win the battle; No matter how the guns and sabers rattle.
For the right, then; Honor bright, then; We will march on our journey thro' the world;
We'll be strong, then, 'Gainst the wrong, then, And we'll work till the setting of the sun;
Col-ors fly - ing, Ev-er try-ing To be true, as our banner is un-furled.
Col-ors fly - ing, Ev-er try-ing To be faithful un-til the vict'ry's won.
CHORUS.
1
Then see us marching as to war; . . . With purpose steady, Our hearts are
Our gal-lant Lead-er goes be- [Omit.] . . . .

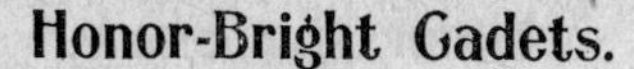
Honor-Bright Cadets.

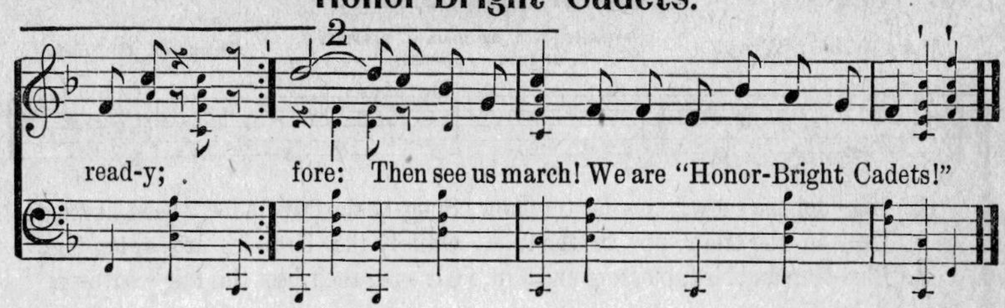
2
read-y;
fore: Then see us march! We are "Honor-Bright Cadets!"

No. 167. Hurrah for the Red, White and Blue.

E. L. McCord. USED BY PERMISSION. W. W. Gilchrist.

1. I know three lit-tle sis-ters, I think you know them, too, For
2. I know three lit-tle les-sons These lit-tle sis-ters tell, The
one is red, and one is white, And the oth-er one is blue.
first is Love, then Pu-ri-ty, And Truth we love so well.
CHORUS.
Hurrah for these three lit-tle sis-ters! Hur-rah for the red, white and blue!
Hur-rah! Hur-rah! Hur-rah! Hur-rah! Hur-rah for the red, white and blue!

No. 168. Under the Snow.

Mary Gilbert-Wray.

Chas. H. Gabriel.

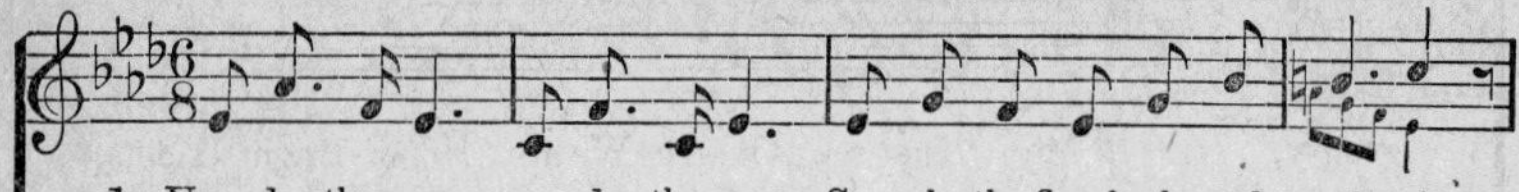

1. Un - der the snow, un - der the snow, Snug-ly the flow'rs have been sleeping;
2. Up in the tree, up in the tree, Gai-ly the bird-ies are swing-ing;
3. Blos-som and bird, blossom and bird, Giv - ing their best this fair weath-er;

Dear lit-tle flowr's, they could not know Je-sus a kind watch was keep - ing.
Hap - py and free, songs full of glee, Cheer - i - ly, cheer - i - ly ring - ing;
With them we come in sweet ac-cord, Sing - ing our car - ols to - geth - er;

Un - der the snow they soft - ly lay, Wait-ing to greet the first spring day;
Building their nests on boughs so high, Teach-ing the ba - by birds to fly;
Brighter are we than blooming flow'rs, Gay-er than birds in leaf - y bow'rs;

REFRAIN.

Soon as the winter passed a-way Brightly the flow'rs came peeping. Sleep, sleep,
God watching o'er them from on high, List to their mer-ry sing-ing. Sing, sing,
Pleading to Christ our ear-ly hours, His we would be for-ev - er. Sweet, sweet,

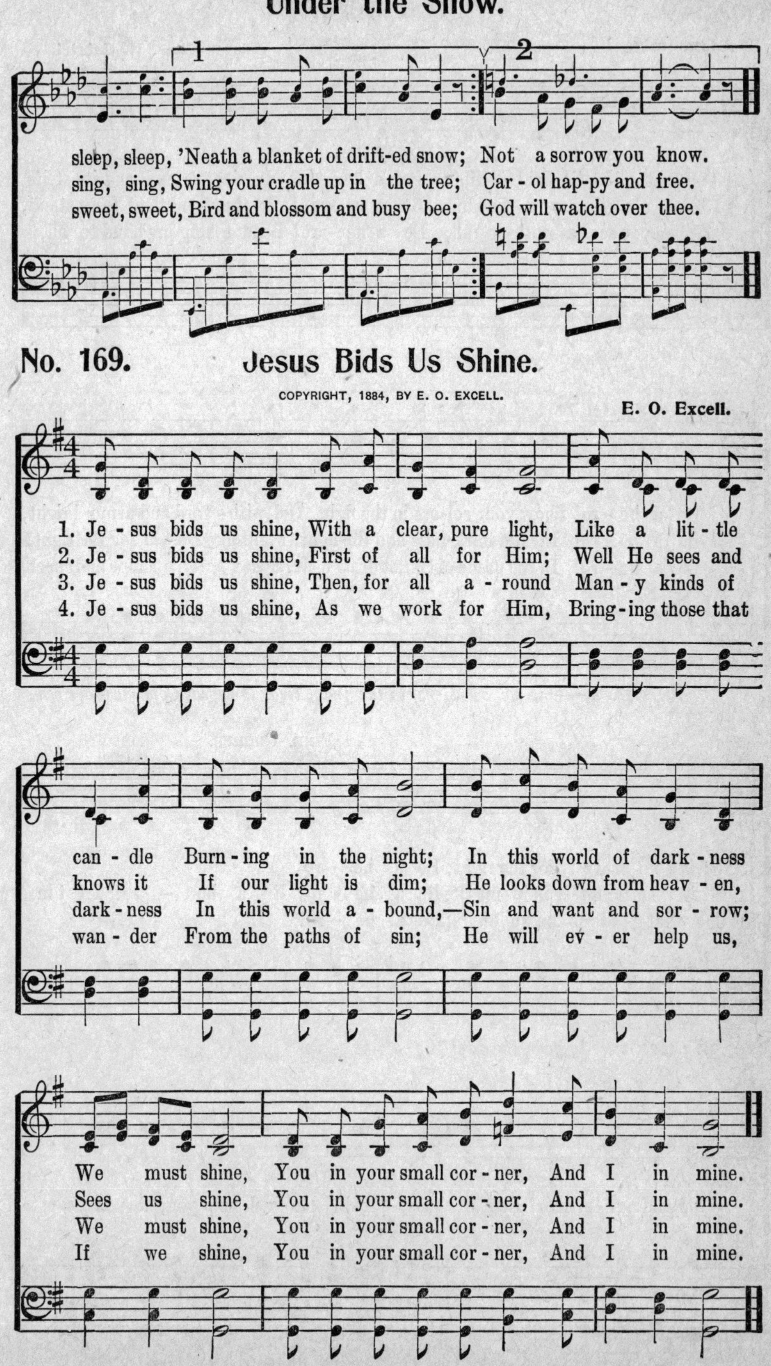
Under the Snow.
1
2
sleep, sleep, 'Neath a blanket of drift-ed snow; Not a sorrow you know.
sing, sing, Swing your cradle up in the tree; Car - ol hap-py and free.
sweet, sweet, Bird and blossom and busy bee; God will watch over thee.
No. 169.
Jesus Bids Us Shine.
COPYRIGHT, 1884, BY E. O. EXCELL.
E. O. Excell.
1. Je - sus bids us shine, With a clear, pure light, Like a lit - tle
2. Je - sus bids us shine, First of all for Him; Well He sees and
3. Je - sus bids us shine, Then, for all a - round Man - y kinds of
4. Je - sus bids us shine, As we work for Him, Bring - ing those that
can - dle Burn - ing in the night; In this world of dark - ness
knows it If our light is dim; He looks down from heav - en,
dark - ness In this world a - bound,—Sin and want and sor - row;
wan - der From the paths of sin; He will ev - er help us,
We must shine, You in your small cor - ner, And I in mine.
Sees us shine, You in your small cor - ner, And I in mine.
We must shine, You in your small cor - ner, And I in mine.
If we shine, You in your small cor - ner, And I in mine.

No. 170. Be a Hero.

Adam Craig. COPYRIGHT, 1897, BY E. O. EXCELL. WORDS AND MUSIC. Chas. H. Gabriel.

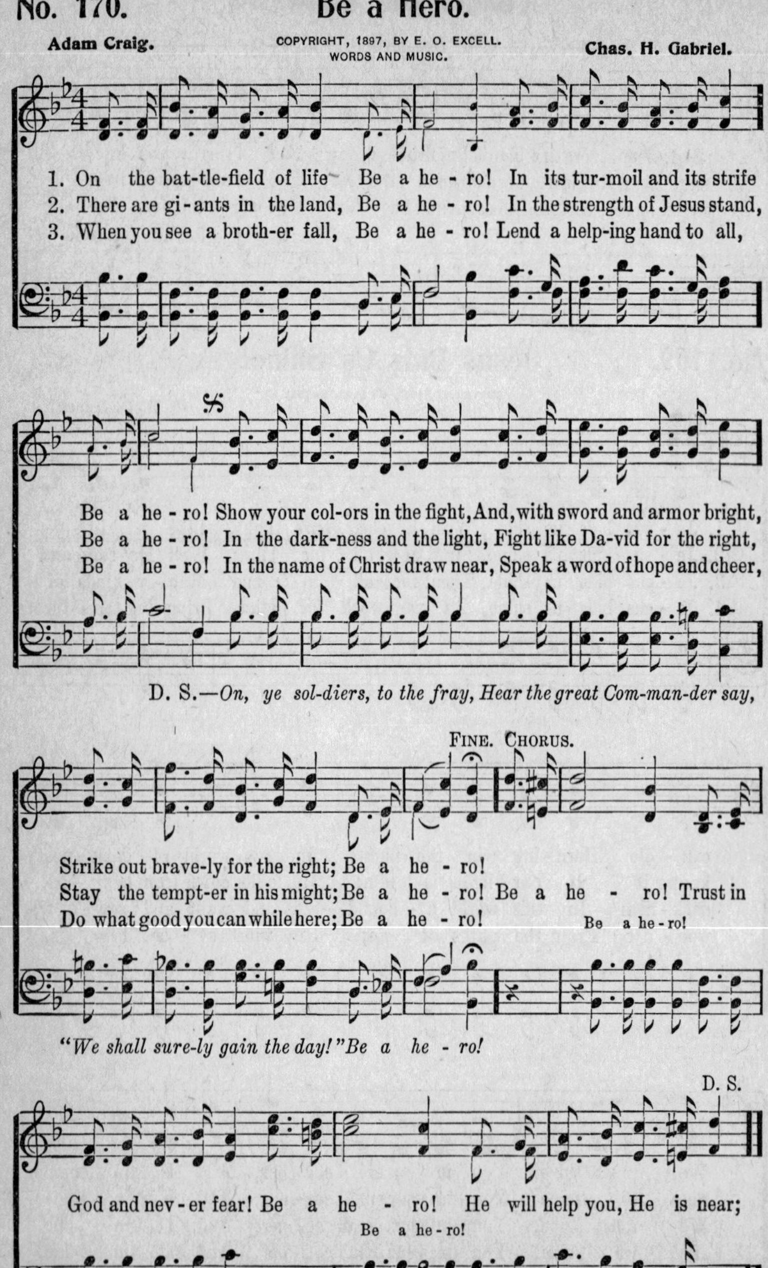

1. On the bat-tle-field of life Be a he - ro! In its tur-moil and its strife
2. There are gi-ants in the land, Be a he - ro! In the strength of Jesus stand,
3. When you see a broth-er fall, Be a he - ro! Lend a help-ing hand to all,
Be a he - ro! Show your col-ors in the fight, And, with sword and armor bright,
Be a he - ro! In the dark-ness and the light, Fight like Da-vid for the right,
Be a he - ro! In the name of Christ draw near, Speak a word of hope and cheer,
D. S.—On, ye sol-diers, to the fray, Hear the great Com-man-der say,
FINE. CHORUS.
Strike out brave-ly for the right; Be a he - ro!
Stay the tempt-er in his might; Be a he - ro! Be a he - ro! Trust in
Do what good you can while here; Be a he - ro!
Be a he-ro!
"We shall sure-ly gain the day!" Be a he - ro!
D. S.
God and nev-er fear! Be a he - ro! He will help you, He is near;
Be a he-ro!

No. 171. Rose, Rose, Rose.
Charlotte G. Homer.
COPYRIGHT, 1908, BY CHAS. H. GABRIEL.
WORDS AND MUSIC. E. O. EXCELL, OWNER.
Chas. H. Gabriel.
1. What is sweeter, tell me, Than a pret-ty rose? Fra-grant in its beau - ty, Loveliest flow'r that grows.
2. If a rose could whisper, Could it, think you, tell Of that bless-ed coun - try Where the an-gels dwell?
3. Je - sus, keep me ev - er Like un-to this flow'r— Pure and sweet and mod-est, Ev - 'ry day and hour.
Waltz time.
REFRAIN.
Rose, rose, rose, Pret-ti-est flow'r that grows, Em-blem of love that came from heaven, Thro' which a Savior, Christ, was giv-en;
Rose, rose, rose, Not till the whole world knows Of my dear Sav - ior King, Will I cease to sing, Sweet rose, rose, rose. . .
1
2

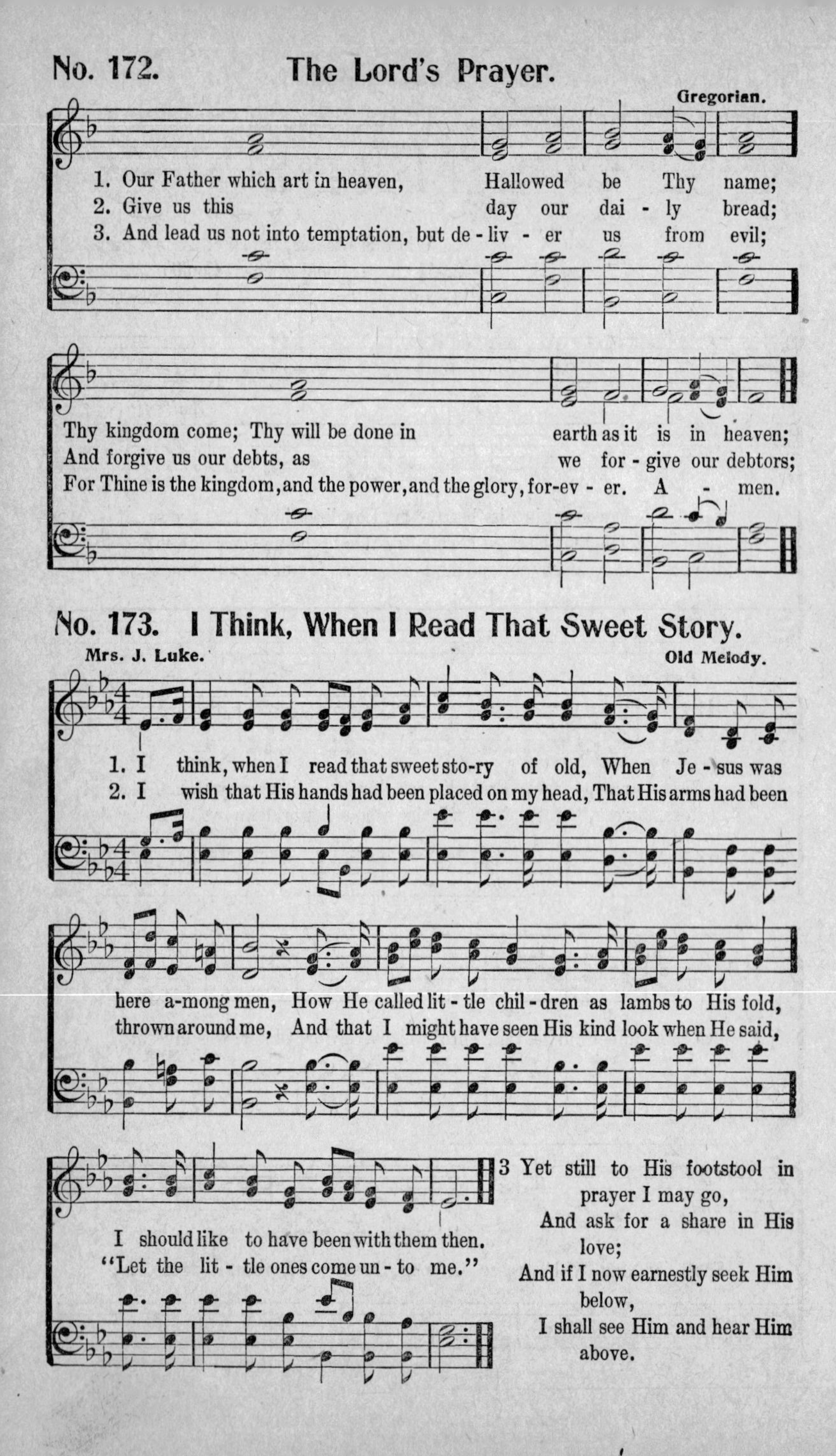
No. 172. The Lord's Prayer.
Gregorian.
1. Our Father which art in heaven, Hallowed be Thy name;
2. Give us this day our dai - ly bread;
3. And lead us not into temptation, but de - liv - er us from evil;
Thy kingdom come; Thy will be done in earth as it is in heaven;
And forgive us our debts, as we for - give our debtors;
For Thine is the kingdom, and the power, and the glory, for-ev - er. A - men.
No. 173. I Think, When I Read That Sweet Story.
Mrs. J. Luke.
Old Melody.
1. I think, when I read that sweet sto-ry of old, When Je - sus was
2. I wish that His hands had been placed on my head, That His arms had been
here a-mong men, How He called lit - tle chil - dren as lambs to His fold,
thrown around me, And that I might have seen His kind look when He said,
I should like to have been with them then.
"Let the lit - tle ones come un - to me."
3 Yet still to His footstool in prayer I may go,
And ask for a share in His love;
And if I now earnestly seek Him below,
I shall see Him and hear Him above.

Special Selections

No. 174. Behold, I Stand at the Door.
F. M. D.
COPYRIGHT, 1894, BY E. O. EXCELL.
WORDS AND MUSIC.
Frank M. Davis.
Be - hold, I stand at the door and knock, knock, knock, knock;
1. If an - y one . . . . will hear my voice, . . . And o-pen wide . . . .
2. And shall I stand . . . and knock in vain . . . . At thy heart's door, . .
3. O wear-y heart, . . . O trem-bling soul, ... Un-do the door, ...
If an - y one
will hear my voice,
And o-pen wide
to me the door, . . . I will come in . . . . and sup with him, . . And he with
O child of sin? . . . . I've waited long . . . and patient-ly. . . . Un-do the
long closed with sin; . . I bring you joy . . . from heav'n above, And glad-ly
to me the door,
I will come in
and sup with him,
rit.
me . . . for-ev-er - more, . . And he with me for-ev - er - more. . . .
door . . and let me in, . . . Un-do the door and let me in. . . . .
I . . . . would enter in, . . . And glad-ly I would en-ter in. . . . .
And he with me
for-ev-er-more,
for-ev-er-more.

No. 175. Going Down to the Grave.

Unknown. COPYRIGHT, 1878, BY GEO. ORBIN. USED BY PERMISSION. Rev. Geo. Orbin.

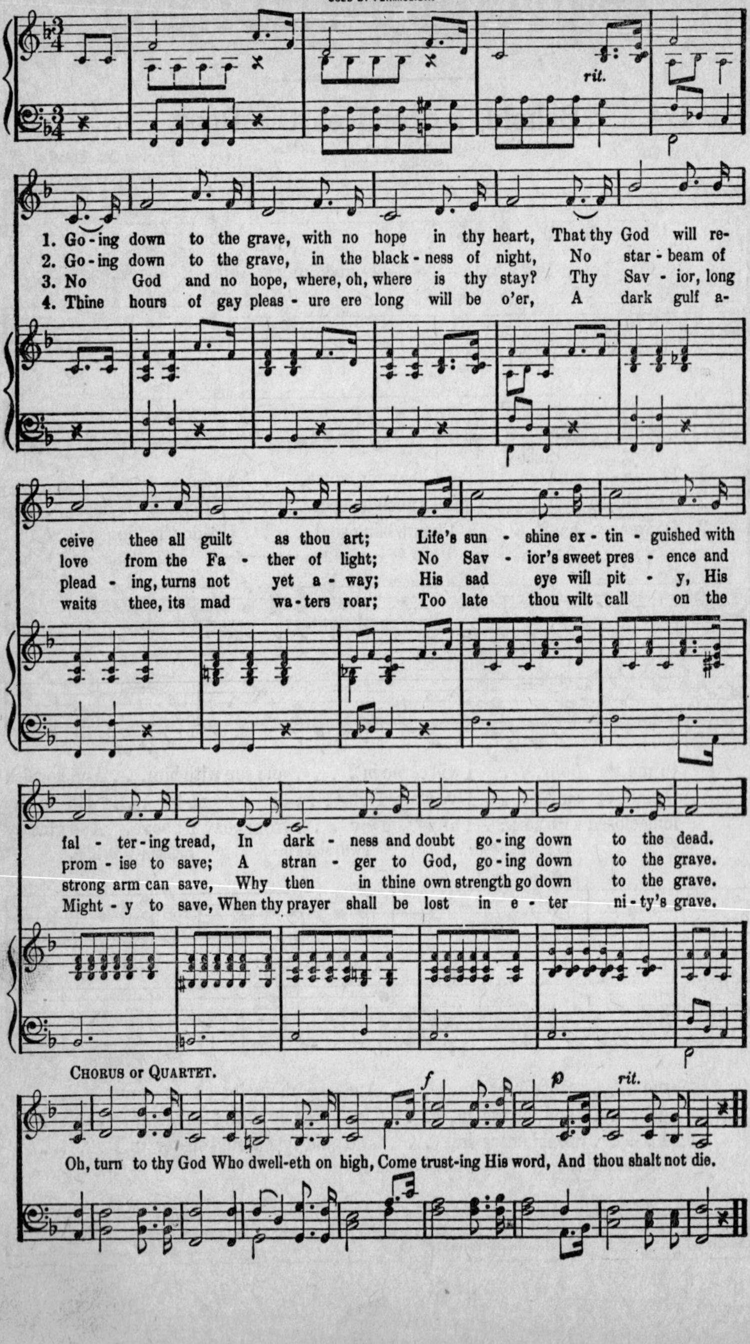

1. Going down to the grave, with no hope in thy heart, That thy God will receive thee all guilt as thou art; Life's sunshine extinguished with faltering tread, In darkness and doubt going down to the dead.

2. Going down to the grave, in the blackness of night, No star-beam of love from the Father of light; No Savior's sweet presence and promise to save; A stranger to God, going down to the grave.

3. No God and no hope, where, oh, where is thy stay? Thy Savior, long pleading, turns not yet away; His sad eye will pity, His strong arm can save, Why then in thine own strength go down to the grave.

4. Thine hours of gay pleasure ere long will be o'er, A dark gulf awaits thee, its mad waters roar; Too late thou wilt call on the Mighty to save, When thy prayer shall be lost in eternity's grave.

CHORUS OR QUARTET.

Oh, turn to thy God Who dwelleth on high, Come trusting His word, And thou shalt not die.

No. 176.
I'm Not Your Judge.
Sarah Spencer-Ruff.
COPYRIGHT, 1910, BY E. O. EXCELL. WORDS AND MUSIC.
Chas. H. Gabriel.
Introduction. f
1. I'm not your judge, Nay! God for - bids Me judge the rec-ord of your deeds; But
2. I'm not your judge, Nay! I'm un - fit, God plainly tells in ho - ly writ; He
3. I'm not your judge, Nay! One on high Will read your sentence by and by; But
4. I'm not your judge, Nay! One up - on His throne will judge in love, His own; So,
tells me wait, with read - y hand, To love and help and un - der - stand; But tells me
bids me raise and lift you up, Then pass to you the lov - ing - cup; He bids me
while we jour - ney side by side, I am your friend what-e'er be - tide; But while we
o - ver all your faults I cast Love's sa-cred man - tle to the last; So o - ver
wait, with read - y hand, To love, and help, and un - der - stand.
raise and lift you up, Then pass to you the lov - ing - cup.
jour - - ney side by side, I am your friend what-e'er be - tide.
all your faults I cast Love's sacred man - tle to the last.
Response.
Judge not, that ye be not judged; Judge not, that ye be not judged.

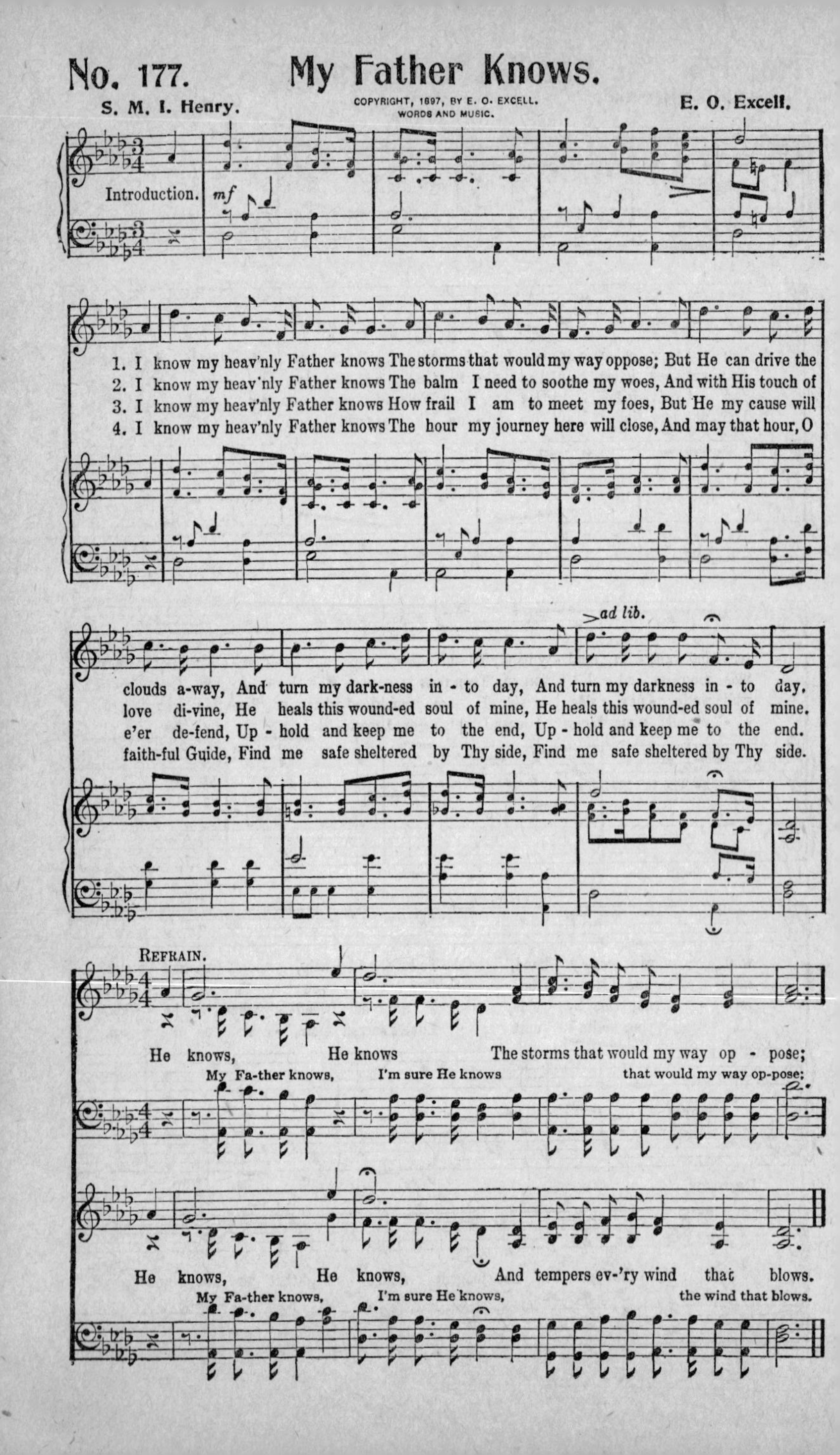
No. 177.
My Father Knows.
S. M. I. Henry.
COPYRIGHT, 1897, BY E. O. EXCELL. WORDS AND MUSIC.
E. O. Excell.
Introduction.
mf
1. I know my heav'nly Father knows The storms that would my way oppose; But He can drive the clouds a-way, And turn my dark-ness in-to day, And turn my darkness in-to day.
2. I know my heav'nly Father knows The balm I need to soothe my woes, And with His touch of love di-vine, He heals this wound-ed soul of mine, He heals this wound-ed soul of mine.
3. I know my heav'nly Father knows How frail I am to meet my foes, But He my cause will e'er de-fend, Up-hold and keep me to the end, Up-hold and keep me to the end.
4. I know my heav'nly Father knows The hour my journey here will close, And may that hour, O faith-ful Guide, Find me safe sheltered by Thy side, Find me safe sheltered by Thy side.
ad lib.
REFRAIN.
He knows, He knows The storms that would my way op-pose;
My Fa-ther knows, I'm sure He knows that would my way op-pose;
He knows, He knows, And tempers ev-'ry wind that blows.
My Fa-ther knows, I'm sure He knows, the wind that blows.

No. 178. His Love For Me.

F. M. Eastwood. Fred H. Byshe.

Introduction.

1. You have heard of the sto - ry of Je - sus—Of His grace, flowing boundless and free, ...
2. You have heard how He blessed lit - tle chil-dren: "Come, all ye that are weary," said He; . .
3. You have heard how the blind as they sought Him, Found their sight, when He bade them to see; . .
4. You have heard how He spake to the tem - pest—How His words, "Peace, be still!" calmed the sea;

But there's no one can tell you the ful - ness Of His won - der - ful love for me. . . . .
So I came, and He gave me the bless - ing Of His won - der - ful love for me. . . . .
So my sin-blind-ed eyes have been o - pened By His won - der - ful love for me. . . . .
So my soul found the peace that it longed for In His won - der - ful love for me. . . . .
CHORUS.*
His love for me, His love for me! High as the heav'n, deep as the sea;
Love that will last thro' e - ter - ni - ty, His love for me, His love for me!

*Small notes may be used as a Soprano Obligato after last stanza.

No. 179. Just For His Sake.
Mrs. S. M. I. Henry.
COPYRIGHT, 1889, BY E. O. EXCELL.
M. H. Evans.
Introduction.
1. I have toiled all night and for man - y a day; For they say there are fish in the sea,
2. So he bent and la-bored at wash-ing his net, While the Sav-ior walked down to the sea;
3. And just how 'twas done on-ly Je - sus can tell, But the net was so full that it brake;
And yet I have caught nothing, my la - bor is vain, And there cometh no increase to me.
Straight-way en-ter-ing in - to the ship, Je-sus said, "Thrust the boat out a lit - tle for Me,
For they launched out their ship and they cast in their net, As He bade them to do for His sake.
I will wash out my net, I will hang it a-way, And my fish-ing-boat draw to the shore;
Launch it out in the deep, quickly let down the net," But the fish-er-man answered, "In vain
Therefore, tho' you have labored in vain un - til now, Lo, the Sav-ior is say - ing to thee,
It is use - less to me; I will cast out my net In these bar-ren sea wa-ters no more.
We have la-bored all night, Yet at Thy bid-ding, Lord, I will cast in my net once a - gain."
"Launch out in - to the deep, Quickly cast in the net; There are fish in the depths of the sea."

No. 180.
I Know.
W. H. O. and C. H. G.
COPYRIGHT, 1903, BY E. O. EXCELL.
Chas. H. Gabriel.
Introduction.
1. You ask me how I gave my heart to Christ? O yes, I know! There came a yearning in my soul for
2. You ask me when I gave my heart to Christ? Yes, I can tell! The day, and just the hour, indeed, I
3. You ask me where I gave my heart to Christ? Yes, I can say! That sacred place can never fade from
Him, So long ago. I found earth's fairest flow'rs would fade and die; I wept for something that would satis-
now Remember well. It was when I was struggling all a - lone, The light of His for-giv-ing Spir - it
sight, As yes-ter-day. Perhaps He tho't it better I should not Forget the place, for I should love the
fy; . . . And, in my grief, somehow, I seemed to dare . . To lift my bro-ken heart to Him in
shone . . In - to my heart all clouded o'er with sin, . . That I un-locked the door and let Him
spot; . . And un-til I be-hold Him face to face, . . 'T will be to me, on earth, the dear-est
prayer. O yes, I know! And I can tell you how; I know, I know He is my Savior now. . .
in. . . . O yes, I know! And I can tell you when; I know, I know He is so dear since then.
place. . O yes, I know! And I can tell you where; I know, I know He came and blest me there.

No. 181. God Is Not Far Away.

Ada Powell. COPYRIGHT, 1914, BY E. O. EXCELL. WORDS AND MUSIC. Chas. H. Gabriel.

1. This tho't gives sweetest com - fort, How - ev - er dark the day, . . As long and drear the
2. My heart grows faint and wear - y, But I can tru - ly say, . . I trust Him thro' temp-
3. His love is strong and change - less, And bears me thro' the fray, . . When fierce the bat - tle
jour - ney— God is not far a - way; . . . When clouds hang dark-ly o - ver me, And
ta - tion— God is not far a - way; . . . No mat - ter where He lead-eth me, I'll
ra - ges— God is not far a - way; . . . His grace and strength He lend-eth me, And
sor-row's ash - es cov-er me, Al-might-y to de - liv - er me,—God is not far a - way. . .
go—for there He needeth me; He lov-eth, keepeth, feedeth me—God is not far a - way. . .
from all harm de-fend-eth me; Then come whate'er He sendeth me—God is not far a - way. . .
CODA.
God is not far . . . . a - way, . . . God is not far . . . . a - way, ... I
have the sweet as - sur - ance God is not far a - way. . . .

No. 182. His Love is All I Need.
E. O. E.
COPYRIGHT, 1908, BY E. O. EXCELL.
INTERNATIONAL COPYRIGHT.
E. O. Excell.
Andante.
Introduction.
mf Con espress.
1. The love of Je - sus, who can tell, Tho' he may know it, oh, so well? The love that ev - 'ry want sup-plies, The love that al - ways sat - is - fies; His love is all I need!
2. The love of Je - sus, oh, what bliss To hear Him whis - per I am His! Tho' I may fal - ter on the way, He will not let me go a-stray; His love is all I need!
3. The love of Je - sus, oh, how sweet To hide in such a safe re - treat! Tho' Sa - tan would my hopes destroy, My Sav-ior's love is still my joy; His love is all I need!
p
f
rit.
CHORUS.
So won - der - ful, His love to me, More won-der - ful how could it be? My ev - 'ry sin on Him was laid, My ev - 'ry debt by Him was paid; His love is all I need!
f ten.
ten.
rit.

No. 183. What Would You Have Done?

Jennie E. Hussey.

Chas. H. Gabriel.

Introduction.
SOLO.
1. Had you dwelt in Beth-l'hem Cit - y When from Heav'n to earth came
2. Had you dwelt in some fair val - ley 'Mong the hills of Gal i -
3. Had your eyes be - held the scourg - ing, Pur - ple robe, and crown of
4. Had you, like the lov - ing Ma - ry, Ear - ly has - tened thro' the
down Je - sus Christ, the King of Glo - ry, Who for us left throne and
lee, When the Christ with His dis - ci - ples Walked and talked be - side the
thorn, When the un - be - liev - ers mocked Him Would you then have shared their
gloom, Would your lips have framed the ques - tion, "Who has borne Him from the
crown, Would you then, like watch - ing shep - herds, Ear-nest - ly the Child have
sea, Teach - ing les - sons from the lil - ies, How they nei - ther toil nor
scorn? Or, like quick, im - pet - uous Pe - ter, Read - y e'en with Him to
tomb?" Then what joy to hail Him ris - en, On that morn - ing fair and
sought— Would you, like the three who jour-neyed, Pre-cious gifts to Him have brought?
spin, Yet your Heav'nly Fa - ther robes them—Would your heart have let Him in?
die, O - ver - come by Sa - tan's pow - er, Just as read - y to de - ny?
bright, From the grave that could not pris - on Christ, the Lord of life and light!

No. 184. God Reaches Down.
Ada Blenkhorn.
COPYRIGHT, 1912, BY E. O. EXCELL.
WORDS AND MUSIC.
Samuel W. Beazley.
Introduction.
SOLO. For low voice.
1. God reach-es down, and straightway clasps The hand up-lift - ed to His own,
2. God reach-es down,—no depths too great His ev - er watch-ful eyes to see;
3. God reach-es down to lift the soul To heights of love and hope sub lime;
4. God reach-es down to thee to - day, O soul, wher-ev - er you may be;
And leads that soul in - to the light That shines from His e - ter - nal throne.
No soul too sin - ful to be saved; From sin's deep gulf to be set free.
Sin's dis-cord lost, the soul can hear Heav'n's glad, sweet, ho - ly mu - sic chime.
If thou wilt reach thine hand to Him, His gra-cious love will res - cue thee.
rit.
CHORUS OR QUARTET.
God reaches down, . . . God reaches down, His pow'r di-vine can set you free; . . . .
He reaches down, He reaches down, can set you free;
His mighty arm, ... His heart of love, From sin's dark gulf can res-cue thee.
His might-y arm, His heart of love.

No. 185. How Sweet is His Love.

James Rowe.
COPYRIGHT, 1902, BY E. O. EXCELL.
WORDS AND MUSIC.
E. O. Excell.
Introduction.
1. When troub-led my soul, and when peace I would find, How sweet is the love of Je - sus! . .
2. When faint - ing and help-less I fall in de - spair, How sweet is the. love of Je - sus! . .
3. When dark is the night, and when sore-ly distressed, How sweet is the love of Je - sus! . .
When lone - ly I feel, and when friends are un-kind, How sweet is His love to me! . . .
When suf-f'ring with pain, and when sor-row I bear, How sweet is His love to me! . . .
When long-ing my soul for His com-fort and rest, How sweet is His love to me! . . .
CHORUS.
O . . . how sweet, O how sweet is His love, . . How sweet is His love to
me! . . When friends all have gone, and I suf - fer a - lone, How sweet is His love to me! . .

No. 186. O Make Me Pure.
E. O. E.
WORDS AND MUSIC COPYRIGHT, 1905, BY E. O. EXCELL.
INTERNATIONAL COPYRIGHT SECURED.
E. O. Excell.
Andante.
mp
rit.
1. Be - cloud - ed long my way has been, Be - cause of doubts and fears with - in;
2. Thy grace I claim from day to day; Thy blood to wash my guilt a - way;
3. Long as I jour - ney here be - low, Be Thou my Guide wher - e'er I go;
p
Lord, take a - way my ev - 'ry sin, And make me pure, O make me pure.
Thy - self to teach me how to pray; O make me pure, O make me pure.
Thy pres-ence, Lord, I need it so, To make me pure, To make me pure.
rit.
Chorus.
My one de - sire, my on - ly plea, That I some day Thy face may see,
rit.
And live with Thee e - ter - nal - ly; O make me pure, O make me pure.
rit.

No. 187. The Good Old-Fashioned Way.

Rev. Johnson Oatman, Jr.

E. O. Excell.

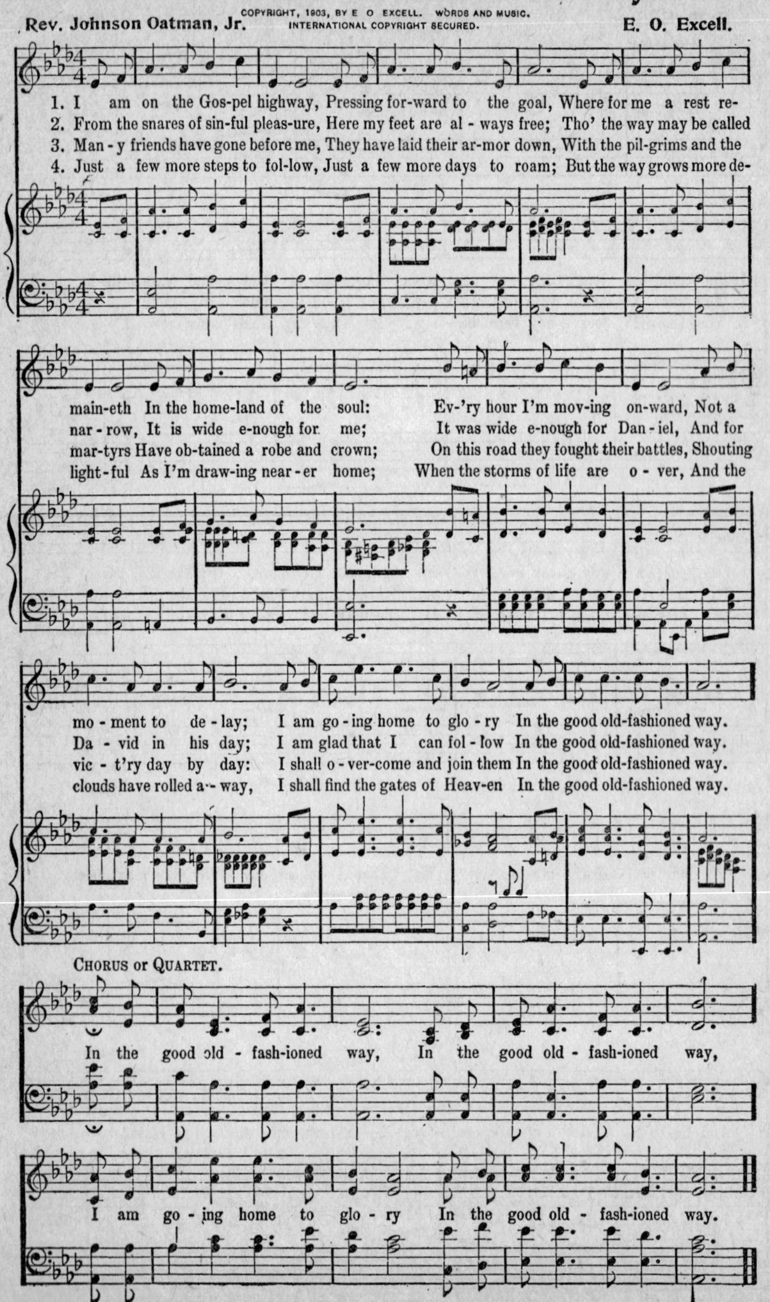
1. I am on the Gos-pel highway, Pressing for-ward to the goal, Where for me a rest re-
2. From the snares of sin-ful pleas-ure, Here my feet are al - ways free; Tho' the way may be called
3. Man - y friends have gone before me, They have laid their ar-mor down, With the pil-grims and the
4. Just a few more steps to fol-low, Just a few more days to roam; But the way grows more de-
main-eth In the home-land of the soul: Ev-'ry hour I'm mov-ing on-ward, Not a
nar - row, It is wide e-nough for me; It was wide e-nough for Dan - iel, And for
mar-tyrs Have ob-tained a robe and crown; On this road they fought their battles, Shouting
light-ful As I'm draw-ing near - er home; When the storms of life are o - ver, And the
mo - ment to de - lay; I am go - ing home to glo - ry In the good old-fashioned way.
Da - vid in his day; I am glad that I can fol - low In the good old-fashioned way.
vic - t'ry day by day: I shall o - ver-come and join them In the good old-fashioned way.
clouds have rolled a - way, I shall find the gates of Heav-en In the good old-fashioned way.
CHORUS OR QUARTET.
In the good old - fash-ioned way, In the good old - fash-ioned way,
I am go - ing home to glo - ry In the good old - fash-ioned way.

No. 188.
It Is Jesus.
T. O. Chisholm.
COPYRIGHT, 1909 BY E. O. EXCELL. WORDS AND MUSIC.
Chas. H. Gabriel.
1. Be - hold! One com-eth in the way, In hum-ble garments clad; The poor-est of the poor is He, No pil-low for His head; The hun-gry, wea-ry, sick and sad In crowds about Him press,— To ev-'ry one He gives re-lief,—What manner of man is this?
2. What words of grace and truth He speaks, Ne'er heard on earth before: The burdened sin-ner hears that voice, And feels his sins no more; He calls the dead to life a-gain, Bids winds and bil-lows cease,—None other man such works hath done,—What manner of man is this?
3. They lead Him forth to Cal-va-ry,— O see Him bleed and die! His parch-ed lips are plead-ing now For those who cru-ci - fy! His head is bowed, the cup has passed, His Spir - it finds re-lease,— He suf-fered thus for you and me,—What manner of man is this?
4. But lo! what wondrous thing is done? The grave has lost its dead! To weep-ing ones He re - ap-pears, When all their hopes had fled; He lin - gers but a lit - tle while, To com - fort and to bless; The heav'ns receive Him from their sight,—What manner of man is this?
CHORUS.
It is Je-sus, it is Je-sus, The Man of Gal-i-lee; It is Je-sus, bless-ed Je-sus who died on Cal-va-ry.
Introduction.
rit.
dim.

No. 189.
Sweet Galilee.
Neal A. McAulay.
WORDS AND MUSIC COPYRIGHT, 1903, BY E. O. EXCELL.
INTERNATIONAL COPYRIGHT SECURED.
E. O. Excell.
Introduction.
1. I stood by the side of the mur-mur-ing sea, Sweet Gal-i-lee, sweet Gal-i-lee, When the
2. I sailed in a ship on that bil-low-y sea, Sweet Gal-i-lee, sweet Gal-i-lee, While the
3. I love to re-call the bright sil-ver-y sea, Sweet Gal-i-lee, sweet Gal-i-lee, For its
sun-shine its beau-ty re-vealed un-to me, Sweet Gal-i-lee, sweet Gal-i-lee; Then I
voice of the tempest was say-ing to me, Sweet Gal-i-lee, sweet Gal-i-lee; Then I
won-der-ful sto-ry is pre-cious to me, Sweet Gal-i-lee, sweet Gal-i-lee; As it
tho't of my Sav-ior who years long a-go Came to tell the glad sto-ry, His love to be-stow,
tho't of the hearts who once tossed on the wave, When they cried in their peril to Him who could save;
tells of my Sav-ior who came from a-bove, With the treasures of mer-cy and in-fi-nite love,
As He stood by the side of that mur-mur-ing sea, Sweet Gal-i-lee, sweet Gal-i-lee.
How the Mas-ter spoke peace to that bil-low-y sea, Sweet Gal-i-lee, sweet Gal-i-lee.
Standing there by the side of that sil-ver-y sea, Sweet Gal-i-lee, sweet Gal-i-lee.

No. 190. Somebody Knows.

Alfred H. Ackley.
COPYRIGHT, 1908 AND 1909, BY F. G. FISCHER.
WORDS AND MUSIC. E. O. EXCELL, OWNER.
B. D. Ackley.
Introduction.
Legato.
1. Fail - ing in strength when op - prest by my foes, Some - bod - y knows, Some-bod-y knows;
2. Why should I fear when the care - bil-lows roll? Some - bod - y knows, Some-bod-y knows;
3. Wound-ed and help - less and sick with dis - tress, Some - bod - y knows, Some-bod-y knows;
Wait - ing for some - one to ban - ish my woes, Some-bod-y knows,—'tis Je - sus.
When the deep shad - ows sweep o - ver my soul, Some-bod-y knows,—'tis Je - sus.
Long - ing for home and a moth-er's ca - ress, Some-bod-y knows,—'tis Je - sus.
Chorus or Quartet.
Some-bod - y knows, Some-bod - y knows When I am tempt-ed and tried by my foes;
He is the One who will keep me— Some-bod - y knows— 'tis Je - sus.

No. 191. Alone At the Beautiful Gate.

Jessie Brown Pounds. Samuel W. Beazley.

Intro.

SOLO.

1. I dreamed that I stood at the por-tal of Heav'n, With saints of the a-ges whom Christ has for-giv'n; But I was a-lone in the midst of the throng, And some-thing I missed from the heav-en-ly song.
2. "Why came I a-lone?" to an an-gel I said; "All oth-ers have dear ones whom here they have led; Have I none who love me, who watch and who wait To en-ter with me thro' the Beau-ti-ful Gate?"
3. "A-las!" said the an-gel, "None saw in thy face The smile of the Mas-ter, the heav-en-ly grace; He asked for thy-self, but the price was too great, And so thou art lone-ly at Heav-en's own gate."
4. I woke from my dream with a cry in my soul; "O Lord, take my life,—not a part, but the whole; No toil is a bur-den, no price is too great For one who has dreamed of the Beau-ti-ful Gate!'

rit.

CHORUS OR QUARTET.

A-lone! a-lone at the Beau-ti-ful Gate! A-lone! a-lone at the Beau-ti-ful Gate! O

Alone At the Beautiful Gate.

rit.
pit-y of pit-ies, O sor-row-ful fate, To jour-ney a-lone to the Beau-ti-ful Gate!
No. 192. Eternity.
F. A. S.
COPYRIGHT, 1908, BY E. O. EXCELL. WORDS AND MUSIC.
Frank A. Simpkins.
1. There is a City, I am told, Where all the streets are paved with gold;
2. Me-thinks I hear the heav'n-ly song, In hal-le-lu-jahs loud and long,
3. Our loved ones who have gone be-fore, Are beck'ning us to that bright shore,
4. Some day my bless-ed Lord will call, In tones that gen-tly rise and fall;
A Home pre-pared for you and me, Where we may spend e-ter-ni-ty,
Come float-ing o'er the might-y sea, A mes-sage from e-ter-ni-ty,
That we may from our cares be free, And sing thro' all e-ter-ni-ty,
And He will say, "Come home with Me, To dwell in blest e-ter-ni-ty,
E-ter-ni-ty, e-ter-ni-ty, Where we may spend e-ter-ni-ty.
E-ter-ni-ty, e-ter-ni-ty, A mes-sage from e-ter-ni-ty.
E-ter-ni-ty, e-ter-ni-ty, And sing thro' all e-ter-ni-ty.
E-ter-ni-ty, e-ter-ni-ty, And dwell in blest e-ter-ni-ty."

No. 193. When I Shall Fall Asleep.

Moses Gage Shirley. Chas. H. Gabriel.

Introduction.
1. Some day the sun of life shall set, and I shall fall a - sleep, And,
2. Some day the cares of life will cease, and I shall fall a - sleep, And,
3. Some day my work will all be done, and I shall fall a - sleep, But
leav-ing all that I hold dear, will find the si - lence deep,— That mys-ter-y which, still un-
pass-ing from you, I shall see a - far the gold-en street, And sainted forms of those who
O what joy to know that I shall wake to nev - er weep! For where I go we know that
solved, God and His an - gels know, (And those who walk by crystal streams where
dwell up - on the oth - er shore, Be - hold the loved ones who from us a-
God has promised per - fect rest And peace for ev - 'ry ach-ing heart, and
heav'nly breez - es blow,) Where grief nor sor-row ev - er come, nor troub - le's bil-lows
while have gone be - fore, Where soft and cool-ing pathways lie, where none shall ev - er
ev - 'ry troub - led breast; And love more last-ing than our own He'll give to me to

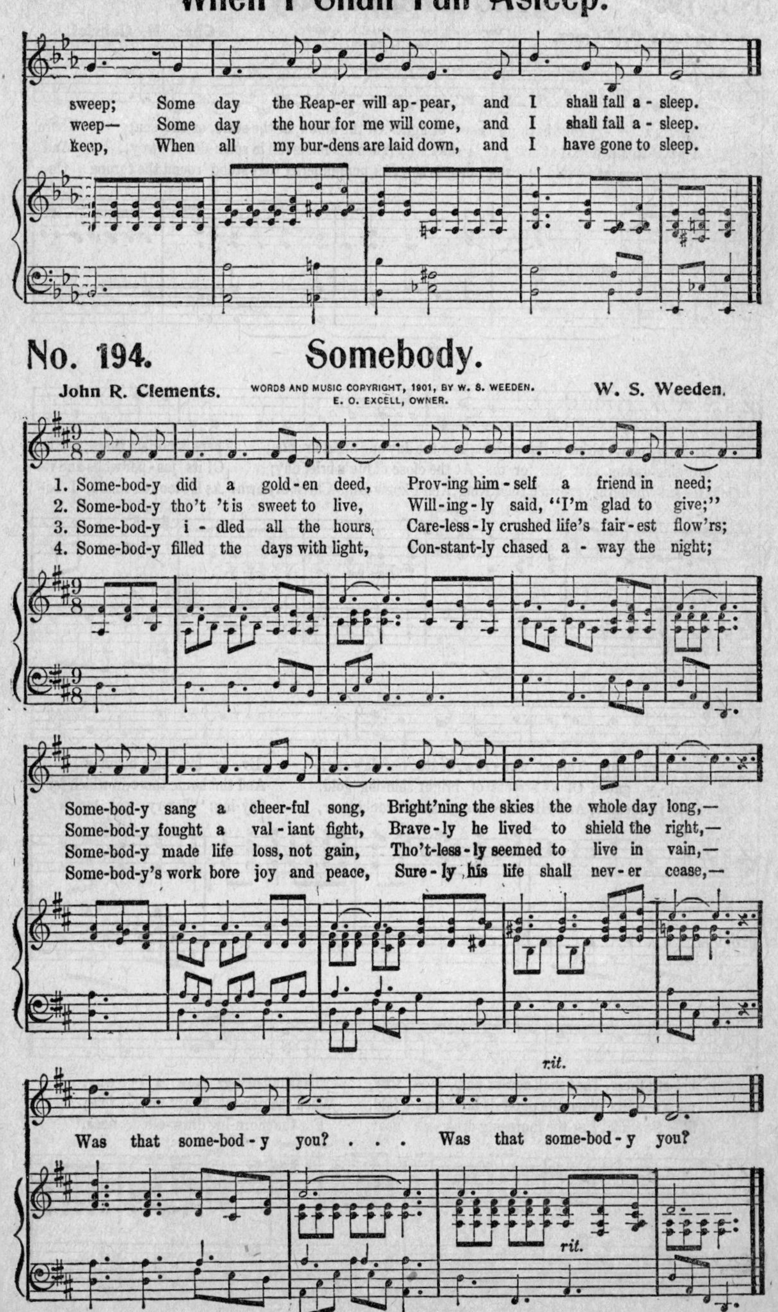
When I Shall Fall Asleep.
sweep; Some day the Reap-er will ap-pear, and I shall fall a - sleep.
weep— Some day the hour for me will come, and I shall fall a - sleep.
keep, When all my bur-dens are laid down, and I have gone to sleep.
No. 194. Somebody.
John R. Clements.
WORDS AND MUSIC COPYRIGHT, 1901, BY W. S. WEEDEN. E. O. EXCELL, OWNER.
W. S. Weeden.
1. Some-bod-y did a gold-en deed, Prov-ing him-self a friend in need;
2. Some-bod-y tho't 't is sweet to live, Will-ing-ly said, "I'm glad to give;"
3. Some-bod-y i - dled all the hours, Care-less-ly crushed life's fair-est flow'rs;
4. Some-bod-y filled the days with light, Con-stant-ly chased a - way the night;
Some-bod-y sang a cheer-ful song, Bright'ning the skies the whole day long,—
Some-bod-y fought a val - iant fight, Brave-ly he lived to shield the right,—
Some-bod-y made life loss, not gain, Tho't-less-ly seemed to live in vain,—
Some-bod-y's work bore joy and peace, Sure-ly his life shall nev-er cease,—
rit.
Was that some-bod-y you? . . . Was that some-bod-y you?
rit.

No. 195.
The Dream City.
Charlotte G. Homer.
COPYRIGHT, 1907, BY CHAS. H. GABRIEL.
E. O. EXCELL, OWNER.
Chas. H. Gabriel.
Solo.
1. There's a cit - y that hath no need of light Of the moon, or the stars, or the sun; There
2. I have dreamed of that cit - y I shall see, When the mists roll in splen-dor a - way, And
3. I have thought I could hear the an-gels sing, As, unnumbered, they stood 'round the throne On
For Introduction see first four measures.
is no noon, neither is there night, For the day and night are one; There is no sin there, neither
morning dawns, as it will for me, At the close of life's brief day; Of its jas - per walls and its
which One sat whom they crown'd their King, And I knew Him–Christ my own! As He looked on me, I be-
pain or care, Toil or sor - row, death, nor de - cay; Ev - er - last - ing beaut - y a -
pearl - y gates, Of its streets of bright shin-ing gold, And the home there-in which for
held Him smile, And His ten - der voice I could hear, Say-ing: "Tar-ry yet but a
bid-eth there, That shall nev-er pass a - way, That shall nev-er pass a - way.
me a-waits When the por-tals bright un - fold, When the por-tals bright un - fold.
lit - tle while, For the morn-ing draw-eth near, For the morn-ing draw-eth near."

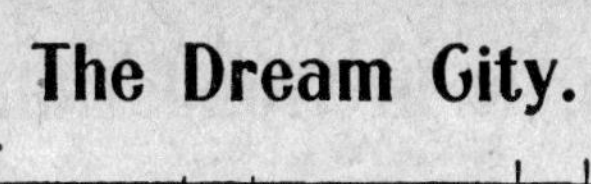

The Dream City.

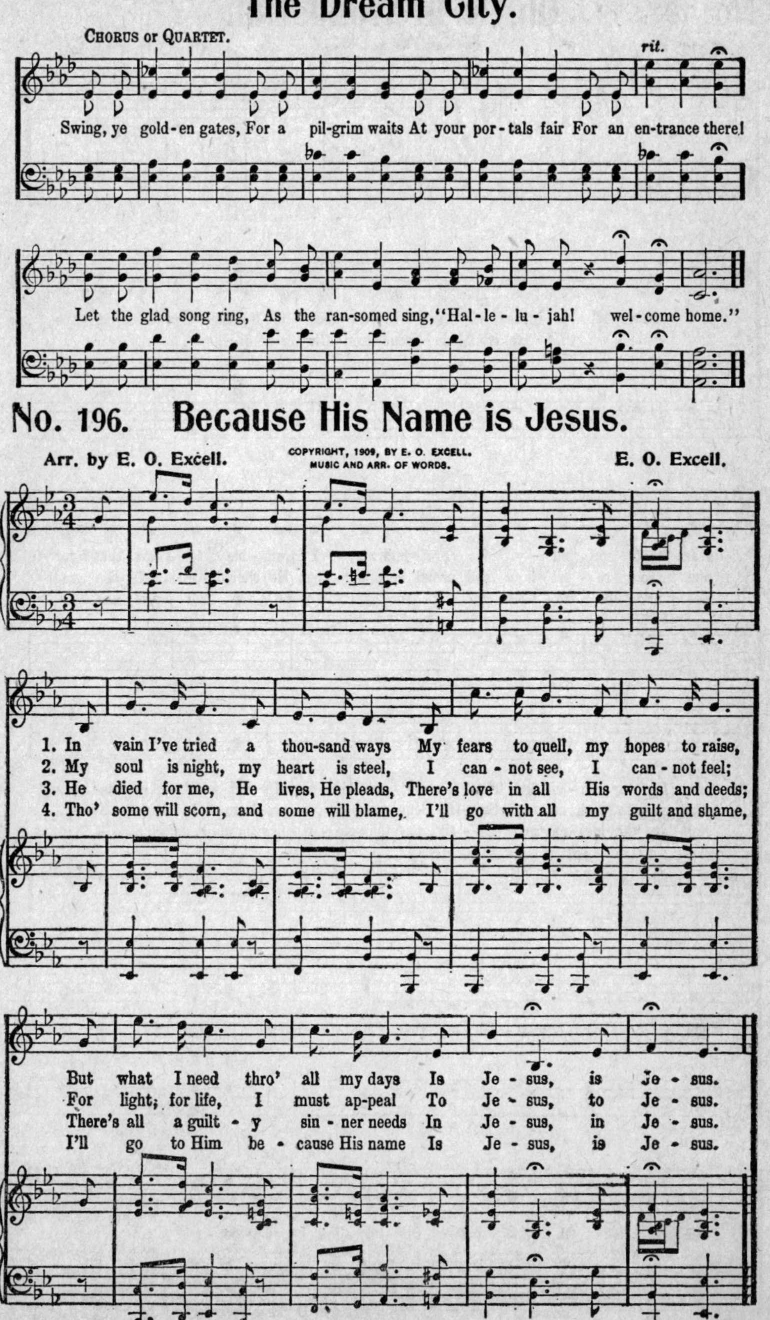

Chorus or Quartet.
rit.
Swing, ye gold-en gates, For a pil-grim waits At your por-tals fair For an en-trance there!
Let the glad song ring, As the ran-somed sing, "Hal-le-lu-jah! wel-come home."
No. 196. Because His Name is Jesus.
Arr. by E. O. Excell.
COPYRIGHT, 1909, BY E. O. EXCELL. MUSIC AND ARR. OF WORDS.
E. O. Excell.
1. In vain I've tried a thou-sand ways My fears to quell, my hopes to raise,
2. My soul is night, my heart is steel, I can-not see, I can-not feel;
3. He died for me, He lives, He pleads, There's love in all His words and deeds;
4. Tho' some will scorn, and some will blame, I'll go with all my guilt and shame,
But what I need thro' all my days Is Je-sus, is Je-sus.
For light, for life, I must ap-peal To Je-sus, to Je-sus.
There's all a guilt-y sin-ner needs In Je-sus, in Je-sus.
I'll go to Him be-cause His name Is Je-sus, is Je-sus.

No. 197. Oh, It Is Wonderful!
C. H. G.
COPYRIGHT, 1898, BY E. O. EXCELL. WORDS AND MUSIC.
Chas. H. Gabriel.
Introduction.
1. I stand all a - mazed at the love Je - sus of - fers me, Con - fused at the
2. I mar - vel that He would de - scend from His throne di - vine, To res - cue a
3. I think of His hands, pierced and bleed - ing, to pay the debt! Such mer - cy, such
grace that so full - y He prof - fers me; I trem - ble to know that for
soul so re - bel - lious and proud as mine; That He should ex - tend His great
love and de - vo - tion can I for - get? No, no, I will praise and a -
me He was cru - ci - fied, That for me, a sin - ner, He suf - fered, He bled and died.
love un - to such as I, Suf - fi - cient to own, to re - deem and to jus - ti - fy.
dore at the mer - cy - seat, Un - til at the glo - ri - fied throne I kneel at His feet.
rit.
Chorus.
Oh, it is won - der - ful that He should care for me, E - nough to
won - der - ful!
die for me! Oh, it is won - der - ful, won - der - ful to me!
won - der - ful!

No. 198. The Slighted Stranger.
C. H. G.
WORDS AND MUSIC, COPYRIGHT, 1908, BY CHAS. H. GABRIEL.
E. O. EXCELL, OWNER.
Chas. H. Gabriel.
Introduction.
Moderato. mf
1. A Stran-ger stands out-side the door, And longs thy guest to be; He knows thy name, for
2. From lone-ly, dark Geth-sem - a - ne, Thro' Pi-late's hall of shame, Up o - ver cru - el
3. Yet still He waits and calls to thee, Al - tho' ye scarce can hear The plead - ing voice, so
o'er and o'er He soft - ly calls to thee! His hands are pierced, His brow is torn, His
Cal - va - ry, To thee in love He came! De - spised! re-ject - ed! cru - ci - fied! O
oft - en has It fal - len on thine ear: O soul, a - rise and let Him in, Lest
face is sad, but sweet—It is the Lord of Par - a - dise! A - rise, thy Sav-ior greet.....
love, O grace un-known, That He should still re-mem-ber thee, And claim thee for His own!....
from the bolt-ed door In sor-row He should turn a-way, To call for thee no more.....
CHORUS.
He was wound-ed for thy trans-gres-sions; He was bruis - ed for thy sin;
Yet He stands at thy heart's door plead - ing, Why, O why not let Him in?

No. 199. That Beautiful Stream.
E. Torbey.
COPYRIGHT, 1889, BY E. O. EXCELL.
E. O. Excell.
1. I'll sing of a stream, . . . of a beau-ti-ful stream, . . . 'T is flow-ing to-
2. I'll sing of a stream, . . . of a beau-ti-ful stream, . . . Which gladdens the
3. I'll sing of a stream, . . . of a beau-ti-ful stream, . . . That fountain that
(1.) I'll sing of a stream, of a beau-ti-ful stream,
day . . . . thro' the sweet Canaan Land; . . . Its waters gleam bright . . .
hearts . . . . in the Cit-y of God; . . . . . It flows from a-bove, ...
now . . . . and for-ev-er is free; . . . . I'll sing of that flood . . . .
'T is flowing to-day thro' the sweet Canaan Land; Its waters gleam bright,
in their heav-en-ly light, ... And spark - les o'er sil-ver-y sand. Go wash,
thro' God's in-fi-nite love, ... And spreads . . its sweet wa-ters a-broad. Go wash,
which is crimsoned with blood, . . . From sin, . . . He has cleansed e-ven m Go wash,
in their heavenly light, And spark-les o'er sil-ver-y sand. Go wash,
CHORUS.
Go wash . . in that beau-ti-ful stream, ... Go wash . . in that
Go wash, go wash in that beau-ti-ful stream, in that beautiful stream, Go wash, go wash in that
beau-ti-ful stream, ... Go, 'T is flow-ing at the cross for you. . .
beau-ti-ful stream, in that beautiful stream, 'T is flow-ing at the cross for you. . .

No. 200. I'm a Pilgrim.

Mary S. B. Dana. COPYRIGHT, 1910, BY E. O. EXCELL. Chas. H. Gabriel.

1. I'm a pil-grim, and I'm a stran-ger; I can tar - ry but a night!
2. Of that Cit - y to which I jour - ney, My Re-deem - er is the Light;
3. There the sun-beams are ev - er shin - ing,— O my long - ing heart is there;
(1) I can tar-ry but a night, I can tar-ry but a night!
Do not de-tain me, for I am go - ing To where the foun-tains are ev - er flow - ing;
There is no sor - row, nor an - y sigh - ing, Nor an - y tears there, nor an - y dy - ing;
Here in this coun - try, so dark and drear - y, I long have wan-dered, forlorn and wear - y;
(1.) Do not de-tain me, for I am go - ing To where the fountains are ever flow - ing;
rit.
Do not de-tain me, for I am go - ing To where the foun-tains are ev - er flow - ing.
There is no sor - row, nor an - y sigh - ing, Nor an - y tears there, nor an - y dy - ing.
Here in this coun - try, so dark and drear - y, I long have wan-dered, forlorn and wear - y.
(1.) Do not de-tain me, for I am go - ing To where the fountains are ever flow - ing.
CHORUS.
I'm a pil - grim, and I'm a stran - ger; I can tar - ry but a night;
I'm a pilgrim and a stranger, I'm a pilgrim and a stranger; I can tarry but a night, I can tarry but a night; For
I'm a pil - grim, and I'm a stran - ger, I can tar-ry, I can tar-ry but a night.
I'm a pilgrim and a stranger, I'm a pilgrim and a stranger,

No. 201. Clinging Close to His Hand.

Lizzie DeArmond. COPYRIGHT, 1910, BY E. O. EXCELL. WORDS AND MUSIC. Samuel W. Beazley.

1. As I cling to the hand of my Lord each day, . . What a glad-ness is mine in the heav'nward way! . . Bless - ed fel-low-ship ours all the way a - long, As my glad - ness voi-ces it-self in song. . .
2. If I cling to His hand when the way grows dim, . . What is there I need fear, since I trust in Him? . For His love lights the way that my feet must tread, And Faith's day - star bright-ens the path a - head. . .
3. I will cling to the hand whose nail-prints I see, . . And will rest in the love that is full and free; . . Cling - ing ev-er to Him, of His grace I sing, Christ, my Sav - ior, ev - er to be my King. . .
CHORUS.
Clinging, clinging by faith to my Savior's hand; Clinging, clinging to Him who my way hath planned;
Cling-ing, cling-ing to Je-sus, my Hope, my All; Cling-ing, clinging, clinging, I can-not fall.

No. 202. Raise Me, Jesus, to Thy Bosom.
Geo. Birdseye.
COPYRIGHT, 1885, BY W. F. SHAW. USED BY PERMISSION.
Wm. A. Huntley.
DUET.
1. Raise me, Je - sus, to Thy bos - om, From this world . . . of sin and woes; . .
2. Raise me, Je - sus, to Thy bos - om, For my heart . . . is slave to fear, . .
3. Raise me, Je - sus, to Thy bos - om, Hear a con - trite spir-it's prayer; .
Let me feel Thine arms a - round me, Then my soul may know re - pose. . .
That will van - ish as a shad - ow, When it feels Thy pres - ence near. . .
Raise me from the sin a - round me Ere I yield me to de - spair. . .
SOLO.
I am wear-y with my bur-den, And I come to Thee for rest; . . Knee-ling at Thy feet, I
In my anguish deign to hear me All my sin and grief con - fess; . . By the promise Thou hast
Oh, I feel that Thou wilt hear me, And will give me ho - ly rest; . . Now I feel Thy glo - ry
CHORUS OR QUARTET.
pray Thee Lift me, Je - sus, to Thy breast. . .
giv - en, Lift me, Je - sus, to Thy breast. . . Raise me, Je-sus, to Thy bos - om, From this
near me, Lift me, Je - sus, to Thy breast. . .
world of sin and woes; Let me feel Thine arms a - round me, Then my soul may know re-pose.

No. 203. Sometime, Somewhere.

Mrs. Ophelia G. Adams. COPYRIGHT, 1894, BY CHARLIE D. TILLMAN. E. O. EXCELL, OWNER. Charlie D. Tillman.

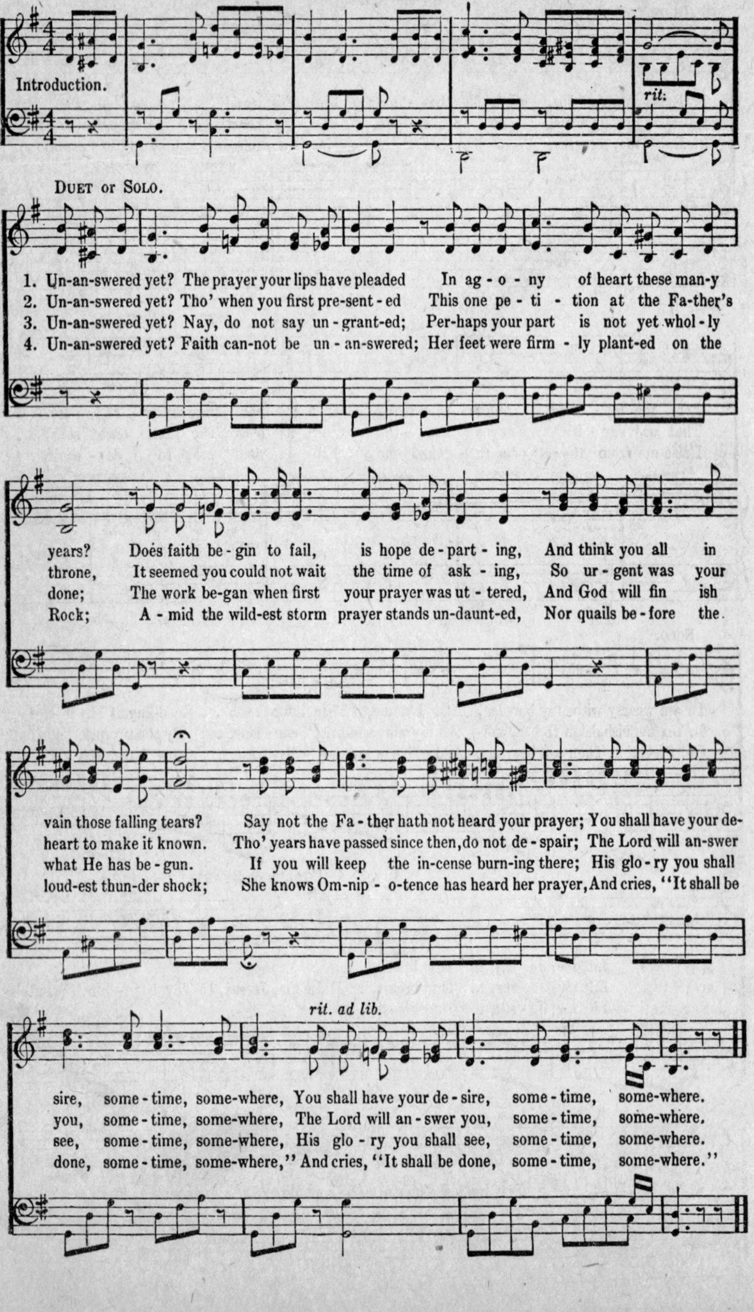

Introduction.

rit.

DUET OR SOLO.

1. Un-an-swered yet? The prayer your lips have pleaded In ag - o - ny of heart these man-y
2. Un-an-swered yet? Tho' when you first pre-sent - ed This one pe - ti - tion at the Fa-ther's
3. Un-an-swered yet? Nay, do not say un - grant-ed; Per-haps your part is not yet whol - ly
4. Un-an-swered yet? Faith can-not be un - an-swered; Her feet were firm - ly plant-ed on the

years? Does faith be - gin to fail, is hope de - part - ing, And think you all in
throne, It seemed you could not wait the time of ask - ing, So ur - gent was your
done; The work be-gan when first your prayer was ut - tered, And God will fin ish
Rock; A - mid the wild-est storm prayer stands un-daunt-ed, Nor quails be - fore the

vain those falling tears? Say not the Fa - ther hath not heard your prayer; You shall have your de-
heart to make it known. Tho' years have passed since then, do not de - spair; The Lord will an-swer
what He has be - gun. If you will keep the in-cense burn-ing there; His glo - ry you shall
loud-est thun-der shock; She knows Om-nip - o-tence has heard her prayer, And cries, "It shall be

rit. ad lib.

sire, some - time, some-where, You shall have your de - sire, some - time, some-where.
you, some - time, some-where, The Lord will an - swer you, some - time, some-where.
see, some - time, some-where, His glo - ry you shall see, some - time, some-where.
done, some - time, some-where," And cries, "It shall be done, some - time, some-where."

No. 204. I Am Happy In Him.
E. O. E.
COPYRIGHT, 1902, BY E. O. EXCELL.
WORDS AND MUSIC.
E. O. Excell.
Introduction.
1. My soul is so hap-py in Je - sus, For He is so pre-cious to me;
2. He sought me so long ere I knew Him, When wan - d'ring a-far from the fold;
3. His love and His mer-cy sur-round me, His grace like a riv - er doth flow;
4. They say I shall some day be like Him, My cross and my bur-den lay down;
His voice it is mu-sic to hear it, His face it is Heav-en to see. . . . .
Safe home in His arms He hath bro't me, To where there are pleasures un-told. . . . .
His Spir - it, to guide and to com - fort, Is with me wher-ev-er I go. . . . .
Till then I will ev - er be faith - ful, In gath - er-ing gems for His crown. . . .
CHORUS or QUARTET.
I am hap-py in Him, ... I am hap-py in Him; . . . . .
I . . . . . am hap - py in Him, I . . . . . am hap - py in Him:
My soul with de - light He fills day and night, For I am hap-py in Him.

No. 205. Drifting Away From God.

F. A. S. COPYRIGHT, 1899, BY E. O. EXCELL. WORDS AND MUSIC. Frank A. Simpkins.

DUET. Tenor and Baritone. (As sung by Gabriel & Excell.)

1. Drift - ing a - way from the Sav - ior, Drift - ing to lands un - known,
2. Drift - ing a - way from the Sav - ior, He who would bear your load;

SOLO or QUARTET.

3. Drift - ing a - way from the Sav - ior, Fear - less - ly on you go;
4. Drift - ing a - way from the Sav - ior, E - ven the an - gels weep;

Drift - ing a - way by night and by day, Drift - ing, yes, drift - ing a - lone.
Drift - ing a - way by night and by day, Drift - ing, yes, drift - ing from God.

Drift - ing a - way by night and by day, Drift - ing to re - gions of woe.
Still you drift on with mirth and with song, Out on the fath - om - less deep.

REFRAIN.

Drift - ing a - way from the Sav - ior, Drift - ing a - way from His love, While the

Drift - ing a - way from the Sav - ior, Drift - ing a - way from His love, While the

Sav - ior is ten - der - ly call - ing, You are drift - ing a - way from God.

Sav - ior is ten - der - ly call - ing, You are drift - ing a - way from God.

No. 206. Speak It For the Savior.

James Rowe. E. O. Excell.

DUET. Tenor and Baritone. (As sung by Gabriel & Excell.)

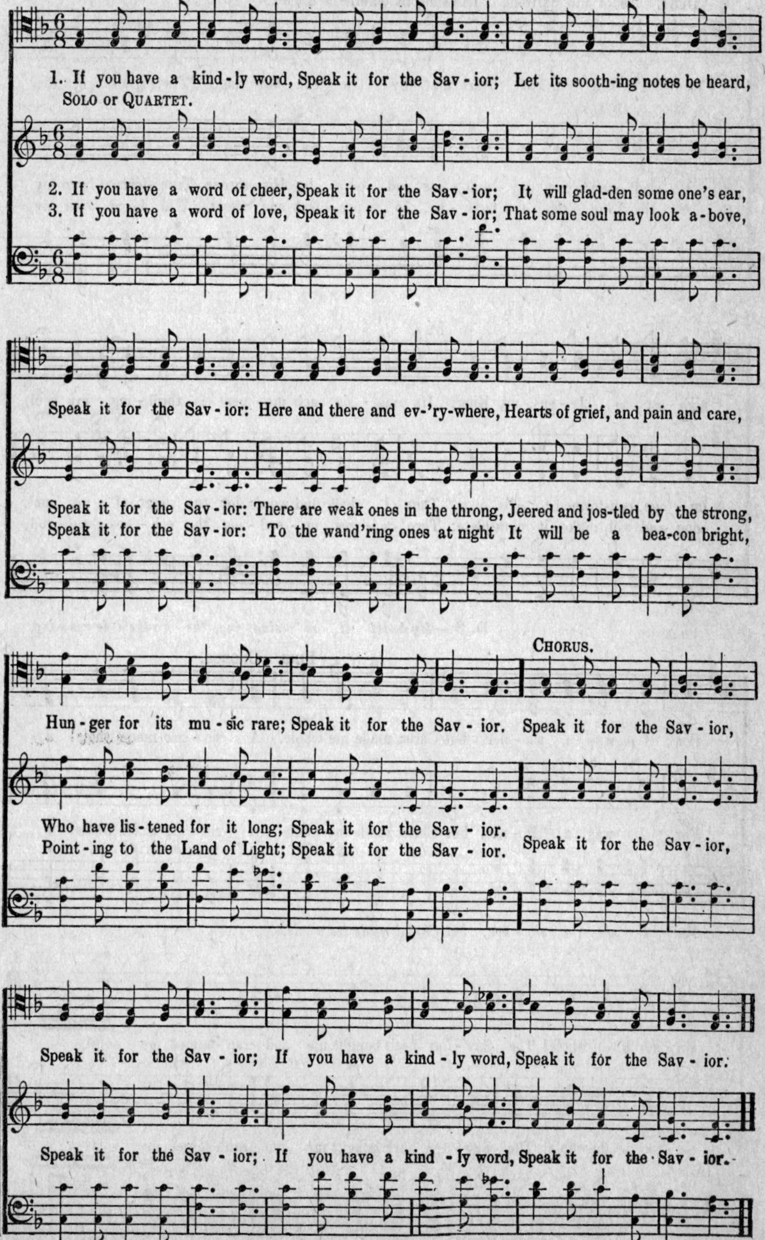

SOLO or QUARTET.

1. If you have a kind-ly word, Speak it for the Sav-ior; Let its sooth-ing notes be heard, Speak it for the Sav-ior: Here and there and ev-'ry-where, Hearts of grief, and pain and care, Hun-ger for its mu-sic rare; Speak it for the Sav-ior.

2. If you have a word of cheer, Speak it for the Sav-ior; It will glad-den some one's ear, Speak it for the Sav-ior: There are weak ones in the throng, Jeered and jos-tled by the strong, Who have lis-tened for it long; Speak it for the Sav-ior.

3. If you have a word of love, Speak it for the Sav-ior; That some soul may look a-bove, Speak it for the Sav-ior: To the wand'ring ones at night It will be a bea-con bright, Point-ing to the Land of Light; Speak it for the Sav-ior.

CHORUS.

Speak it for the Sav-ior, Speak it for the Sav-ior; If you have a kind-ly word, Speak it for the Sav-ior.

No. 207. A Sinner Made Whole.

W. M. Lighthall. Chas. H. Gabriel.

DUET. Tenor and Baritone. (As sung by Gabriel & Excell.)

1. There's a song in my heart that my lips can-not sing, 'Tis praise in the high-est to Je-sus, my King; Its mu-sic each mo-ment is thrill-ing my soul, For I was a sin-ner, but Christ made me whole.

SOLO or QUARTET.

2. I shall stand one day fault-less and pure by His throne, Trans-formed from my im-age, con-formed to His own; Then I shall find words for the song of my soul, For I was a sin-ner, but Christ made me whole.

3. All the mu-sic of heav-en, so per-fect and sweet, Will blend with my song and will make it com-plete; Thro' a-ges un-end-ing the ech-oes will roll, For I was a sin-ner, but Christ made me whole.

D. S.—*My heart it is sing-ing, the an-them is ring-ing, For I was a sin-ner, but Christ made me whole.*

FINE. CHORUS.

A sin-ner made whole! a sin-ner made whole! The Sav-ior hath bought me and ran-somed my soul! *rit.* D. S.

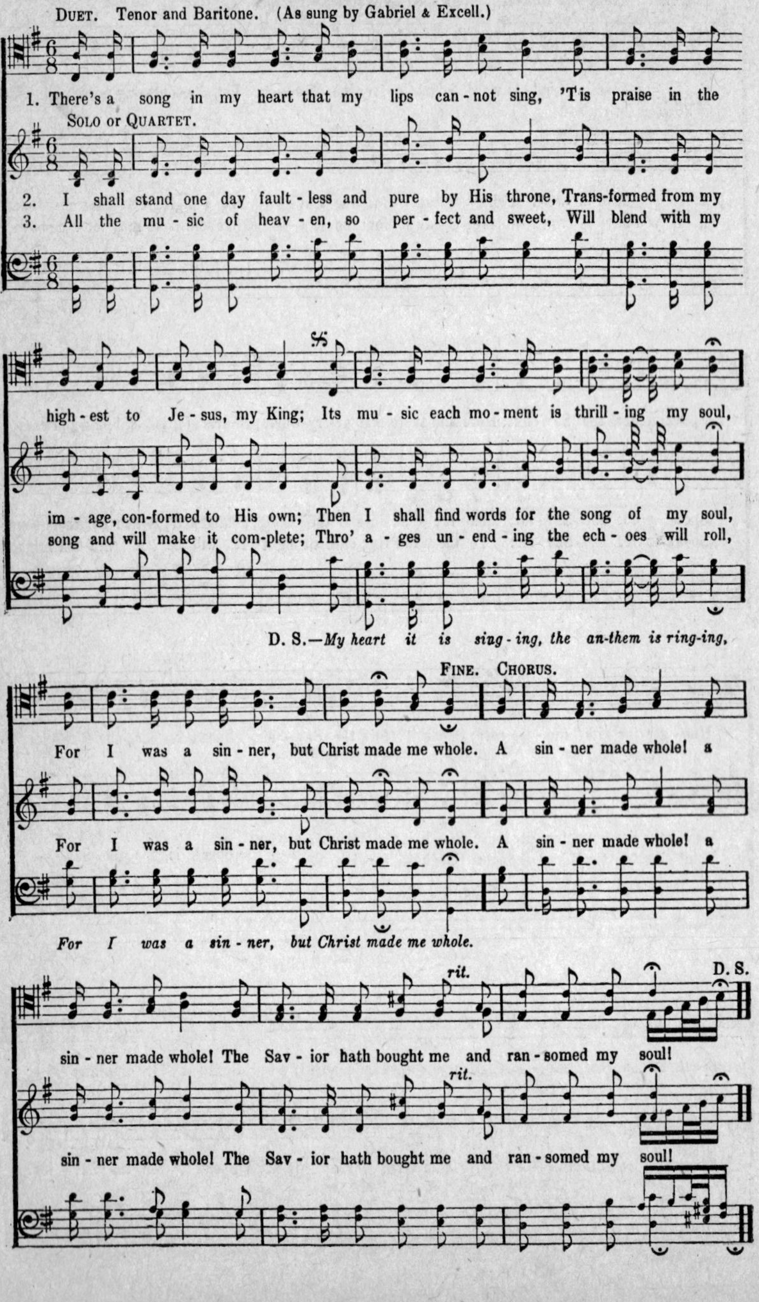

No. 208. His Love Can Never Fail.

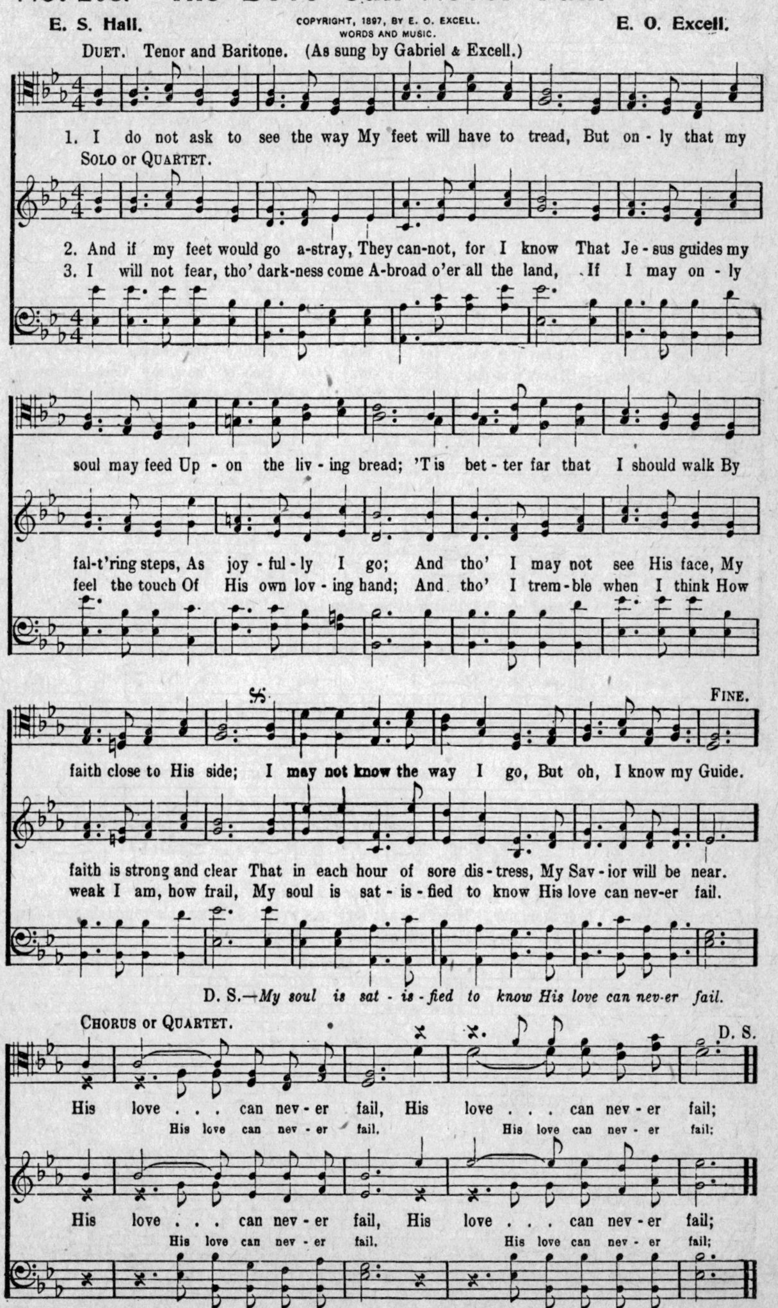
E. S. Hall.
COPYRIGHT, 1897, BY E. O. EXCELL.
WORDS AND MUSIC.
E. O. Excell.
DUET. Tenor and Baritone. (As sung by Gabriel & Excell.)
1. I do not ask to see the way My feet will have to tread, But on - ly that my
SOLO or QUARTET.
2. And if my feet would go a-stray, They can-not, for I know That Je - sus guides my
3. I will not fear, tho' dark-ness come A-broad o'er all the land, If I may on - ly
soul may feed Up - on the liv - ing bread; 'Tis bet - ter far that I should walk By
fal-t'ring steps, As joy - ful - ly I go; And tho' I may not see His face, My
feel the touch Of His own lov - ing hand; And tho' I trem - ble when I think How
FINE.
faith close to His side; I may not know the way I go, But oh, I know my Guide.
faith is strong and clear That in each hour of sore dis - tress, My Sav - ior will be near.
weak I am, how frail, My soul is sat - is - fied to know His love can nev-er fail.
D. S.—My soul is sat - is - fied to know His love can nev-er fail.
CHORUS or QUARTET.
D. S.
His love . . . can nev - er fail, His love . . . can nev - er fail;
His love can nev - er fail. His love can nev - er fail;
His love . . . can nev - er fail, His love . . . can nev - er fail;
His love can nev - er fail. His love can nev - er fail;

No. 209. "Heaven Is Not Far Away."
J. E. Ramsey.
COPYRIGHT, 1913, BY E. O. EXCELL.
WORDS AND MUSIC.
Roger Cox.
1. Kneel - ing by my trun-dle bed, Moth - er's hand up - on my head, She would kiss my
2. Dark-ness comes with guilt-y fears, Sin and shame bring bit - ter tears, Pray - ing there, night
cheek and say, "Heav'n is not far a - way." Man-y years have rolled be-tween,
turns to day;— "Heav'n is not far a - way." Ho - ly now, my Beth - el ground,
D. S.—Then how sweet will be my bliss;
Mother's feet have en-tered in, Still that whis-per when I pray, "Heav'n is not far a - way."
An-gel hosts en-camped a-round, In my dreams I hear them say, "Heav'n is not far a - way."
Dear-er than a moth-er's kiss—On His breast my head to lay, "Heav'n is not far a - way."
FINE.
Still that whis-per when I pray, "Heav'n is not far a - way."
In my dreams I hear them say, "Heav'n is not far a - way." 3. When at last 'mid shadows deep,
On His breast my head to lay, "Heav'n is not far a - way."
D. S. AL FINE.
I shall "lay me down to sleep," He who keeps my soul will say, "Heav'n is not far a - way."

No. 210. The Sinner and the Song.
W. L. T.
BY PER. W. L. THOMPSON & CO.
Will L. Thompson.
Solo.
Organ.
1. A sin-ner was wand'ring at e - ven-tide, His tempter was watching close by at his side,
2. He stopped and listened to ev-'ry sweet chord, He remembered the time he once loved the Lord,
In his heart raged a battle for right against wrong, But hark! from the church he hears the sweet song;
Come on! says the tempter, come, on with the throng, But hark! from the church a-gain swells the song,
pp Quartet.
Solo.
1. Je - sus, lov - er of my soul, Let me to Thy bo - som fly,
2. While the bil-lows near me roll, while the tem-pest still is high,
Organ.
Oh, tempter, de-part,
I have served thee too long, I fly to the Sav - ior, He dwells in that song, O Lord,
can it be that a sin - ner like me, May find a sweet ref - uge by com - ing to Thee?
pp Quartet.
Solo.
Oth - er ref - uge have I none; Hangs my help-less soul on Thee.
Organ.
I come, Lord, I
pp Quartet.
come, Thou'lt for-give the dark past, And O, re - ceive my soul at last.

No. 211. Jesus and His Love.
John R. Clements.
WORDS AND MUSIC COPYRIGHT, 1908, BY E. O. EXCELL.
INTERNATIONAL COPYRIGHT SECURED.
E. O. Excell.
Solo. For Introduction see last brace.
1. A voice is sweet-ly sing-ing Its mes-sage in my heart, And oft-en, o'er it
2. How oft-en, when life's path-way Is heaped a-bout with care, And ev-'ry step that's
3. I fan-cy, when the morn-ing Of heav-en's day shall break, And I from earth for-
mu-sing, The tears un-bid-den start; No day can be so drear-y But this a balm will
tak-en Re-veals some hid-den snare, Will this sweet song of com-fort A ben-e-dic-tion
ev-er My journey thence shall take, No song of an-gel voic-es More sweet to me shall
prove: Tell me the old, old sto-ry, Of Je-sus and His love;
CHORUS. This Chorus used by permission of the Author, Dr. W. H. Doane.
Tell me the old, old sto-ry, Tell me the old, old sto-ry, Tell me the old, old
sto-ry Of Je-sus and His love.
FINE. Introduction.
Moderato.

No. 212. My Mother's Song.
J. E. Ramsey.
COPYRIGHT, 1908, BY E. O. EXCELL. WORDS AND MUSIC.
E. O. Excell.
1. Sing me the song my moth-er sang In ac-cents sweet and low, That dear old song she sang to me In childhood long a - go; Me thinks I hear her voice a-gain, And see her smil - ing face, As when she sang that sweet re-frain .Of God's A-maz - ing Grace.
2. O sing it as she sang that day, So tender and so sweet, When pen - i - tent I knelt to pray, Be - fore the mer - cy - seat; It seemed a song from angel tongue, My bro-ken heart to bless, When mother sang that dear old song Of God's A-maz - ing Grace.
3. Sing me the dear old song a-gain, It brings a sweet re - lief; 'Twas mother's song in joy or pain, Her balm for ev - 'ry grief; In vale or on the mountain steep, She sang her song of praise,—The Lord my soul will safe-ly keep, Thro' His A-maz - ing Grace.
4. Sing as she sang, with faith so strong, When called by an - gel band, To join her song with ser-aph throng, In heav'n's sweet sum-mer land; Still sing-ing God's re-deem-ing love, His glo - ry on her face, She winged her way to realms a-bove, Thro' God's A-maz - ing Grace.
After each stanza sing the corresponding stanza of the following hymn: "Amazing Grace,"
No. 213. Amazing Grace.
John Newton.
Arr. by E. O. Excell.
1 2
1. Amazing grace! how sweet the sound, That saved a wretch like me! I once was lost, but now am found, Was blind, but now I see.
2 'Twas grace that taught my heart to fear And grace my fears relieved; How precious did that grace appear The hour I first believed!
3 Thro' many dangers, toils and snares, I have already come; 'Tis grace hath bro't me safe thus far, And grace will lead me home.
4 When we've been there ten thousand years Bright shining as the sun, We've no less days to sing God's praise Than when we first begun.

No. 214. Echoes of Old Hymns.

Rose Keene. | COPYRIGHT, 1898, BY E. O. EXCELL. WORDS AND MUSIC. | E. O. Excell.

1. A lit - tle maid with soft blue eyes Was sing - ing at her play The lull - a - by her
2. A stranger chanced to pass that way, His heart was lone and sad; "I used to hear that
3. The stranger's life had sin - ful been, It pierced him like a dart; His eyes were run - ning
4. The stranger knelt, and as he prayed He fixed his eyes on Heav'n; "O God," he cried, "I
5. The lit - tle maid kept sing - ing on While at her child-ish play, And who but God can
moth - er sang To her at close of day; Her child-ish voice rose sweet and clear, Up-
song," he said, "When I was but a lad." Then like a flash there came to him The
o'er with tears, The song had reached his heart; He heard a - gain his moth-er's voice, In
come to Thee, And ask to be for - giv'n." An - oth - er song came float - ing near, While
tell the hearts Her songs had reached that day. The stran-ger rose with sins for-giv'n, The
on the sum-mer air, . . . And o'er and o'er these words she sang: (Omit, see No. 1.....)
mem - 'ries of the past; . . He saw his lov-ing moth-er's face, With sor-row o - ver-cast.
hum - ble, earnest prayer, . The while the lit - tle maid sang on, (Omit, see No. 2.....)
there on bend-ed knee; . . He heard the lit - tle maid-en sing, (Omit, see No. 3.....)
Sav - ior heard his plea, . . And then he sang that pre-cious song, (Omit, see No. 4.....)
No. 1. Sing after 1st stanza.
No. 2. Sing after 3rd stanza.
Hush, my babe, lie still and slum-ber, Ho-ly an - gels guard thy bed. Ho-ly an-gels guard thy bed.

Echoes of Old Hymns.

No. 3. *Sing after 4th stanza.*

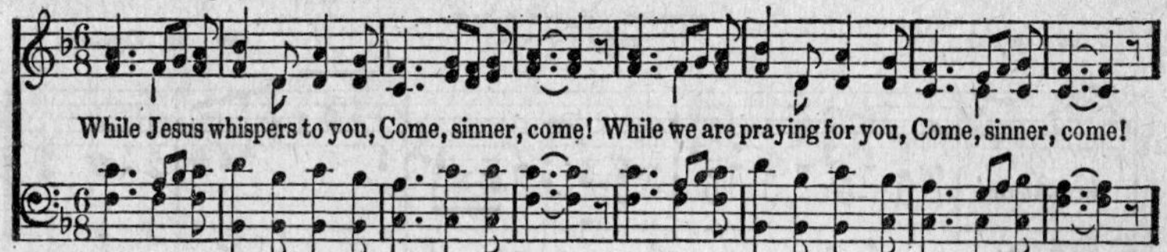

While Jesus whispers to you, Come, sinner, come! While we are praying for you, Come, sinner, come!

No. 4. *Sing after 5th stanza.*

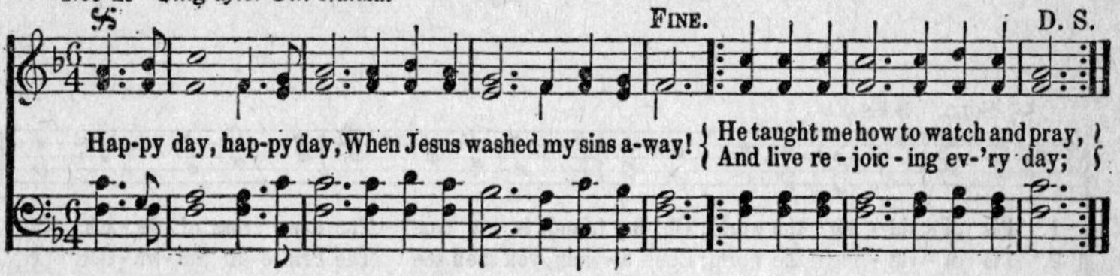

FINE. D. S.

Hap-py day, hap-py day, When Jesus washed my sins a-way! { He taught me how to watch and pray, And live re - joic - ing ev-'ry day; }

No. 215. My Savior's Voice.

C. H. G.

Chas. H. Gabriel.

DUET.

1. Like mu-sic, float-ing on the eve-ning air; Like ves-pers, ring-ing out the hour of prayer; Like ech - oes, answ'ring round me ev-'ry-where, My Sav - ior's voice falls on my ear.
2. As when it rose a-bove the an-gry sea; And it in love commanded: "Fol-low Me!" As when it plead in dark Geth-sem-a-ne, My Sav - ior's voice falls on my ear.
3. As when it spake the dead to life a-gain; As to the sleep-ing ones He called in vain; And as it rang with His ex-pir-ing pain, My Sav - ior's voice falls on my ear.
4. When earth-ly cares and sor-rows all are past, And at His feet my gold-en sheaves I cast, I'll sing His praise for-ev-er, when at last My Sav - ior's voice falls on my ear.

CHORUS OR QUARTET.

He speaks, and darkness changes in - to day; He speaks, and all my sor-rows flee a-way; He speaks, and in my soul I hear Him say: "I died for thee, O come to Me!"

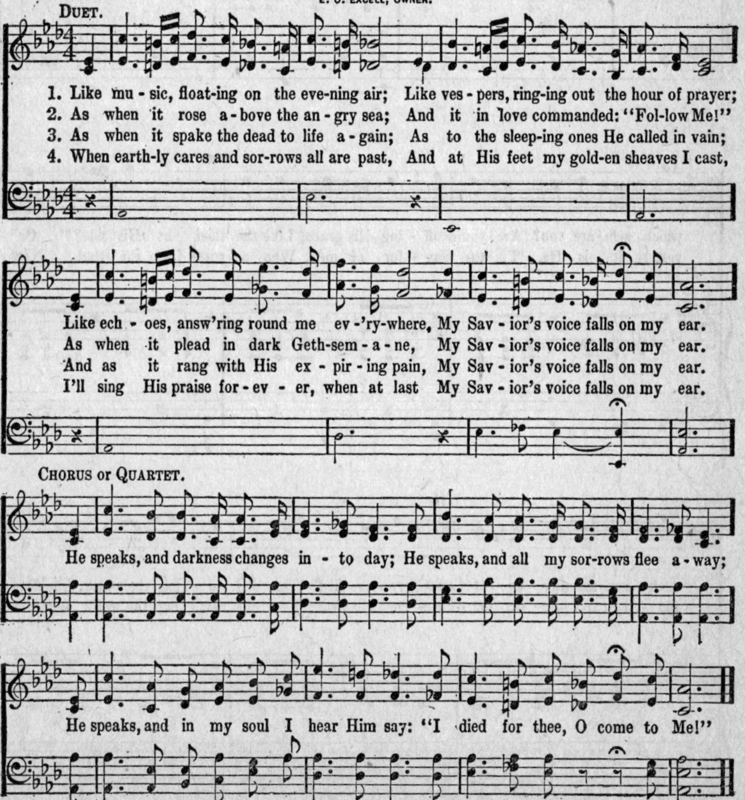

No. 216. 'Tis Dividing the World.

COPYRIGHT, 1887, BY E. O. EXCELL.
WORDS AND MUSIC.
W. A. O.
W. A. Ogden.
Introduction.
Solo. Bass.
1. 'Tis di - vid - ing the world; Oh! my friend, is it true? The dear cross of Je - sus, On which side are you? Are you scoff - ing His grace, Like the thief at His side? Or seek - ing the mer - cy of Christ cru - ci - fied? 'Tis di - vid - ing the world; Look a-
2. 'Tis di - vid - ing the world; Look a - gain, you shall see The Prince of Sal - va - tion: Oh, yes, it is He, 'Tis the Sav - ior of men, Who a - rose from the dead. Now glo - ry and hon - or en - cir - cle His head; 'Tis di - vid - ing the world, But His
rit.
8
8

'Tis Dividing the World.

broad and be-hold, The ar - mies of Sa - tan, de - fi - ant and bold; With the
prom - is - es are, A crown and a robe for the faith - ful to wear, And the
weap - ons of sin they u - ni - ted - ly stand, O - bey - ing the cap - tain of
song of the vic - tor at last he shall sing, Who bat - tles for Je - sus, our
rit.
ad lib.
sin's dark command, O - bey - ing the cap - tain of sin's dark command. On which side,
Sav - ior and King, Who bat - tles for Je - sus, our Sav - ior and King. On which side,
rit.
which side, On which side are you? Arrayed with God's en - e-mies, or friends tried and true?
which side, On which side are you? Arrayed with God's en - e-mies, or friends tried and true?
Interlude.
f

No. 217. A Thought of Him.
C. L.
COPYRIGHT, 1904, BY CHAS. H. GABRIEL.
E. O. EXCELL, OWNER.
Chas. H. Gabriel.
1. If ev - er Je - sus has need of me, Some-where in the fields of sin,
2. I'll fill each day with lit - tle things, As the pass - ing moments fly;
I'll go where the darkest pla - ces be, And let the sun-shine in;
The tendril, which to the great oak clings, Grows strong as it climbs on high;
I'll be con-tent with the low-liest place, To earth's re-mot - est rim,
I'll trust my Lord, tho' I can - not see, Nor let my faith grow dim;
I know I'll see His smil-ing face, If it's done with a tho't of Him;
He'll smile—and that's e-nough for me, If it's done with a tho't of Him;
If it's done with a tho't of Him, If it's done with a tho't of Him.

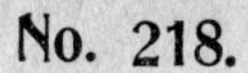

But For a Moment.

Jno. R. Clements.

E. O. Excell.

1. "But for a mo-ment" this weight of af-flic-tion; "But for a mo-ment" this darkness, this gloom; Then the bright to-mor-row, Then no more sin or sor-row; Morn-ing of bliss be-yond the tomb, Morn-ing of bliss be-yond the tomb.
2. "But for a mo-ment" this bond of re-strain-ing; "But for a mo-ment" this tri-al, this care; Then the glad a-wak-ing, Then Heaven's glo-ry break-ing; Dawn-ing of life be-yond com-pare, Dawn-ing of life be-yond com-pare.
3. "But for a mo-ment" this day of a-lone-ness; "But for a mo-ment" this pa-thos, this blight; Then the morn of glo-ry, Then, then the new, new, sto-ry; Heav-en, and joy with-out a night, Heav-en, and joy with-out a night.

No. 219. Holy Bible, Book Divine.

John Burton.
COPYRIGHT 1900, BY E. O. EXCELL.
E. O. Excell.
Slow, with dignity.
1. Ho - ly Bi - ble, Book di - vine, Pre-cious treas-ure, thou art mine:
2. Mine to chide me when I rove; Mine to show a Sav-ior's love;
3. Mine to com-fort in dis - tress, Suf-f'ring in this wil - der - ness;
4. Mine to tell of joys to come, And the reb - el sin-ner's doom:
rit.
Mine to tell me whence I came; Mine to tell me what I am;
Mine thou art to guide and guard; Mine to pun - ish or re - ward;
Mine to show, by liv - ing faith, Man can tri - umph o - ver death;
O thou ho - ly Book di - vine, Pre-cious treas-ure, thou art mine.
CHORUS.
Ho - ly Bi - ble, Book di - vine, Pre-cious treas - ure, thou art mine;
O thou ho - ly Book di - vine, Pre-cious treas - ure, thou art mine!

No. 220. **Better Than I Know.**

Ina Duley Ogdon. COPYRIGHT, 1914, BY E. O. EXCELL. INTERNATIONAL COPYRIGHT. B. D. Ackley.

1. Christ found me lost in sor-row's night, Up - on my soul a crim-son blight;
2. He drew me to His lov - ing heart, And bade me nev - er-more de - part;
3. When I, in weak-ness, al - most fail, Still does His love for me pre - vail,

My stain of sin He made as snow,—He loves me bet - ter than I know.
No love like His, a - bove, be - low,—He loves me bet - ter than I know.
Still does He grace and mer - cy show; He loves me bet - ter than I know.

CHORUS.

He loves me bet - ter than I know; Wher-e'er I stray His love will go—

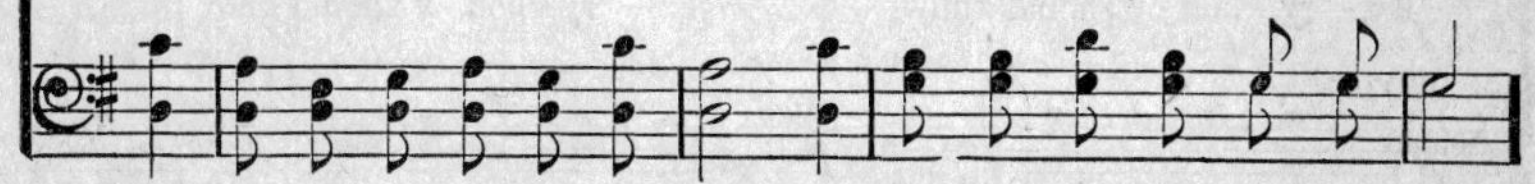

There is no oth - er loves me so, He loves me bet - ter than I know.

No. 221. Everybody Should Know.

Mrs. Frank A. Breck.

E. O. Excell.

1. I have such a won-der-ful Sav - ior, Who helps me wher-ev-er I go,
2. His mer - cy and love is un-bound-ed, His riv - ers of grace o - ver - flow;
3. He helps me when tri-als sur-round me, His love and His goodness to show;
4. My life and my love I will give Him, And faith-ful -ly serve Him be - low,

That I must be tell - ing His good-ness That ev - 'ry-bod - y should know.
Yes, He is "The Chief of ten thou-sand" That ev - 'ry-bod - y should know.
How can I but love and a - dore Him That ev - 'ry-bod - y should know?
Who bro't me His won-drous sal - va - tion, That ev - 'ry-bod - y should know.

CHORUS.

Ev - 'ry - bod - y should know, should know, Ev - 'ry - bod - y should know; should know;
I have such a won-der - ful Sav - ior, That ev - 'ry - bod - y should know.

rit.

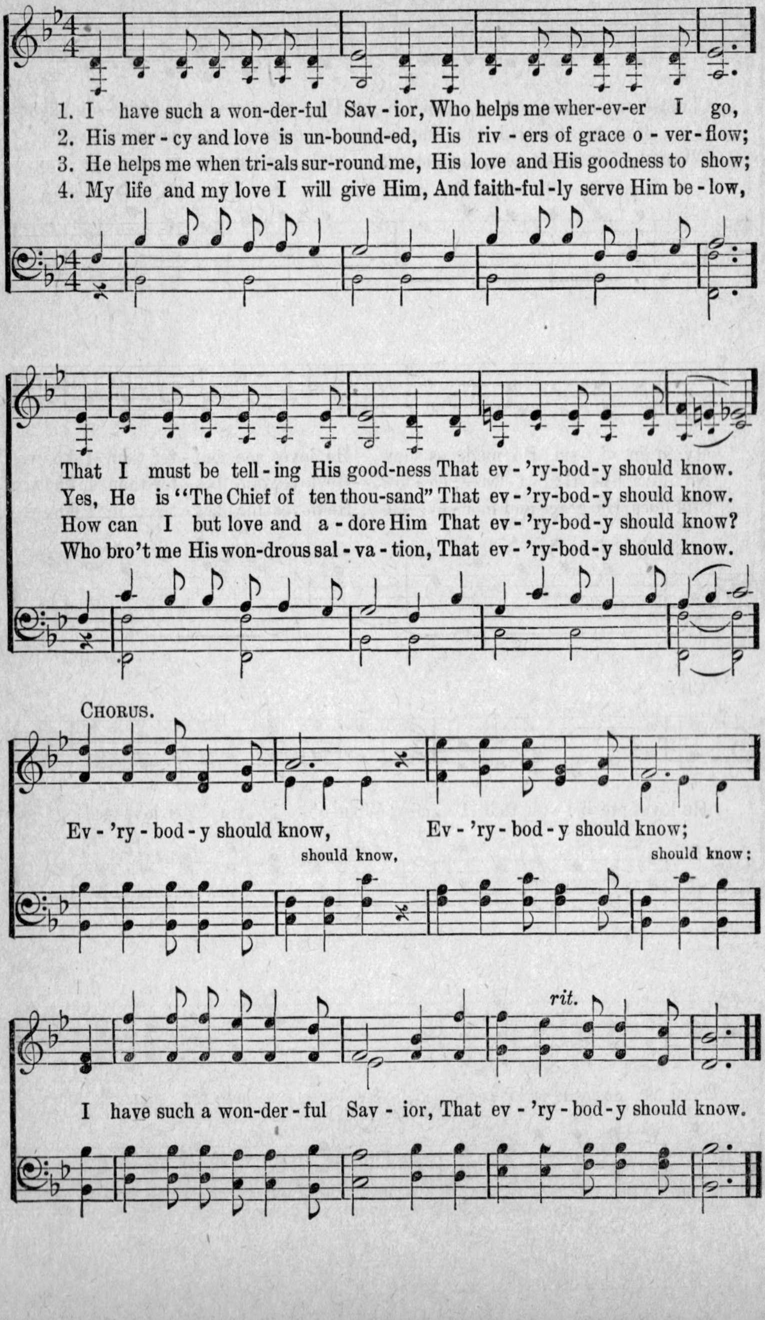

No. 222. Jesus Will!

Ina Duley Ogdon.
COPYRIGHT, 1912, BY W. E. BIEDERWOLF.
B. D. Ackley.
DUET.
1. Who will o-pen mer-cy's door? Je-sus will! Je-sus will!
2. Who can take a-way my sin? Je-sus will! Je-sus will!
3. Who can conquer doubts and fears? Je-sus will! Je-sus will!
4. Who will be my dear-est Friend? Je-sus will! Je-sus will!
As for par-don I im-plore? Je-sus, bless-ed Je-sus will!
Make me pure, with-out, with-in? Je-sus, bless-ed Je-sus will!
Share my joys and dry my tears? Je-sus, bless-ed Je-sus will!
Love and keep me to the end? Je-sus, bless-ed Je-sus will!
CHORUS.
Je-sus will, Je-sus will! Yes, your lov-ing Sav-ior will;
sure-ly will;
He will each and ev-'ry need ful-fill, Je-sus, bless-ed Je-sus will!

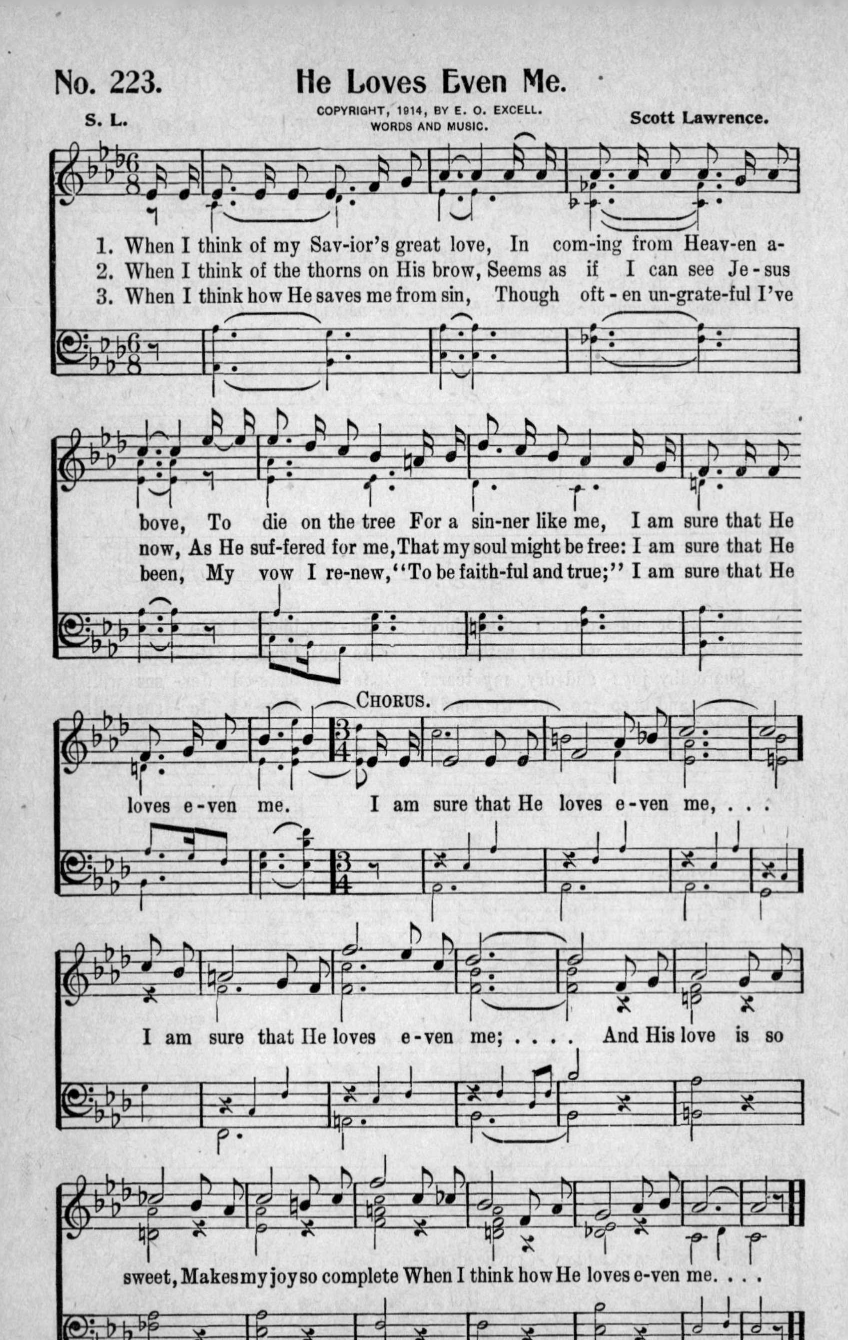
No. 223.
He Loves Even Me.
S. L.
COPYRIGHT, 1914, BY E. O. EXCELL.
WORDS AND MUSIC.
Scott Lawrence.
1. When I think of my Sav-ior's great love, In com-ing from Heav-en a-bove, To die on the tree For a sin-ner like me, I am sure that He loves e-ven me.
2. When I think of the thorns on His brow, Seems as if I can see Je-sus now, As He suf-fered for me, That my soul might be free: I am sure that He loves e-ven me.
3. When I think how He saves me from sin, Though oft-en un-grate-ful I've been, My vow I re-new, "To be faith-ful and true;" I am sure that He loves e-ven me.
CHORUS.
I am sure that He loves e-ven me, . . . I am sure that He loves e-ven me; . . . . And His love is so sweet, Makes my joy so complete When I think how He loves e-ven me. . . .

No. 224. He Knows It All.

Mrs. Ophelia Adams.
COPYRIGHT, 1905, BY E. O. EXCELL. WORDS AND MUSIC.
INTERNATIONAL COPYRIGHT SECURED.
C. M. Davis.
1. I love to think my Fa-ther knows Why I have missed the path I chose,
2. I love to think my Fa-ther knows The thorns I pluck with ev-'ry rose,
3. I love to think my Fa-ther knows The strength or weakness of my foes,
And that I soon shall clear-ly see The way He led was best for me.
The dai-ly griefs I seek to hide From the dear souls I walk be-side.
And that I need but stand and see Each con-flict end in vic-to-ry.
REFRAIN.
He knows it all, . . . He knows it all, . . . My Fa-ther
He knows it all, He knows it all,
knows, . . He knows it all; . . . Thy bit-ter tears . . . how
My Fa-ther knows He knows it all; Thy bit-ter tears
fast they fall!— He knows, My Fa-ther knows it all.
how fast they fall!—

No. 225. He Understands.
Sophie E. Morgan.
COPYRIGHT, 1914, BY E. O. EXCELL. WORDS AND MUSIC.
INTERNATIONAL COPYRIGHT.
E. O. Excell.
1. There's a qui - et re-treat, where with Je-sus I meet, And my bur-dens I place in His hands; Ev-'ry sor-row I bear, ev-'ry heart-breaking care,
2. When o'er-come by my grief, noth-ing brings such re-lief As the touch of His com-fort-ing hands; Ev-'ry bur-den He bore for my sins o'er and o'er,
3. When my friends all for-sake, and my sad heart would break, I reach out to His beck-on-ing hands; They were wounded for me, that thro' faith I might see,
4. Wheth-er wear-y or sad, whether cheer-ful or glad, I will cling to those nail-pierc-ed hands; For they point day by day to my Home far a-way,
FINE.
REFRAIN.
D. S.—Je-sus knows, and He un-der-stands.
Je-sus knows, and He un-der-stands. He knows,................ He knows,................
Je-sus knows, and He un-der-stands.
Je-sus knows, and He un-der-stands. And He un-der-stands, And He un-der-stands;
Ev-'ry sor-row I bear, ev'ry heart-breaking care,
Ev-'ry bur-den He bore for my sins o'er and o'er,
They were wounded for me, that thro' faith I might see,
For they point day by day to my Home far a-way,
D. S.

No. 226. Refuge.

Charles Wesley. E. O. Excell.

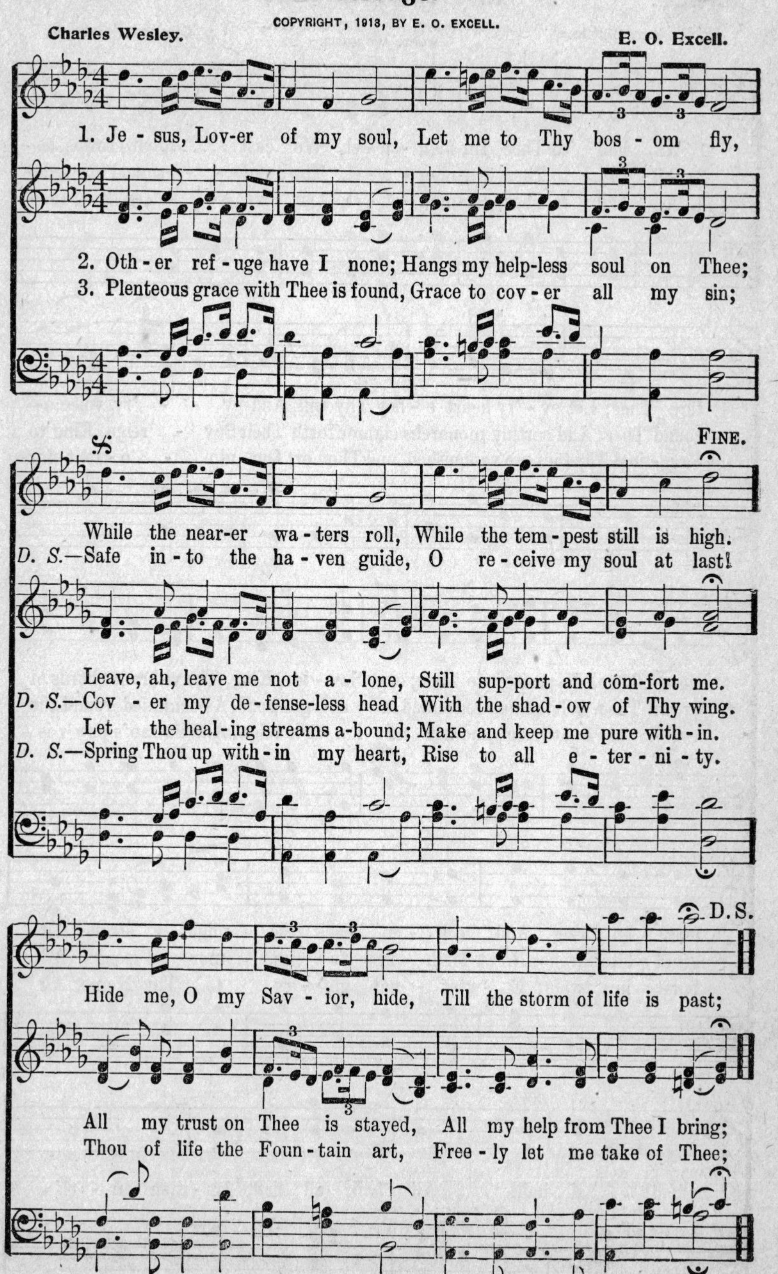
1. Je - sus, Lov-er of my soul, Let me to Thy bos - om fly,
2. Oth - er ref - uge have I none; Hangs my help-less soul on Thee;
3. Plenteous grace with Thee is found, Grace to cov - er all my sin;
Fine.
While the near-er wa - ters roll, While the tem - pest still is high.
D. S.—Safe in - to the ha - ven guide, O re - ceive my soul at last!
Leave, ah, leave me not a - lone, Still sup-port and com-fort me.
D. S.—Cov - er my de - fense-less head With the shad - ow of Thy wing.
Let the heal - ing streams a-bound; Make and keep me pure with - in.
D. S.—Spring Thou up with - in my heart, Rise to all e - ter - ni - ty.
D.S.
Hide me, O my Sav - ior, hide, Till the storm of life is past;
All my trust on Thee is stayed, All my help from Thee I bring;
Thou of life the Foun - tain art, Free - ly let me take of Thee;

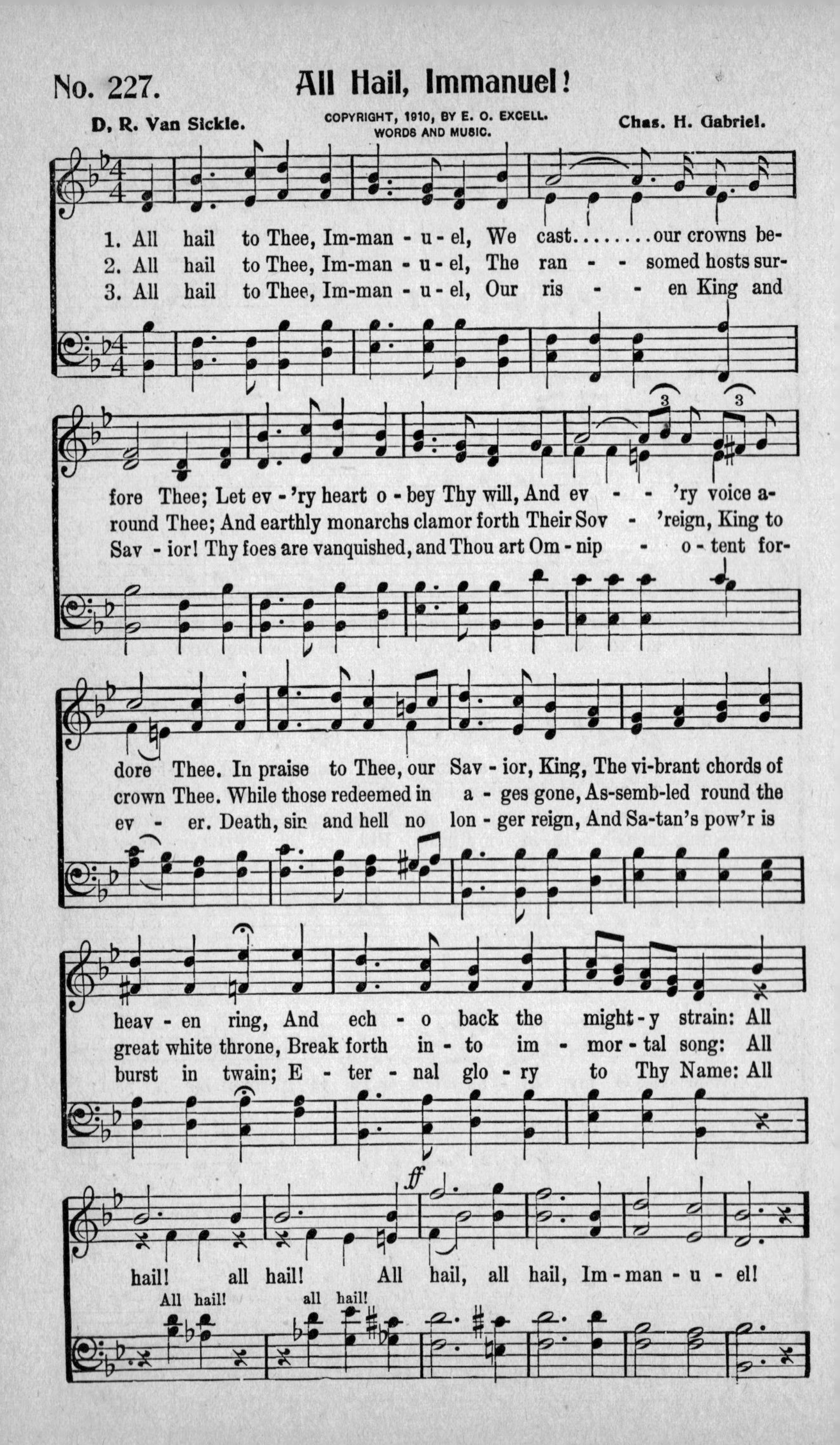
No. 227. All Hail, Immanuel!
D. R. Van Sickle.
COPYRIGHT, 1910, BY E. O. EXCELL. WORDS AND MUSIC.
Chas. H. Gabriel.
1. All hail to Thee, Im-man - u - el, We cast........our crowns be-
2. All hail to Thee, Im-man - u - el, The ran - - somed hosts sur-
3. All hail to Thee, Im-man - u - el, Our ris - - en King and
fore Thee; Let ev - 'ry heart o - bey Thy will, And ev - - 'ry voice a-
round Thee; And earthly monarchs clamor forth Their Sov - 'reign, King to
Sav - ior! Thy foes are vanquished, and Thou art Om - nip - o - tent for-
dore Thee. In praise to Thee, our Sav - ior, King, The vi-brant chords of
crown Thee. While those redeemed in a - ges gone, As-sem-bled round the
ev - er. Death, sin and hell no lon - ger reign, And Sa-tan's pow'r is
heav - en ring, And ech - o back the might - y strain: All
great white throne, Break forth in - to im - mor - tal song: All
burst in twain; E - ter - nal glo - ry to Thy Name: All
hail! all hail! All hail, all hail, Im - man - u - el!
All hail! all hail!
ff

All Hail, Immanuel!

CHORUS.
Hail, ... Im-man-u-el, Im-man-u-el! Hail, ...
Hail to the King we love so well, Hail, Im - man - u - el! Hail to the King we love so well,
Hail! . . . .
Im-man-u - el, Im-man-u - el!
Hail, Im - man - u - el! Glo - ry and hon - or and maj - es - ty,
Hail! . . . . Glo - - ry and maj - es - ty,
Wis-dom and pow-er be un - to Thee, Now and ev - er - more!
Wis - - dom be un - to Thee,
Hail, ... Im-man-u-el, Im-man-u-el! Hail, ...
Hail to the King we love so well, Hail, Im - man - u - el! Hail to the King we love so well,
Hail! . . . .
Im-man-u-el, Im-man-u-el!
Hail, Im - man - u - el! King of kings and Lord of lords, All hail, Im-man-u-el!
Hail! . . . .

No. 228. Homeward and Heavenward.

Eben E. Rexford. | COPYRIGHT, 1913, BY E. O. EXCELL. WORDS AND MUSIC. | Samuel W. Beazley.

Intro.
Unison.
1. Trav - 'ling on in the path that the Sav - ior trod, . .
2. Trav - 'ling home to the land where our loved have gone, . .
3. Trav - 'ling homeward and heav'nward by way of the cross, . .
Know - ing that it leads in - to the land of God, . . .
Out of dark-ness of earth to a heav'n - ly dawn, . . .
To the land where no tears are, no pain, no loss, . . .
Trust - ing Je - sus will guide us thro' shade or sun, . . .
Out of sor-row and sin with the Lord to be, ...
To see Je - sus our Sav - ior, our God, our King, . . .

Homeward and Heavenward
Till the jour-ney is o-ver and rest is won. . . .
If He say-eth, "Well done," unto you and me. . . .
Where the songs of re-demp-tion and glo - ry ring. . . .
8
Chorus.
O Heav'n, where Christ my Redeemer has gone, In the sin - less land, . .
sin - less land,
From thy hills those gone on be - fore Wave a beck-on-ing hand. . . . .
beck-on - ing hand.
Some glad day the message will come From that land to me, ...
that land to me.
rit. cres.
ff
"Child of earth, come home-come home, Heav'n has need of thee!"

No. 229.
The King of Kings.
C. H. G.
COPYRIGHT, 1914, BY E. O EXCELL
Chas. H. Gabriel.
1. Joy-ful-ly now our songs are re-sound-ing, As to our Sav-ior each heart a tribute brings; Sweet-ly the ech-oes, too, are re-bound-ing, Ech-oes of prais-es un-to the King of Kings.
2. Strangely He wro't the Fa-ther's commission; Teaching and preaching the Word in Galilee; Bear-ing the scorn of low-ly po-si-tion, That from the burden of sin we might be free.
FINE.
CHORUS.
1. He . . . is Lord of all, . . . And He a-lone is wor-thy of our ad-o-ra - tion! We . . His name ex-tol, . .
2. Bless - - ed be His name, . . His glory shall endure, and He shall reign for-ev - - er! Un - - to us He came . .
1. He is Lord of all, He is Lord of all, He a - lone is wor-thy of our ad-o-ra-tion! We His name ex-tol, We His name ex-tol,
2. Blessed be His name, Bless-ed be His name, He shall reign for - ev-er, He shall reign for-ev-er! Un-to us He came, Un-to us He came

The King of Kings.

For He it was who gave His life for our sal - va - - tion;
The yoke of sin to bear, the bonds of death to sev - - er;
He it was who gave His life for our sal - va - tion;
He it was who came the bonds of death to sev - er;
Won - - der - ful His love! . . . And with our song we will re-
Loud . . ho-san - nas sing! . . . Ho-san - na to the Son of
Won-der - ful His love! Won-der-ful His love! With our
Loud ho-san-nas sing! Loud ho-san-nas sing To the
peat the bless-ed sto - - ry, Till . . . in Heav'n a-
Da - vid, the vic - to - - rious! Crown . . . Him, crown Him
songs, our songs re-peat the bless-ed sto - ry, Till in Heav'n a - bove,
Son, the Son of Da - vid, the vic - to-rious! Crown Him, crown Him King,
D. S.
bove . . With the redeemed of earth we give to Him the glo - ry.
King, . . And make His praise thro'-out the earth forever glo-rious!
Till in Heav'n a - bove, We will give to Him the glo - ry.
Crown Him, crown Him King, Make His praise for - ev - er glo - rious!

No. 230. Crown Him King of Kings.

E. E. Rexford.
COPYRIGHT, 1909, BY E. O. EXCELL.
WORDS AND MUSIC.
DeLoss Smith.
INTRODUCTION.
VOICES IN UNISON.
1. Crown Him, crown Him with glo - ry the King of kings;
2. He who reigns o'er the king-doms of earth to - day,
3. Praise Him, praise Him, the King on the great white throne;
Praise and hom-age each heart as its trib - ute brings;
Sends His bless-ings to those in the heav'n-ward way;
Love Him, serve Him, who rul-eth by love a - lone;
Sing, O earth, and u-nite in the might - y re - frain—
Sing we prais-es with hearts that with love o - ver - flow—
Up to heav-en the shout of the glo - ri - fied rings—

Crown Him King of Kings.

Christ, our Re-deem-er and King, will for - ev - er reign!
Glo - ry to Je - sus who con-quers our ev - 'ry foe!
Laud and a - dore Him, and crown Him the King of kings!
CHORUS.
Sing ho - san - nas, loud let the joy - ful an - thems ring,
Laud and wor - ship Him whom the an - gels a - dore!
Crown Him, crown Him, Sav - ior, Re-deem - er and King,
Glo-ry to God in the high - est— Glo - ry for - ev - er - more!

No. 231. Christ Shall Be King.
Elisha A. Hoffman.
COPYRIGHT, 1905, BY CHAS. H. GABRIEL.
E. O. EXCELL, OWNER.
Chas. H. Gabriel.
1. Christ shall be King o - ver all the na-tions, sea to sea, shore to shore;
2. Christ shall be King! let your swords be gleaming, clean and bright, clean and bright;
3. Christ shall be King! make his reign all-glo-rious! do and dare, do and dare;
Spread a - broad the proc - la - ma-tion, earth's do - min - ions o'er! An-
Soul, why i - dly sleep-ing, dream-ing? quit you for the fight! The
He shall be the Lord vic - to - rious, reign - ing ev - 'ry - where! His
nounce the com - ing king-dom, and the prom-ised vic - to - ry; The
bat - tle must be brave - ly waged, and pressed to vic - to - ry; The
king - dom shall ex - tend - ed be, and make the cap-tives free; The
Lord of lords and King of kings He shall for - ev - er be!
Lord of lords and King of kings He shall for - ev - er be!
Lord of lords and King of kings He shall for - ev - er be!

Christ Shall Be King.

CHORUS.
Christ shall be King! this our bat - tle - cry; Our Christ shall be
Christ shall be the King, the King, and let this be the bat-tle-cry; Our Christ shall be the
King! float His stand-ard high; The Naz-a-rene shall be enthroned, and
King, the King! now float His glorious standard high;
1
set His peo-ple free; The Lord of lords and King of kings He shall for ev - er
be, The Lord of lords and King of kings He shall for - ev - er be.
2
Lord of lords and King of kings He shall for - ev - er be.

No. 232.
Christ is Leading On.
J. F. Williams.
COPYRIGHT, 1910, BY E. O. EXCELL.
WORDS AND MUSIC.
DeLoss Smith.
ff
1. We have heard the cry re-sound-ing from the East and from the West,
2. In the an - nals of the world be - hold the writ - ings of His word;
3. Ere the word of Christ shall fail Him, heav'n and earth shall pass a - way;
4. On-ward then, ye Chris-tian sol-diers, with the truth that makes men free,
Call - ing val - iant men to serve our King, of all the kings the best;
In the ep - och - mak-ing bat - tles see the flash-ing of His sword;
So for one - ness of be - liev - ers we will work, and watch, and pray;
From the mountains and the prai - ries to the is - lands of the sea;
We en - list to brave-ly bat - tle till the na-tions are pos-sessed,
God is swift-ly crushing Sa-tan thro' the strength of Christ the Lord;
We shall see and share the vic-t'ry of that glad tri-um-phant day,
Un - to God shall be the glo - ry, un - to faith the vic - to - ry!

Christ is Leading On.
For Christ, our great Commander, for Christ, Im-man-u - el.
Sin's might - y host shall trem-ble, for venge-ance is our God's.
When Christ shall con-quer Sa - tan, and come in peace to reign.
All hail the name of Je - sus, all hail Im-man-u - el!
CHORUS.
Shout ho - san - na, Christ vic - to - rious! See His
Shout ho - san - na, Christ vic - to - rious!
ban - rer proud-ly wav-ing o - ver us! Sin and er - ror fall be-
Sin and er - ror
fore us, For Christ is lead - ing on; Sin and
fall be - fore us,
er - ror fall be-fore us, For Christ is lead-ing on.
Sin and er - ror fall before us,

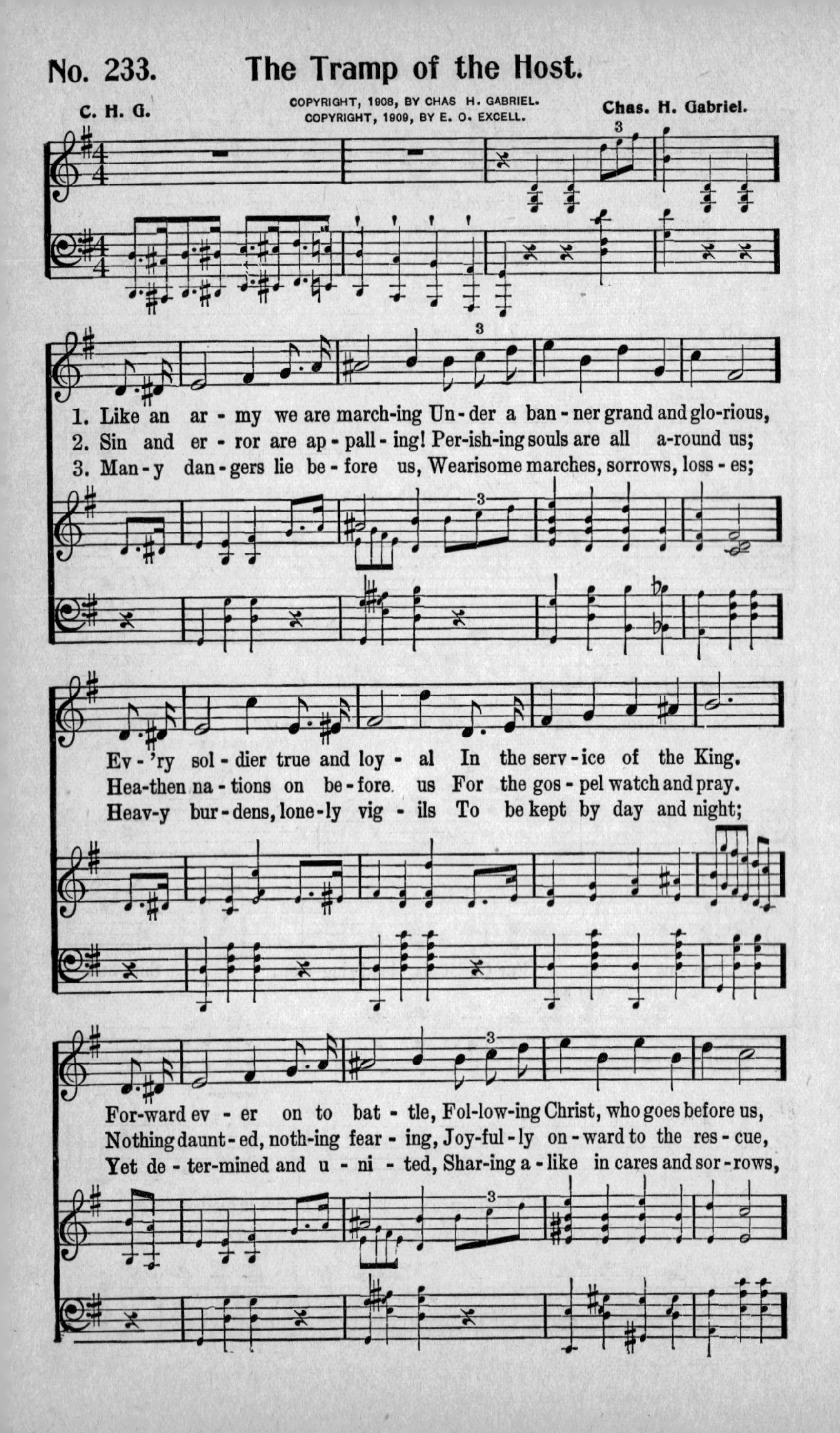
No. 233. The Tramp of the Host.
C. H. G.
COPYRIGHT, 1908, BY CHAS H. GABRIEL.
COPYRIGHT, 1909, BY E. O. EXCELL.
Chas. H. Gabriel.
1. Like an ar - my we are march-ing Un - der a ban - ner grand and glo-rious,
2. Sin and er - ror are ap - pall - ing! Per-ish-ing souls are all a-round us;
3. Man - y dan - gers lie be - fore us, Wearisome marches, sorrows, loss - es;
Ev - 'ry sol - dier true and loy - al In the serv - ice of the King.
Hea-then na - tions on be - fore us For the gos - pel watch and pray.
Heav-y bur - dens, lone - ly vig - ils To be kept by day and night;
For-ward ev - er on to bat - tle, Fol-low-ing Christ, who goes before us,
Nothing daunt - ed, noth-ing fear - ing, Joy-ful - ly on - ward to the res - cue,
Yet de - ter-mined and u - ni - ted, Shar-ing a - like in cares and sor - rows,

The Tramp of the Host.

With a tramp, tramp, tramp, moving onward, While the victor's song we sing.
With a tramp, tramp, tramp, we are marching Where our Savior leads the way.
With a tramp, tramp, tramp, we are marching Upward to the land of light.
Chorus.
Like an ar - my with ban-ners fly - ing, A-gainst the hosts of sin we
March-ing on, march-ing on,
march, march away! Souls in bond-age of sin are dy-ing; "They must and shall be
March-ing on, march-ing on,
free!" rings the war-cry to-day, "They must and shall be free!" rings the war-cry to-day.
3
3
3
3
3

No. 234. Rock of Ages.
A. M. Toplady.
COPYRIGHT, 1912, BY E. O. EXCELL. RENEWAL.
E. O. Excell.
1. Rock . . of A - - ges, cleft . . for me,
2. Could . . my tears . . for - ev - - er flow,
3. While . . I draw . . this fleet - - ing breath,
1. Rock of A - ges, cleft for me, Blest Rock of A - ges, cleft for me,
2. Could my tears for - ev - er flow, Oh! Could my tears for - ev - er flow,
3. While I draw this fleet-ing breath, Yes, While I draw this fleet - ing breath,
Let . . . me hide . . . my - self . . in Thee;
Could . . my zeal . . no lan - - guor know,
When . . mine eyes . . shall close . . in death,
Let me hide my - self in Thee, Oh! Let me hide my - self in Thee;
Could my zeal no lan-guor know, Oh! Could my zeal no lan-guor know,
When mine eyes shall close in death, Yes, When mine eyes shall close in death,
Let . . the wa - - ter and . . the blood,
These . . for sin . . could not . . a - tone;
When . . I rise . . to worlds . . un - known,
Let the wa - ter and the blood, Oh! Let the wa - ter and the blood,
These for sin could not a - tone, No, These for sin could not a - tone;
When I rise to worlds un-known, Yes, When I rise to worlds un-known,

Rock of Ages.

From . . Thy wound - ed side . . which flowed,
Thou . . must save . . and Thou . . a - lone;
And . . be - hold . . Thee on . . . Thy throne,
From Thy wound-ed side which flowed, Yes, From Thy wound-ed side which flowed,
Thou must save and Thou a - lone, Yes, Thou must save and Thou a - lone;
And be - hold Thee on Thy throne, Yes, And be - hold Thee on Thy throne,
rit.
Be . . of sin . . the doub - - le cure,
In . . my hand . . no price . . I bring;
Rock . . of A - - ges, cleft . . for me,
rit.
Be of sin the doub-le cure, Yes, Be of sin the doub-le cure,
In my hand no price I bring, Lord, In my hand no price I bring;
Rock of A - ges, cleft for me, Blest Rock of A - ges, cleft for me,
Repeat pp.
Save . . from wrath . . and make . . me pure.
Sim - - ply to . . . Thy cross . . I cling.
Let . . me hide . . my - self . . . in Thee.
Repeat pp.
Save from wrath and make me pure, Yes, Save from wrath and make me pure.
Sim - ply to Thy cross I cling, Lord, Sim - ply to Thy cross I cling.
Let me hide my - self in Thee, Oh, Let me hide my - self in Thee.

No. 235. Onward, Christian Soldiers.

Sabine Baring-Gould.
COPYRIGHT, 1907, BY E. O. EXCELL.
E. O. Excell.
1. On-ward, Christian, sol - diers! March-ing as to war With the cross of Je - sus Go-ing on be - fore. Christ, the roy - al Mas - ter, Leads a-gainst the foe; . . . . For-ward in - to bat - tle, See, His ban-ners go!
2. At the sign of tri - umph Sa - tan's host doth flee; On, then, Chris-tian sol - diers, On to vic - to - ry! Hell's foun-da - tions quiv - er At the shout of praise; . . . Broth-ers, lift your voi - ces, Loud your anthems raise.
3. Like a might - y ar - my Moves the Church of God; Broth-ers, we are tread - ing Where the saints have trod; We are not di - vid - ed, All one bod - y we, ... One in hope and doc - trine, One in char - i - ty.
4. On-ward, then, ye peo - ple! Join our hap - py throng, Blend with ours your voi - ces In the tri-umph-song; Glo - ry, laud, and hon - or Un - to Christ the King, . . . This thro' count-less a - ges Men and an-gels sing.
CHORUS OR QUARTET.
Arthur S. Sullivan.
On-ward, Chris-tian sol diers! March-ing as to war, With the cross of Je - sus Go - ing on be - fore.
INTRODUCTION and INTERLUDE.

Devotional Hymns

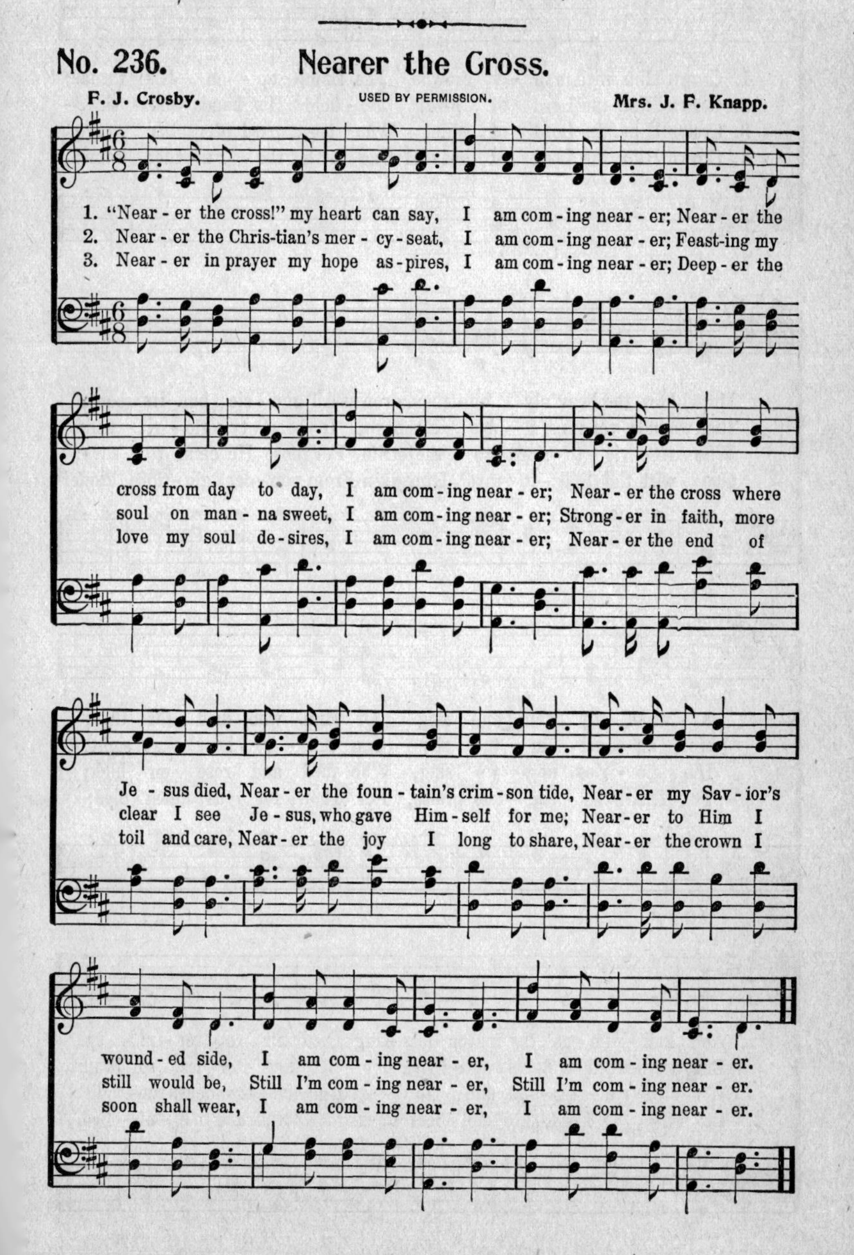
No. 236. Nearer the Cross.
F. J. Crosby.
USED BY PERMISSION.
Mrs. J. F. Knapp.
1. "Near - er the cross!" my heart can say, I am com - ing near - er; Near - er the
2. Near - er the Chris-tian's mer - cy - seat, I am com - ing near - er; Feast-ing my
3. Near - er in prayer my hope as - pires, I am com - ing near - er; Deep - er the
cross from day to day, I am com - ing near - er; Near - er the cross where
soul on man - na sweet, I am com - ing near - er; Strong - er in faith, more
love my soul de - sires, I am com - ing near - er; Near - er the end of
Je - sus died, Near - er the foun - tain's crim - son tide, Near - er my Sav - ior's
clear I see Je - sus, who gave Him - self for me; Near - er to Him I
toil and care, Near - er the joy I long to share, Near - er the crown I
wound - ed side, I am com - ing near - er, I am com - ing near - er.
still would be, Still I'm com - ing near - er, Still I'm com - ing near - er.
soon shall wear, I am com - ing near - er, I am com - ing near - er.

No. 237. Crown Him With Many Crowns.

Matthew Bridges.
George J. Elvey.
1. Crown Him with man - y crowns, The Lamb up - on His throne;
2. Crown Him the Lord of love! Be - hold His hands and side, —
3. Crown Him the Lord of life! Who tri-umphed o'er the grave;
4. Crown Him the Lord of heav'n! One with the Fa - ther known,
Hark! how the heav'nly an - them drowns All mu - sic but its own!
Rich wounds, yet vis - i - ble a - bove, In beau - ty glo - ri - fied:
Who rose vic - to - rious to the strife For those He came to save:
One with the Spir - it thro' Him giv'n From yon - der glo - rious throne!
A - wake, my soul, and sing Of Him who died for thee;
No an - gel in the sky Can full - y bear that sight,
His glo - ries now we sing, Who died and rose on high;
To Thee be end - less praise, For Thou for us hast died;
And hail Him as thy match - less King Thro' all e - ter - ni - ty.
But down-ward bends his won-d'ring eye At mys - ter - ies so bright.
Who died e - ter - nal life to bring, And lives that death may die.
Be Thou, O Lord, thro' end - less days A - dored and mag - ni - fied.

No. 238. O Jesus, I Have Promised.

John E. Bode. Arthur H. Mann.

1. O Je - sus, I have prom - ised To serve Thee to the end;
2. O let me feel Thee near me: The world is ev - er near;
3. O let me hear Thee speak - ing, In ac - cents clear and still,
4. O Je - sus, Thou hast prom - ised To all who fol - low Thee,
Be Thou for - ev - er near me, My Mas - ter and my Friend;
I see the sights that daz - zle, The tempt - ing sounds I hear;
A - bove the storms of pas - sion, The mur - murs of self - will;
That where Thou art in glo - ry There shall Thy serv - ant be;
I shall not fear the bat - tle If Thou art by my side,
My foes are ev - er near me, A - round me and with - in;
O speak to re - as - sure me, To has - ten or con - trol;
And, Je - sus, I have prom - ised To serve Thee to the end;
Nor wan - der from the path - way If Thou wilt be my Guide.
But, Je - sus, draw Thou near - er, And shield my soul from sin.
O speak, and make me lis - ten, Thou Guard - ian of my soul.
O give me grace to fol - low, My Mas - ter and my Friend.

No. 239. Beneath the Cross of Jesus.

Elizabeth C. Clephane. Frederick C. Maker.

1. Be - neath the cross of Je - sus I fain would take my stand,
2. Up - on that cross of Je - sus Mine eye at times can see
3. I take, O cross, thy shad - ow For my a - bid - ing - place:
The shad - ow of a might - y Rock With - in a wear - y land;
The ver - y dy - ing form of One Who suf - fered there for me:
I ask no oth - er sun-shine than The sun - shine of His face;
A home with - in the wil - der - ness, A rest up - on the way,
And from my smit - ten heart with tears Two won - ders I con - fess,—
Con - tent to let the world go by, To know no gain nor loss,
From the burn-ing of the noon - tide heat, And the bur - den of the day.
The won - ders of His glo - rious love, And my own worth - less - ness.
My sin - ful self my on - ly shame, My glo - ry all the cross.

No. 240. A Lamp Within a Stable.

COPYRIGHT, 1913, BY JOHN R. CLEMENTS.
Margaret E. Sangster.
Theo. E. Perkins.
1. No tramp of march-ing ar-mies, No ban-ners flam-ing far;
2. When in the low-ly man-ger The ho-ly moth-er maid
3. No rush of hos-tile ar-mies, But just the hud-dling sheep;
A lamp with-in a sta-ble, And in the sky a star.
In ten-der ad-o-ra-tion Her Babe of Heav-en laid:
Of Christ the an-gels sing-ing, And all the world a-sleep.
Their hymns of peace and glad-ness To earth the an-gels brought;
Born low-ly in the dark-ness, And none so poor as He,
No flame of con-q'ring ban-ners, No le-gions sent a-far;
Their "Glo-ria in Ex-cel-sis" To earth the an-gels taught.
The lit-tle chil-dren of the poor His ver-y own shall be.
A lamp with-in a sta-ble, And in the sky a star.

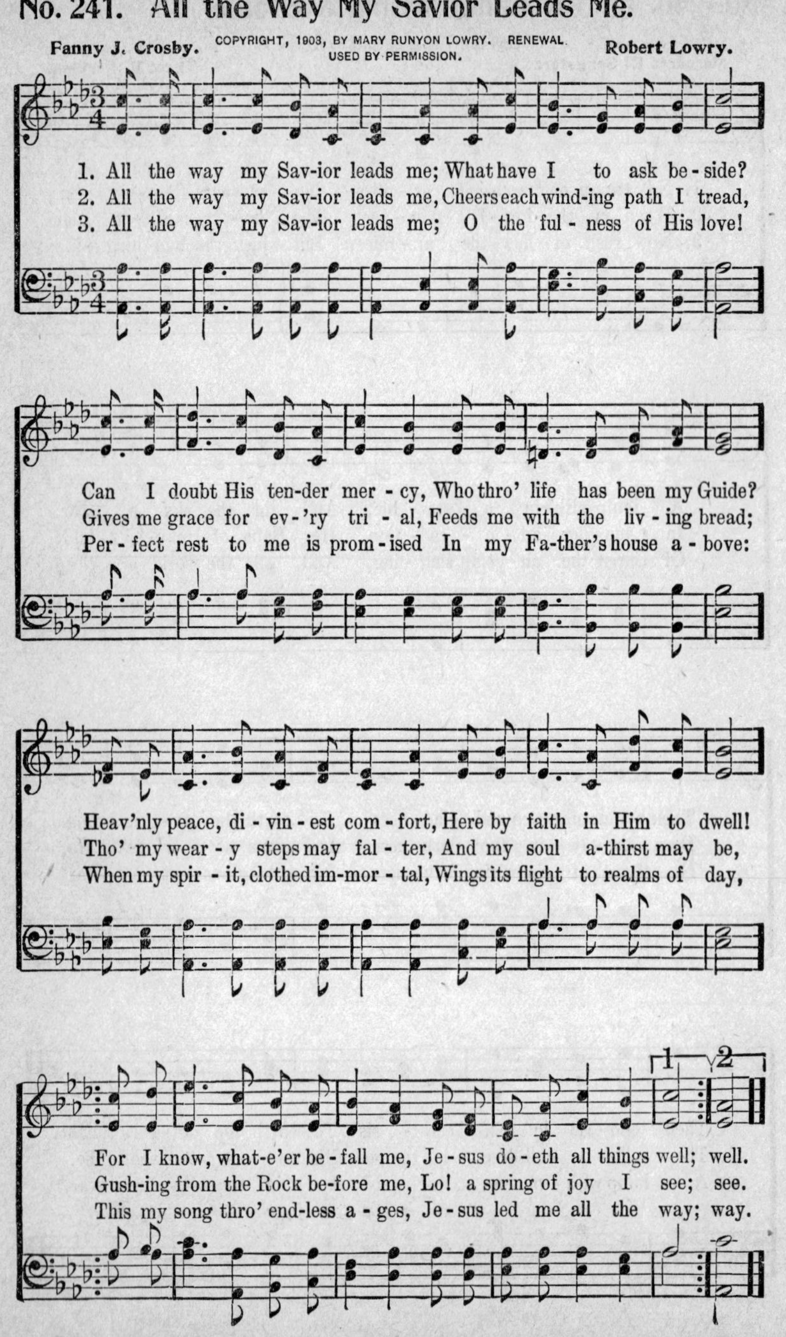
No. 241. All the Way My Savior Leads Me.
Fanny J. Crosby.
COPYRIGHT, 1903, BY MARY RUNYON LOWRY. RENEWAL.
USED BY PERMISSION.
Robert Lowry.
1. All the way my Sav-ior leads me; What have I to ask be - side?
2. All the way my Sav-ior leads me, Cheers each wind-ing path I tread,
3. All the way my Sav-ior leads me; O the ful - ness of His love!
Can I doubt His ten-der mer - cy, Who thro' life has been my Guide?
Gives me grace for ev - 'ry tri - al, Feeds me with the liv - ing bread;
Per - fect rest to me is prom - ised In my Fa-ther's house a - bove:
Heav'nly peace, di - vin - est com - fort, Here by faith in Him to dwell!
Tho' my wear - y steps may fal - ter, And my soul a-thirst may be,
When my spir - it, clothed im-mor - tal, Wings its flight to realms of day,
For I know, what-e'er be - fall me, Je - sus do - eth all things well; well.
Gush-ing from the Rock be-fore me, Lo! a spring of joy I see; see.
This my song thro' end-less a - ges, Je - sus led me all the way; way.
1
2

No. 242. Service is Our W
Wm. Shaw and
Jno. R. Clements.
COPYRIGHT, 1913, BY E. O. E
WORDS AND MUSIC.
No. 243.
Frederick W.
1. Serv - ice is our watch - word, Serv - ice
2. Serv - ice in the home - land Wher - e'er
3. Serv - ice o'er the o - cean, Serv - ing
Serv - ice, fruit - ful serv - ice, Dai - ly ours to bring.
Sac - ri - fi - cial serv - ice Reach - ing un - to all;
Meet - ing ev - 'ry du - ty, Be it toil or pain;
Serv - ice for the need - y, Serv - ice for the lost;
Serv - ice pure, ex - alt - ed; Loy - al and un - priced;
Serv - ice that is Christ - ly, Giv - ing up to God
Self up - on the al - tar; Count - ing not the cost.
Liv - ing, lov - ing chan - nels, Bear - ing forth the Christ.
Ev - 'ry self - ish mo - tive; Tread - ing where Christ trod.

…Hark, Hark, My Soul!

…aber.
J. B. Dykes.
1. Hark, hark, my soul! an - gel - ic songs are swell-ing O'er earth's green fields and
2. On - ward we go, for still we hear them sing - ing, "Come, weary souls, for
3. Far, far a-way, like bells at eve-ning peal-ing, The voice of Je - sus
4. An - gels, sing on! your faith-ful watches keep-ing; Sing us sweet frag-ments
o-cean's wave-beat shore: How sweet the truth those blessed strains are tell - ing
Je - sus bids you come;" And thro' the dark, its ech - oes sweet-ly ring - ing,
sounds o'er land and sea; And la-den souls, by thousands meekly steal - ing,
of the songs a - bove; Till morning's joy shall end the night of weep - ing,
Of that new life when sin shall be no more.
The mu - sic of the gos - pel leads us home.
Kind Shepherd, turn their weary steps to Thee.
And life's long shad-ows break in cloud - less love.
REFRAIN.
An-gels of Je - sus,
an - gels of light, Sing - ing to wel - come the pil-grims of the night,

Hark, Hark, My Soul!
Sing - ing to wel - come the pil - grims, the pil - grims of the night.
No. 244. Angel Voices, Ever Singing.
F. Pott.
A. S. Sullivan.
1. An - gel voi - ces, ev - er sing - ing Round Thy throne of light,
2. Thou, who art be-yond the far - thest Mor - tal eye can scan,
3. In Thy house, great God, we of - fer Of Thine own to Thee;
4. Hon - or, glo - ry, might, and mer - it, Thine shall ev - er be,
An - gel harps, for ev - er ring - ing, Rest not day nor night;
Can it be that Thou re - gard - est Songs of sin - ful man?
And for Thine ac - cept - ance prof - fer, All un - wor - thi - ly,
Fa - ther, Son, and Ho - ly Spir - it, Bless - ed Trin - i - ty:
Thou-sands on - ly live to bless Thee, And con - fess Thee Lord of might.
Can we feel that Thou art near us, And wilt hear us? Yea, we can.
Hearts and minds, and hands and voices, In our choic - est Mel - o - dy.
Of the best that Thou hast giv - en, Earth and heav - en Ren - der Thee.

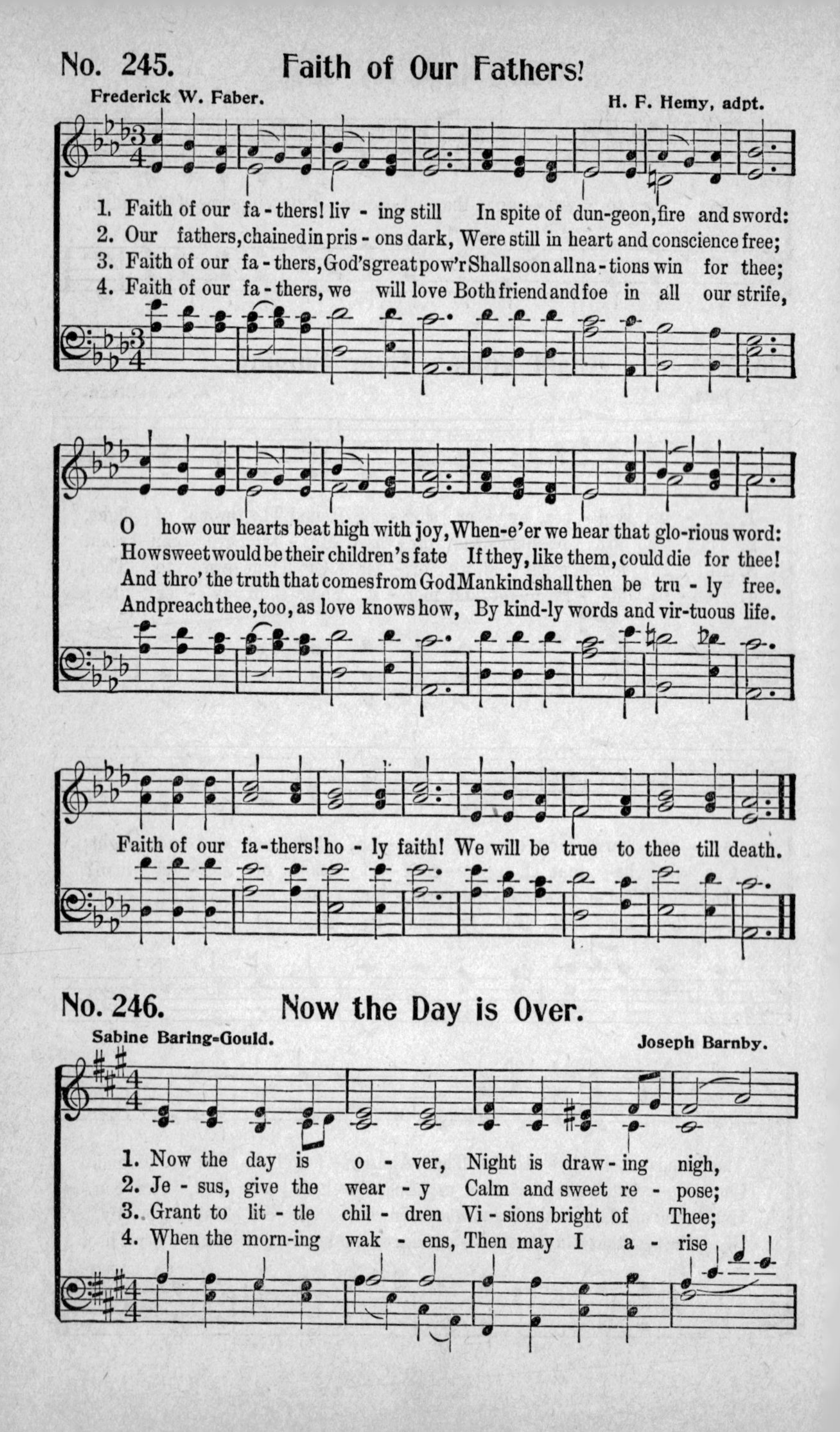
No. 245. Faith of Our Fathers!
Frederick W. Faber.
H. F. Hemy, adpt.
1. Faith of our fa-thers! liv-ing still In spite of dun-geon, fire and sword:
2. Our fathers, chained in pris-ons dark, Were still in heart and conscience free;
3. Faith of our fa-thers, God's great pow'r Shall soon all na-tions win for thee;
4. Faith of our fa-thers, we will love Both friend and foe in all our strife,
O how our hearts beat high with joy, When-e'er we hear that glo-rious word:
How sweet would be their children's fate If they, like them, could die for thee!
And thro' the truth that comes from God Mankind shall then be tru-ly free.
And preach thee, too, as love knows how, By kind-ly words and vir-tuous life.
Faith of our fa-thers! ho-ly faith! We will be true to thee till death.
No. 246. Now the Day is Over.
Sabine Baring-Gould.
Joseph Barnby.
1. Now the day is o-ver, Night is draw-ing nigh,
2. Je-sus, give the wear-y Calm and sweet re-pose;
3. Grant to lit-tle chil-dren Vi-sions bright of Thee;
4. When the morn-ing wak-ens, Then may I a-rise

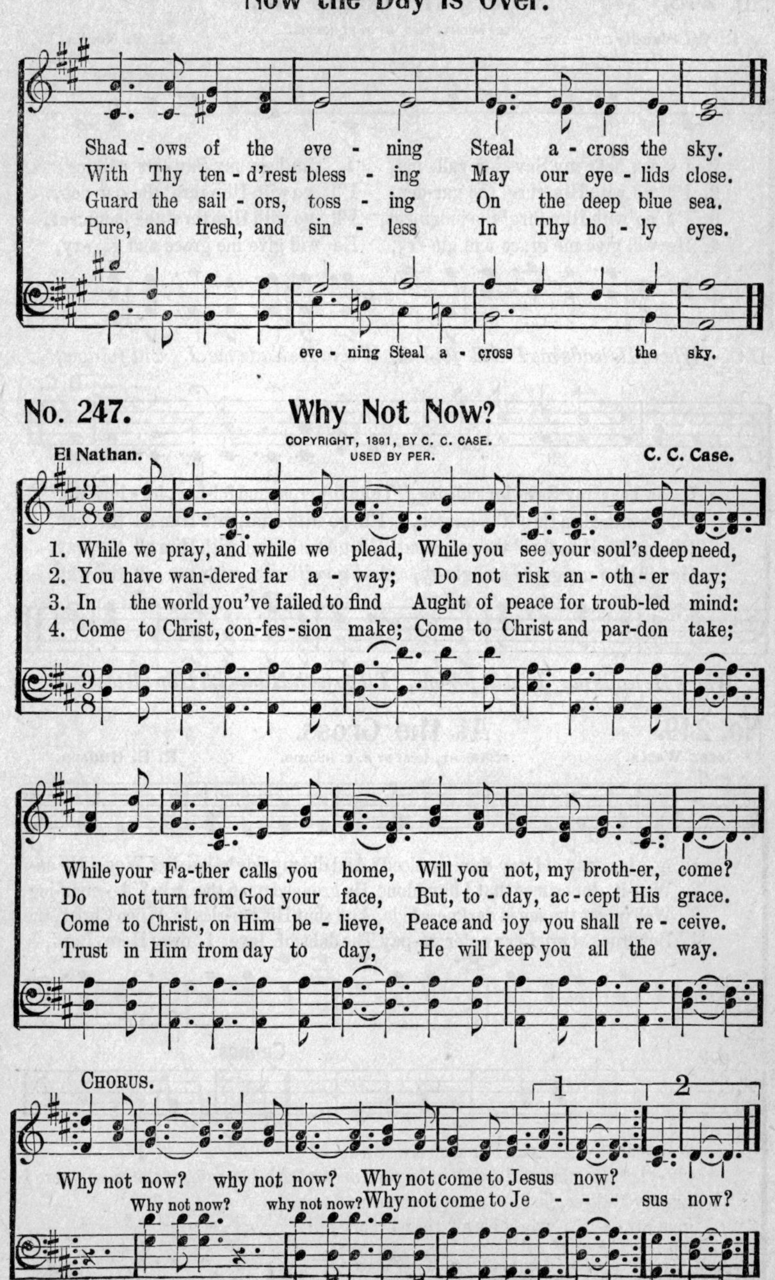
Now the Day is Over.
Shad - ows of the eve - ning Steal a - cross the sky.
With Thy ten - d'rest bless - ing May our eye - lids close.
Guard the sail - ors, toss - ing On the deep blue sea.
Pure, and fresh, and sin - less In Thy ho - ly eyes.
eve - ning Steal a - cross the sky.
No. 247.
Why Not Now?
COPYRIGHT, 1891, BY C. C. CASE.
USED BY PER.
El Nathan.
C. C. Case.
1. While we pray, and while we plead, While you see your soul's deep need,
2. You have wan-dered far a - way; Do not risk an - oth - er day;
3. In the world you've failed to find Aught of peace for troub-led mind:
4. Come to Christ, con-fes - sion make; Come to Christ and par-don take;
While your Fa-ther calls you home, Will you not, my broth-er, come?
Do not turn from God your face, But, to - day, ac - cept His grace.
Come to Christ, on Him be - lieve, Peace and joy you shall re - ceive.
Trust in Him from day to day, He will keep you all the way.
CHORUS.
Why not now? why not now? Why not come to Jesus now?
Why not now? why not now? Why not come to Je - - - sus now?
1
2

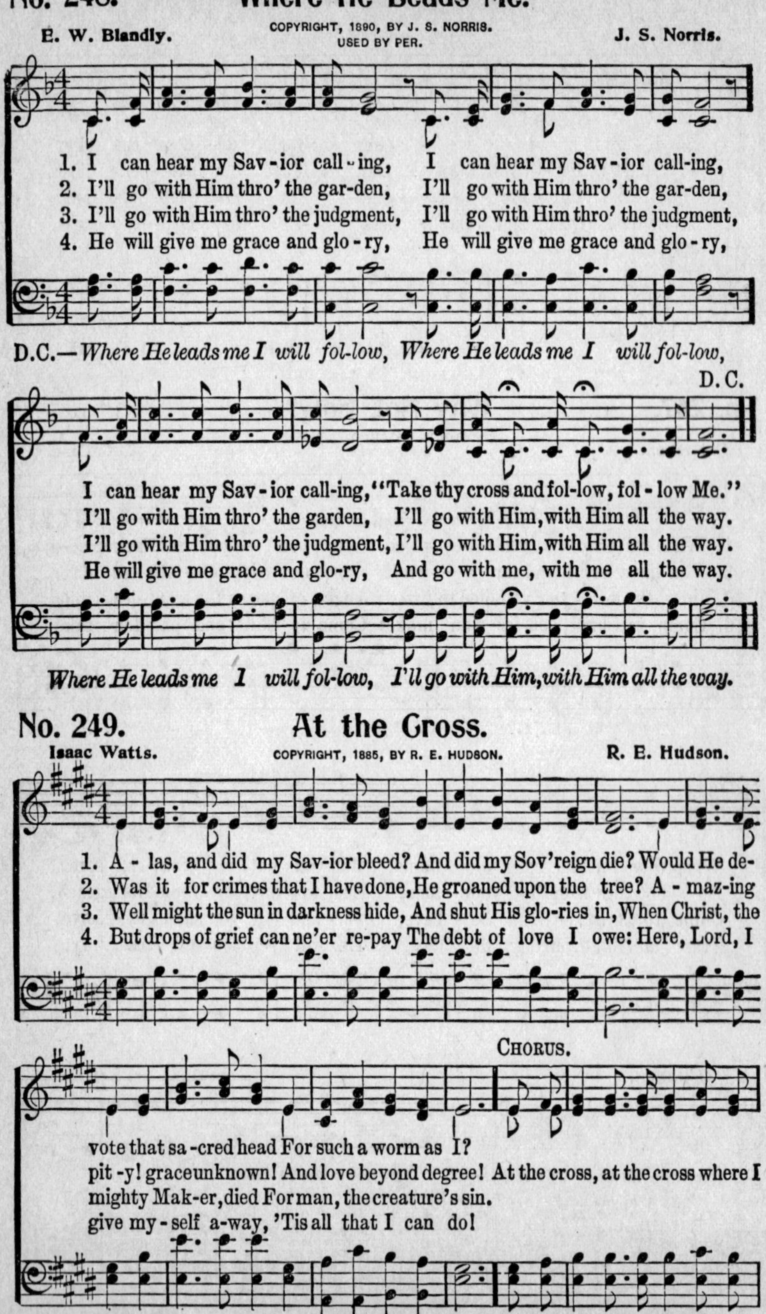
No. 248. Where He Leads Me.
E. W. Blandly.
COPYRIGHT, 1890, BY J. S. NORRIS. USED BY PER.
J. S. Norris.
1. I can hear my Sav-ior call-ing, I can hear my Sav-ior call-ing,
2. I'll go with Him thro' the gar-den, I'll go with Him thro' the gar-den,
3. I'll go with Him thro' the judgment, I'll go with Him thro' the judgment,
4. He will give me grace and glo-ry, He will give me grace and glo-ry,
D.C.—Where He leads me I will fol-low, Where He leads me I will fol-low,
D.C.
I can hear my Sav-ior call-ing, "Take thy cross and fol-low, fol-low Me."
I'll go with Him thro' the garden, I'll go with Him, with Him all the way.
I'll go with Him thro' the judgment, I'll go with Him, with Him all the way.
He will give me grace and glo-ry, And go with me, with me all the way.
Where He leads me I will fol-low, I'll go with Him, with Him all the way.
No. 249. At the Cross.
Isaac Watts.
COPYRIGHT, 1885, BY R. E. HUDSON.
R. E. Hudson.
1. A-las, and did my Sav-ior bleed? And did my Sov'reign die? Would He de-
2. Was it for crimes that I have done, He groaned upon the tree? A-maz-ing
3. Well might the sun in darkness hide, And shut His glo-ries in, When Christ, the
4. But drops of grief can ne'er re-pay The debt of love I owe: Here, Lord, I
CHORUS.
vote that sa-cred head For such a worm as I?
pit-y! grace unknown! And love beyond degree! At the cross, at the cross where I
mighty Mak-er, died For man, the creature's sin.
give my-self a-way, 'Tis all that I can do!

At the Cross.

first saw the light, And the burden of my heart rolled away, (rolled away,) It was
there by faith I received my sight, And now I am hap-py all the day!
No. 250. I Love Him.
London Hymn Book.
USED BY PERMISSION.
S. C. Foster.
1. Gone from my heart the world with all its charm; Gone are my sins and
2. Once I was l st up-on the plains of sin; Once was a slave to
3. Once I was bound, but now I am set free; Once I was blind, but
all that would a-larm; Gone ev-er-more, and by His grace I know The
doubts and fears within; Once was a-fraid to trust a lov-ing God, But
now the light I see; Once I was dead, but now in Christ I live, To
D. S.—Because He first loved me, And
Fine.
Chorus.
D.S.
pre-cious blood of Je-sus cleanses white as snow.
now my guilt is washed a-way in Je-sus' blood. I love Him, I love Him,
tell the world the peace that He a-lone can give.
purchased my sal-va-tion On Calv'ry's tree.

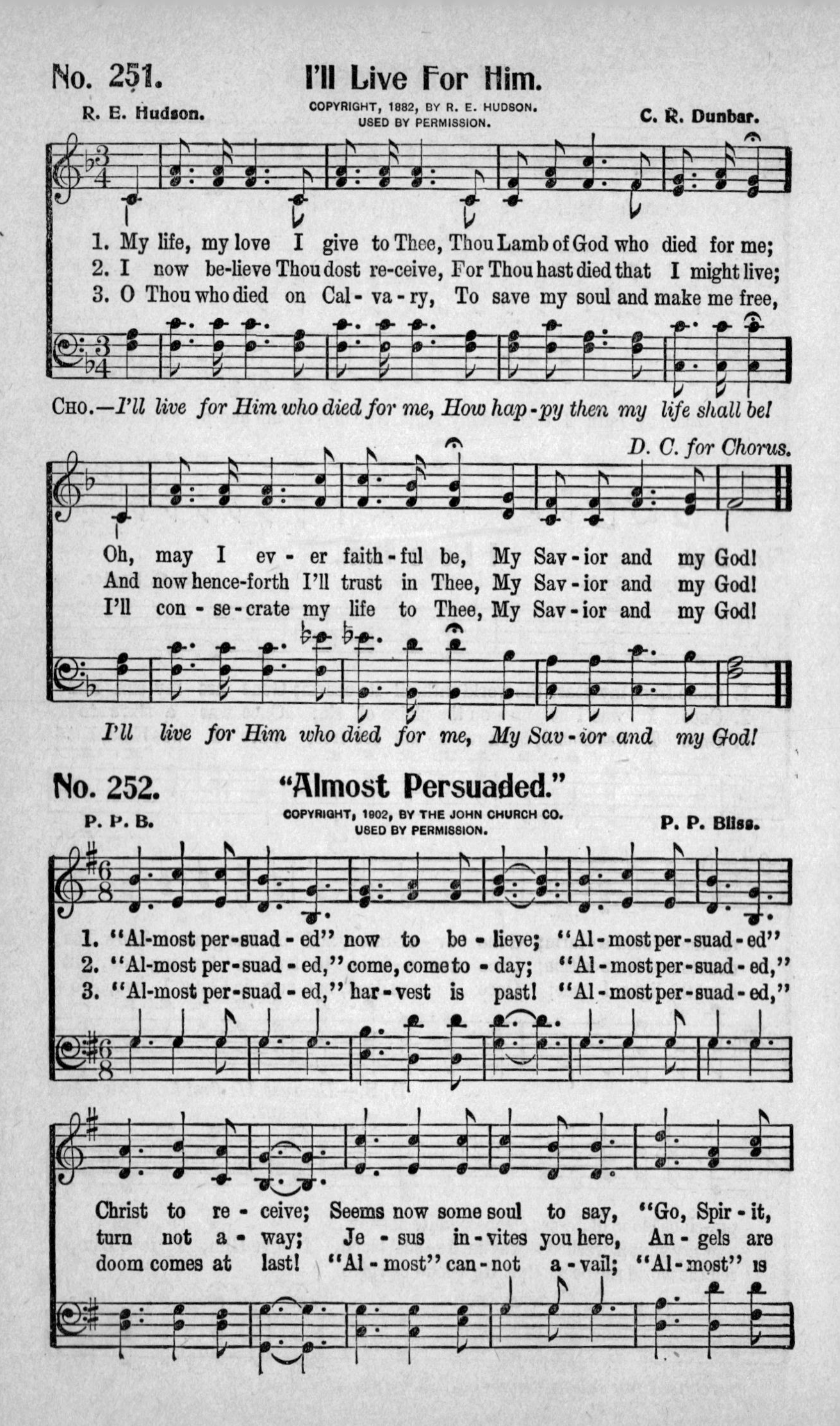
No. 251.
I'll Live For Him.
R. E. Hudson.
COPYRIGHT, 1882, BY R. E. HUDSON.
USED BY PERMISSION.
C. R. Dunbar.
1. My life, my love I give to Thee, Thou Lamb of God who died for me;
2. I now be-lieve Thou dost re-ceive, For Thou hast died that I might live;
3. O Thou who died on Cal-va-ry, To save my soul and make me free,
CHO.—I'll live for Him who died for me, How hap-py then my life shall be!
D. C. for Chorus.
Oh, may I ev-er faith-ful be, My Sav-ior and my God!
And now hence-forth I'll trust in Thee, My Sav-ior and my God!
I'll con-se-crate my life to Thee, My Sav-ior and my God!
I'll live for Him who died for me, My Sav-ior and my God!
No. 252.
"Almost Persuaded."
P. P. B.
COPYRIGHT, 1902, BY THE JOHN CHURCH CO.
USED BY PERMISSION.
P. P. Bliss.
1. "Al-most per-suad-ed" now to be-lieve; "Al-most per-suad-ed"
2. "Al-most per-suad-ed," come, come to-day; "Al-most per-suad-ed,"
3. "Al-most per-suad-ed," har-vest is past! "Al-most per-suad-ed,"
Christ to re-ceive; Seems now some soul to say, "Go, Spir-it,
turn not a-way; Je-sus in-vites you here, An-gels are
doom comes at last! "Al-most" can-not a-vail; "Al-most" is

"Almost Persuaded."

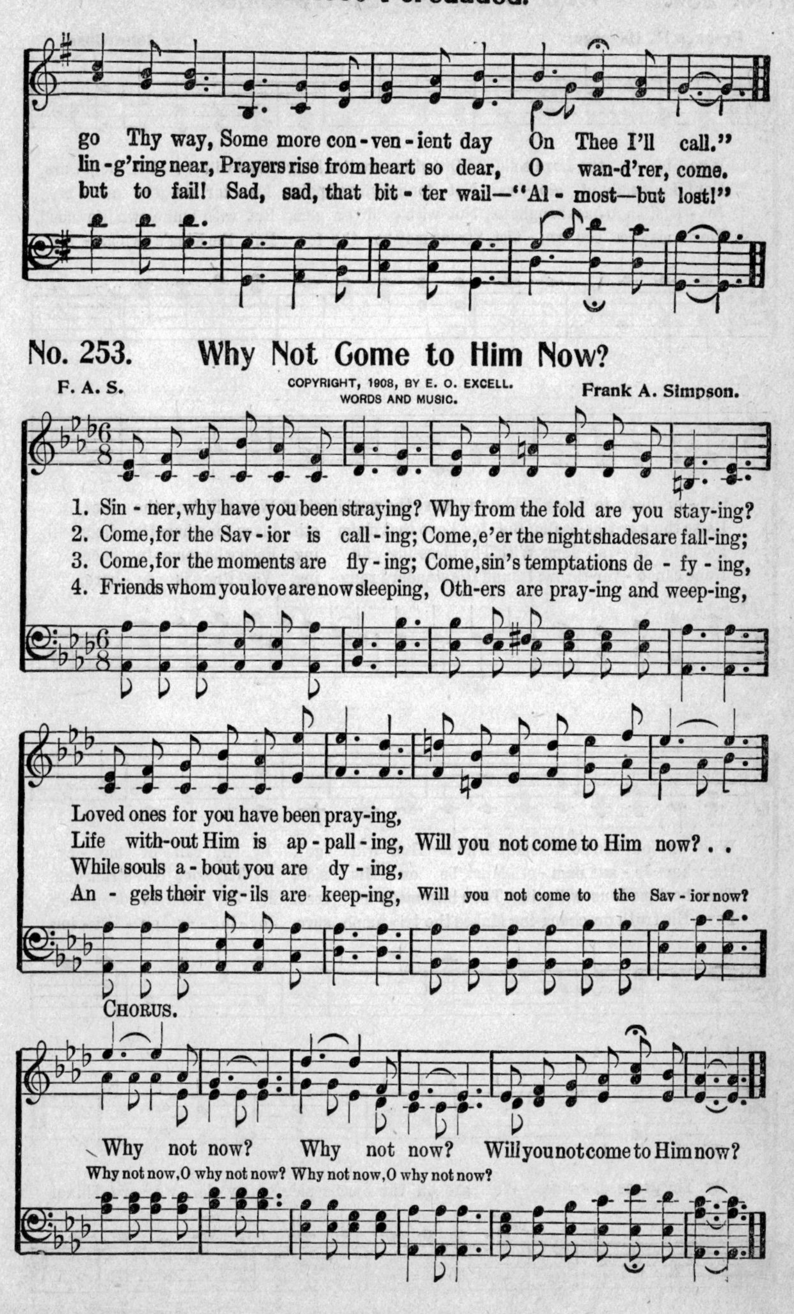
go Thy way, Some more con-ven-ient day On Thee I'll call."
lin-g'ring near, Prayers rise from heart so dear, O wan-d'rer, come.
but to fail! Sad, sad, that bit-ter wail—"Al-most—but lost!"
No. 253. Why Not Come to Him Now?
F. A. S.
COPYRIGHT, 1908, BY E. O. EXCELL.
WORDS AND MUSIC.
Frank A. Simpson.
1. Sin-ner, why have you been straying? Why from the fold are you stay-ing?
2. Come, for the Sav-ior is call-ing; Come, e'er the night shades are fall-ing;
3. Come, for the moments are fly-ing; Come, sin's temptations de-fy-ing,
4. Friends whom you love are now sleeping, Oth-ers are pray-ing and weep-ing,
Loved ones for you have been pray-ing,
Life with-out Him is ap-pall-ing, Will you not come to Him now? . .
While souls a-bout you are dy-ing,
An-gels their vig-ils are keep-ing, Will you not come to the Sav-ior now?
CHORUS.
Why not now? Why not now? Will you not come to Him now?
Why not now, O why not now? Why not now, O why not now?

No. 254. Who is On the Lord's Side?

Frances R. Havergal. Sir John Goss.

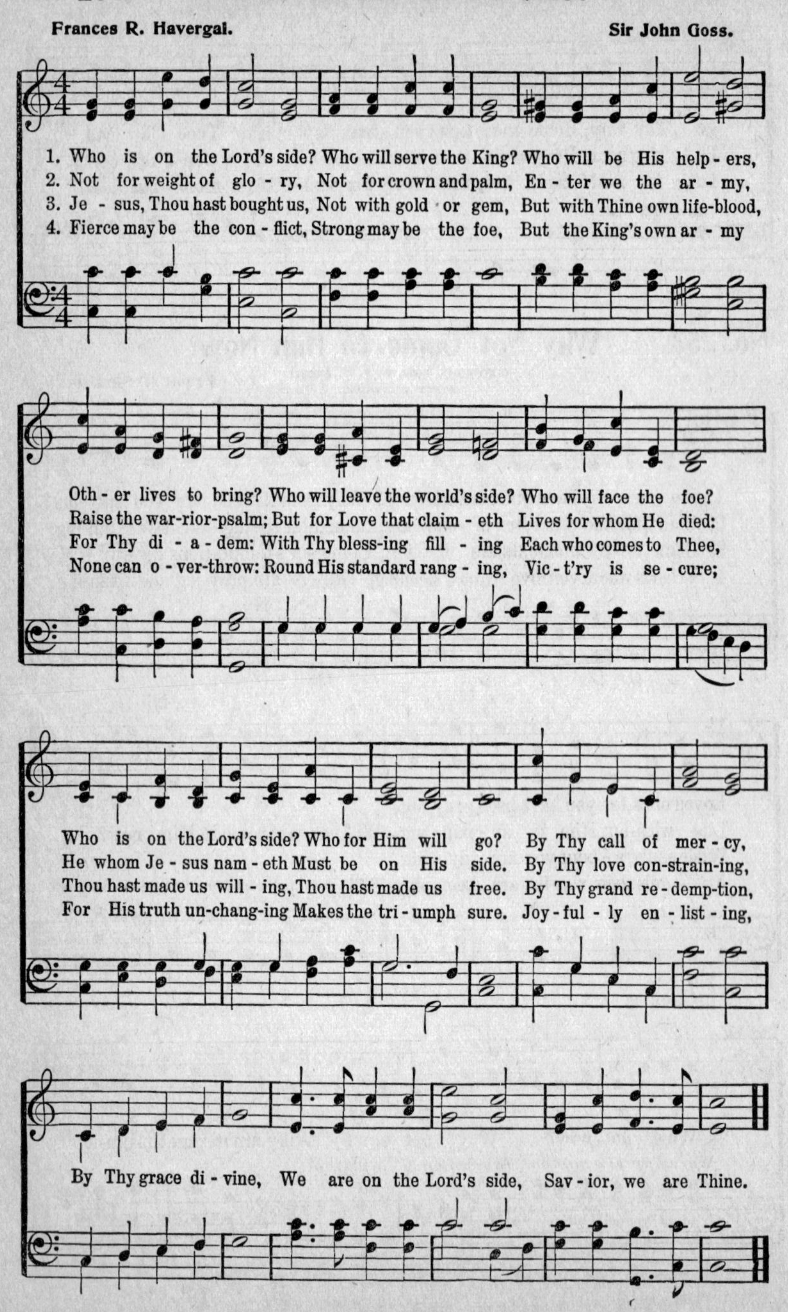

1. Who is on the Lord's side? Who will serve the King? Who will be His help - ers,
2. Not for weight of glo - ry, Not for crown and palm, En - ter we the ar - my,
3. Je - sus, Thou hast bought us, Not with gold or gem, But with Thine own life-blood,
4. Fierce may be the con - flict, Strong may be the foe, But the King's own ar - my
Oth - er lives to bring? Who will leave the world's side? Who will face the foe?
Raise the war-rior-psalm; But for Love that claim - eth Lives for whom He died:
For Thy di - a - dem: With Thy bless-ing fill - ing Each who comes to Thee,
None can o - ver-throw: Round His standard rang - ing, Vic - t'ry is se - cure;
Who is on the Lord's side? Who for Him will go? By Thy call of mer - cy,
He whom Je - sus nam - eth Must be on His side. By Thy love con-strain-ing,
Thou hast made us will - ing, Thou hast made us free. By Thy grand re - demp-tion,
For His truth un-chang-ing Makes the tri - umph sure. Joy - ful - ly en - list - ing,
By Thy grace di - vine, We are on the Lord's side, Sav - ior, we are Thine.

No. 255. Onward, Christian Soldiers.

Sabine Baring-Gould.
Arthur Sullivan.
1. On-ward, Christian sol - diers! Marching as to war, With the cross of Je - sus
2. At the sign of tri - umph Sa-tan's host doth flee; On, then, Christian sol-diers,
3. Like a might-y ar - my Moves the Church of God; Brothers, we are tread - ing
4. On-ward, then, ye peo - ple! Join our hap-py throng; Blend with ours your voices
Go - ing on be - fore! Christ, the roy - al Mas - ter, Leads a-gainst the foe;
On to vic - to - ry! Hell's foun-da-tions quiv - er At the shout of praise;
Where the saints have trod; We are not di - vid - ed, All one bod - y we,
In the tri-umph song; Glo - ry, laud and hon - or Un - to Christ the King,
Refrain.
For-ward in - to bat - tle, See His ban-ner go!
Brothers, lift your voi - ces, Loud your anthems raise. Onward, Christian sol - diers!
One in hope and doc - trine, One in char - i - ty.
This thro' countless a - ges Men and an-gels sing.
March-ing as to war, With the cross of Je - sus Go - ing on be - fore.

No. 256. It Came Upon the Midnight Clear.

E. H. Sears.
R. Storrs Willis.
1. It came up - on the mid - night clear, That glo - rious song of old,
2. Still thro' the clo - ven skies they come, With peace-ful wings un - furled,
3. O ye, be - neath life's crush - ing load, Whose forms are bend - ing low,
4. For lo! the days are hast - 'ning on, By proph-et - bards fore - told,
From an - gels bend - ing near the earth To touch their harps of gold;
And still their heav'n-ly mu - sic floats O'er all the wear - y world;
Who toil a - long the climb - ing way With pain - ful steps and slow,
When with the ev - er - cir - cling years Comes round the age of gold;
"Peace on the earth, good will to men, From heav'n's all - gra - cious King."
A - bove its sad and low - ly plains They bend on hov - 'ring wing,
Look now! for glad and gold - en hours Come swift - ly on the wing;
When peace shall o - ver all the earth Its an - cient splen-dors fling,
The world in sol - emn still - ness lay To hear the an - gels sing.
And ev - er o'er its Ba - bel sounds The bless - ed an - gels sing.
O rest be - side the wear - y road, And hear the an - gels sing.
And the whole world send back the song Which now the an - gels sing.

No. 257. While Shepherds Watched Their Flocks.

Nahum Tate. George F. Handel.

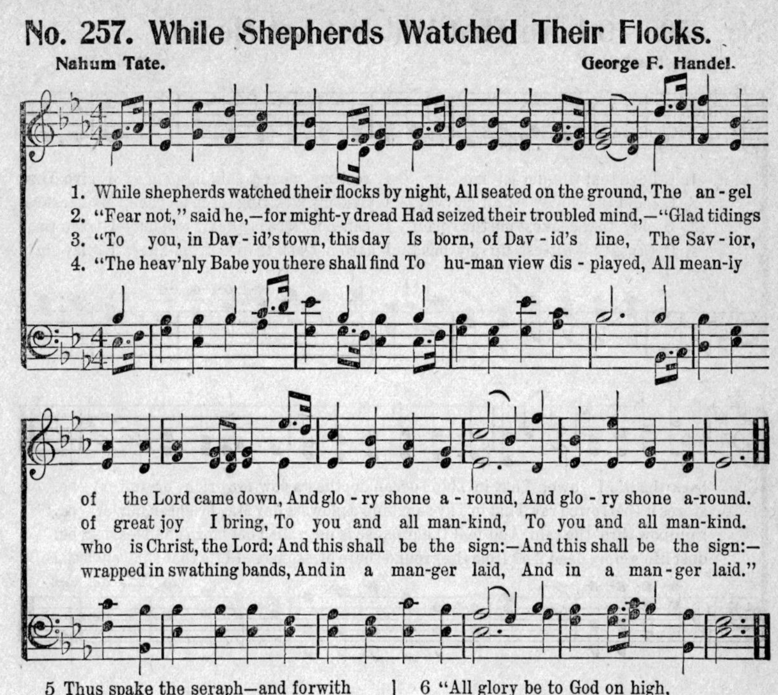
1. While shepherds watched their flocks by night, All seated on the ground, The an-gel of the Lord came down, And glo - ry shone a - round, And glo - ry shone a-round.
2. "Fear not," said he,—for might-y dread Had seized their troubled mind,—"Glad tidings of great joy I bring, To you and all man-kind, To you and all man-kind.
3. "To you, in Dav - id's town, this day Is born, of Dav - id's line, The Sav - ior, who is Christ, the Lord; And this shall be the sign:—And this shall be the sign:—
4. "The heav'nly Babe you there shall find To hu-man view dis - played, All mean-ly wrapped in swathing bands, And in a man-ger laid, And in a man - ger laid."

5 Thus spake the seraph—and forwith
Appeared a shining throng
Of angels, praising God, who thus
Addressed their joyful song:—

6 "All glory be to God on high,
And to the earth be peace;
Good-will henceforth from heaven to men
Begin, and never cease!"

No. 258. Nearer, My God, to Thee.

Sarah F. Adams. Lowell Mason.

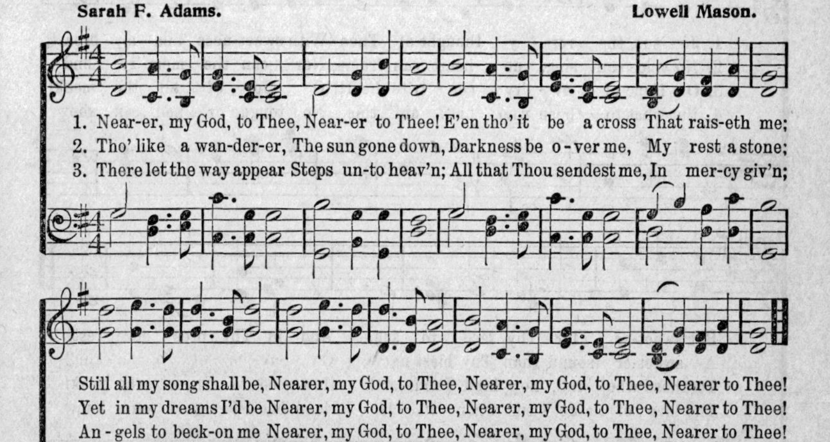
1. Near-er, my God, to Thee, Near-er to Thee! E'en tho' it be a cross That rais-eth me; Still all my song shall be, Nearer, my God, to Thee, Nearer, my God, to Thee, Nearer to Thee!
2. Tho' like a wan-der-er, The sun gone down, Darkness be o - ver me, My rest a stone; Yet in my dreams I'd be Nearer, my God, to Thee, Nearer, my God, to Thee, Nearer to Thee!
3. There let the way appear Steps un-to heav'n; All that Thou sendest me, In mer-cy giv'n; An - gels to beck-on me Nearer, my God, to Thee, Nearer, my God, to Thee, Nearer to Thee!

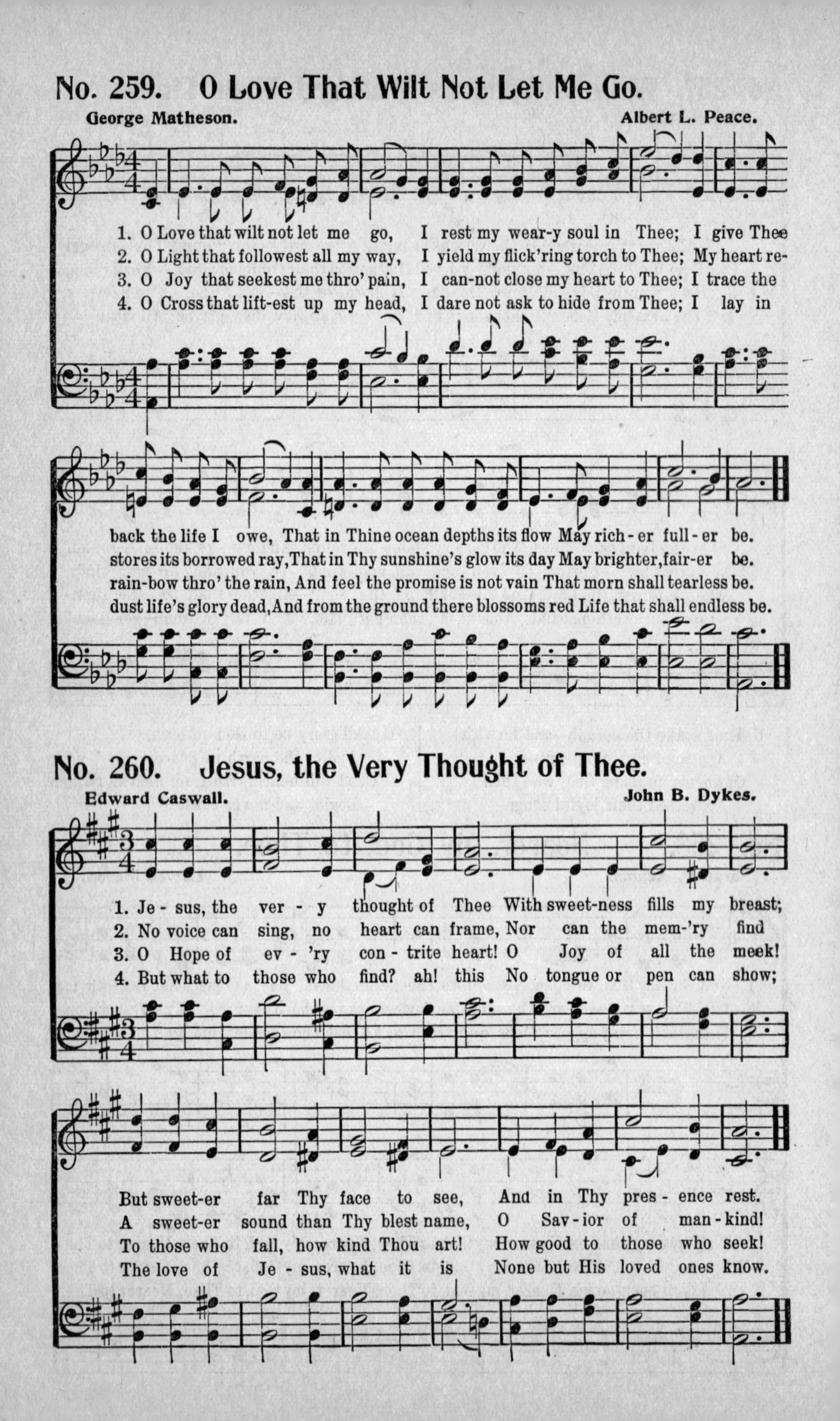
No. 259. O Love That Wilt Not Let Me Go.
George Matheson.
Albert L. Peace.
1. O Love that wilt not let me go, I rest my wear-y soul in Thee; I give Thee back the life I owe, That in Thine ocean depths its flow May rich-er full-er be.
2. O Light that followest all my way, I yield my flick'ring torch to Thee; My heart re-stores its borrowed ray, That in Thy sunshine's glow its day May brighter, fair-er be.
3. O Joy that seekest me thro' pain, I can-not close my heart to Thee; I trace the rain-bow thro' the rain, And feel the promise is not vain That morn shall tearless be.
4. O Cross that lift-est up my head, I dare not ask to hide from Thee; I lay in dust life's glory dead, And from the ground there blossoms red Life that shall endless be.
No. 260. Jesus, the Very Thought of Thee.
Edward Caswall.
John B. Dykes.
1. Je-sus, the ver-y thought of Thee With sweet-ness fills my breast; But sweet-er far Thy face to see, And in Thy pres-ence rest.
2. No voice can sing, no heart can frame, Nor can the mem-'ry find A sweet-er sound than Thy blest name, O Sav-ior of man-kind!
3. O Hope of ev-'ry con-trite heart! O Joy of all the meek! To those who fall, how kind Thou art! How good to those who seek!
4. But what to those who find? ah! this No tongue or pen can show; The love of Je-sus, what it is None but His loved ones know.

No. 261. All Hail the Power.
Edward Perronet.
William Shrubsole.
1. All hail the pow'r of Je-sus' name, Let an-gels pros-trate fall; Bring forth the
2. Crown Him, ye morning stars of light, Who fixed this earthly ball; Now hail the
3. Let ev-'ry kin-dred, ev-'ry tribe, On this ter-res-trial ball, To Him all
4. O that with yon-der sa-cred throng We at His feet may fall; We'll join the
roy-al di-a-dem, And crown Him, crown Him, crown Him, Crown Him Lord of all.
strength of Israel's might, And crown Him, crown Him, crown Him, Crown Him Lord of all.
maj-es-ty ascribe, And crown Him, crown Him, crown Him, Crown Him Lord of all.
ev-er-last-ing song, And crown Him, crown Him, crown Him, Crown Him Lord of all.
No. 262. Jesus Shall Reign.
Isaac Watts.
John Hatton.
1. Je-sus shall reign wher-e'er the sun Does His suc-ces-sive jour-neys run;
2. From north to south the princ-es meet, To pay their homage at His feet;
3. To Him shall end-less prayer be made, And end-less prais-es crown His head;
4. Peo-ple and realms of ev-'ry tongue Dwell on His love with sweet-est song,
His king-dom spread from shore to shore, Till moons shall wax and wane no more.
While western em-pires own their Lord, And sav-age tribes at-tend His word.
His name like sweet per-fume shall rise With ev-'ry morn-ing sac-ri-fice.
And in-fant voi-ces shall pro-claim Their ear-ly bless-ings on His name.

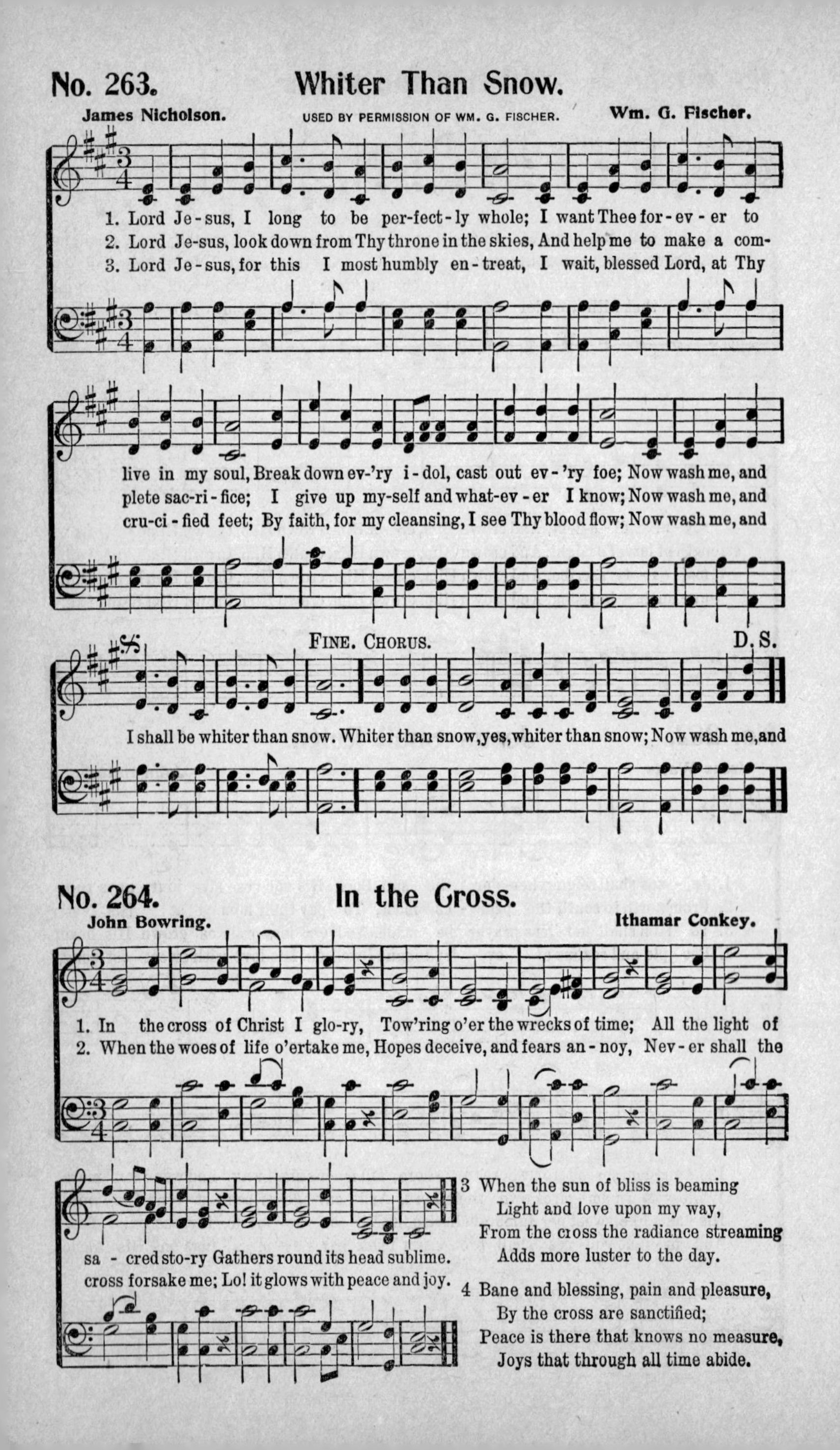
No. 263. Whiter Than Snow.
James Nicholson.
USED BY PERMISSION OF WM. G. FISCHER.
Wm. G. Fischer.
1. Lord Je-sus, I long to be per-fect-ly whole; I want Thee for-ev-er to live in my soul, Break down ev-'ry i-dol, cast out ev-'ry foe; Now wash me, and I shall be whiter than snow.
2. Lord Je-sus, look down from Thy throne in the skies, And help me to make a com-plete sac-ri-fice; I give up my-self and what-ev-er I know; Now wash me, and
3. Lord Je-sus, for this I most humbly en-treat, I wait, blessed Lord, at Thy cru-ci-fied feet; By faith, for my cleansing, I see Thy blood flow; Now wash me, and
FINE. CHORUS.
D. S.
Whiter than snow, yes, whiter than snow; Now wash me, and
No. 264. In the Cross.
John Bowring.
Ithamar Conkey.
1. In the cross of Christ I glo-ry, Tow'ring o'er the wrecks of time; All the light of sa-cred sto-ry Gathers round its head sublime.
2. When the woes of life o'ertake me, Hopes deceive, and fears an-noy, Nev-er shall the cross forsake me; Lo! it glows with peace and joy.
3 When the sun of bliss is beaming
Light and love upon my way,
From the cross the radiance streaming
Adds more luster to the day.
4 Bane and blessing, pain and pleasure,
By the cross are sanctified;
Peace is there that knows no measure,
Joys that through all time abide.

No. 265. O Jesus, Thou Art Standing.
William W. How.
Justin H. Knecht
Edw. Husband.
1. O Je - sus, Thou art stand-ing Out - side the fast-closed door, In low - ly
2. O Je - sus, Thou art knocking; And lo! that hand is scarred, And thorns Thy
3. O Je - sus, Thou art plead-ing In ac - cents meek and low, "I died for
pa-tience wait-ing To pass the threshold o'er: We bear the name of Chris-tians, His
brow en - cir - cle, And tears Thy face have marred: O love that pass-eth knowledge, So
you, my chil-dren, And will ye treat me so?" O Lord, with shame and sor - row We
name and sign we bear; O shame, thrice shame up-on us, To keep Him standing there!
pa - tient-ly to wait! O sin that hath no e - qual, So fast to bar the gate!
o - pen now the door; Dear Sav - ior, en - ter, en - ter, And leave us nev-er - more!
No. 266. Oh, For a Thousand Tongues.
Charles Wesley.
Carl Glasser.
1. Oh, for a thousand tongues, to sing My great Redeemer's praise; The glories of my
2. My gracious Mas-ter and my God, As - sist me to pro - claim, To spread thro' all the
God and King, The triumphs of His grace!
earth a-broad, The hon-ors of Thy name.
3 Jesus! the name that charms our fears,
That bids our sorrows cease;
'T is music in the sinner's ears,
'T is life, and health, and peace.
4 He breaks the power of cancelled sin,
He sets the prisoner free;
His blood can make the foulest clean;
His blood availed for me.

No. 267. Come, Thou Fount.

Robert Robinson.

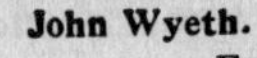
John Wyeth.

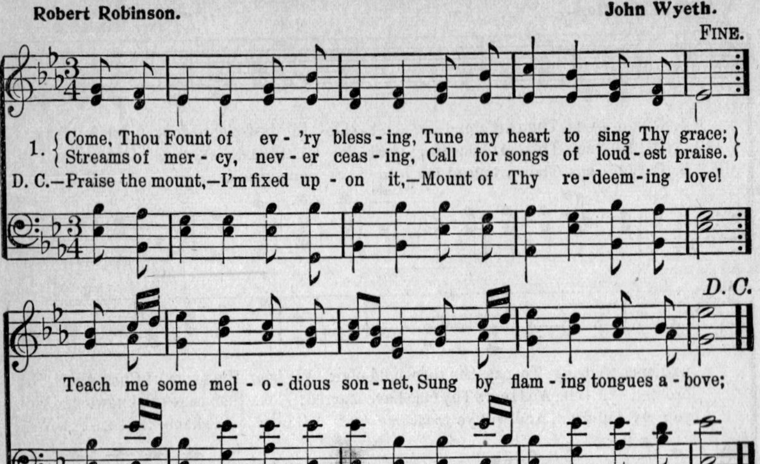
FINE.
1. Come, Thou Fount of ev - 'ry bless - ing, Tune my heart to sing Thy grace;
Streams of mer - cy, nev - er ceas - ing, Call for songs of loud - est praise.
D. C.—Praise the mount,—I'm fixed up - on it,—Mount of Thy re - deem - ing love!
D. C.
Teach me some mel - o - dious son - net, Sung by flam - ing tongues a - bove;

2 Here I'll raise my Ebenezer,
Hither by Thy help I'm come;
And I hope, by Thy good pleasure,
Safely to arrive at home.
Jesus sought me when a stranger,
Wandering from the fold of God;
He, to rescue me from danger,
Interposed His precious blood.

3 Oh, to grace how great a debtor
Daily I'm constrained to be!
Let Thy goodness, like a fetter,
Bind my wandering heart to Thee.
Prone to wander, Lord, I feel it,
Prone to leave the God I love;
Here's my heart, oh, take and seal it,
Seal it for Thy courts above.

No. 268. Walk In the Light.

Bernard Barton. Haydn.

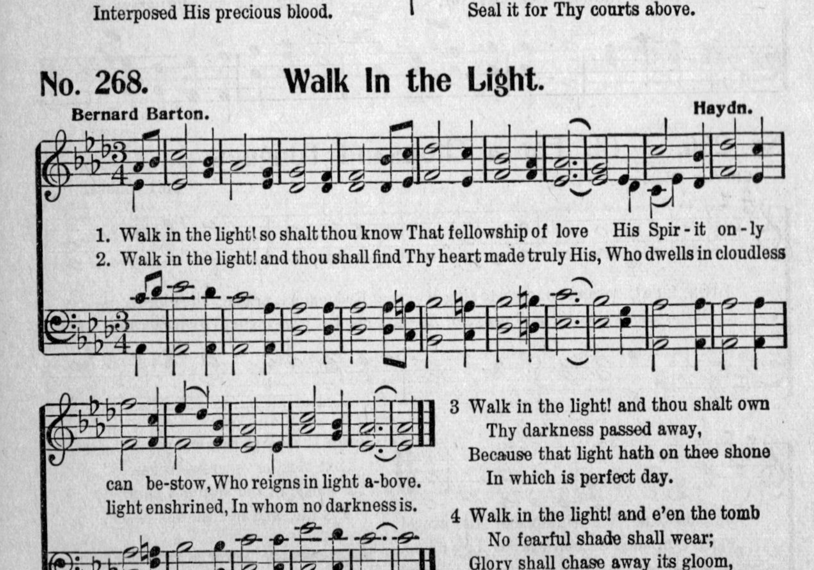
1. Walk in the light! so shalt thou know That fellowship of love His Spir - it on - ly
2. Walk in the light! and thou shall find Thy heart made truly His, Who dwells in cloudless
can be-stow, Who reigns in light a-bove.
light enshrined, In whom no darkness is.

3 Walk in the light! and thou shalt own
Thy darkness passed away,
Because that light hath on thee shone
In which is perfect day.

4 Walk in the light! and e'en the tomb
No fearful shade shall wear;
Glory shall chase away its gloom,
For Christ hath conquered there.

No. 269. Savior, Like a Shepherd.

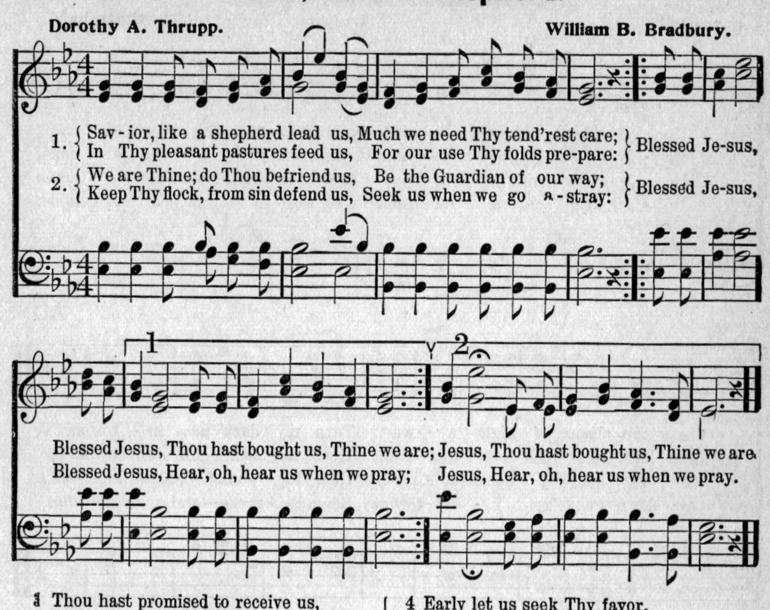
Dorothy A. Thrupp.
William B. Bradbury.
1. Sav-ior, like a shepherd lead us, Much we need Thy tend'rest care;
In Thy pleasant pastures feed us, For our use Thy folds pre-pare:
Blessed Je-sus,
2. We are Thine; do Thou befriend us, Be the Guardian of our way;
Keep Thy flock, from sin defend us, Seek us when we go a-stray:
Blessed Je-sus,
1 2
Blessed Jesus, Thou hast bought us, Thine we are; Jesus, Thou hast bought us, Thine we are.
Blessed Jesus, Hear, oh, hear us when we pray; Jesus, Hear, oh, hear us when we pray.

3 Thou hast promised to receive us,
Poor and sinful though we be;
Thou hast mercy to relieve us,
Grace to cleanse, and power to free:
Blessed Jesus,
We will early turn to Thee.

4 Early let us seek Thy favor,
Early let us do Thy will;
Blessed Lord and only Savior,
With Thy love our bosoms fill:
Blessed Jesus,
Thou hast loved us, love us still.

No. 270. I Love Thy Kingdom, Lord.

Timothy Dwight.
Handel.
1. I love Thy king-dom, Lord, The house of Thine a-bode; The Church our blest Re-deem-er saved With His own precious blood.
2. I love Thy Church, O God! Her walls be-fore Thee stand, Dear as the ap-ple of Thine eye, And gra-ven on Thy hand.

3 For her my tears shall fall,
For her my prayers ascend;
To her my cares and toil be given,
Till toils and cares shall end.

4 Beyond my highest joy
I prize her heavenly ways,
Her sweet communion, solemn vows,
Her hymns of love and praise.

No. 271. Holy Ghost, With Love Divine.

No. 272. Jesus, Savior, Pilot Me.

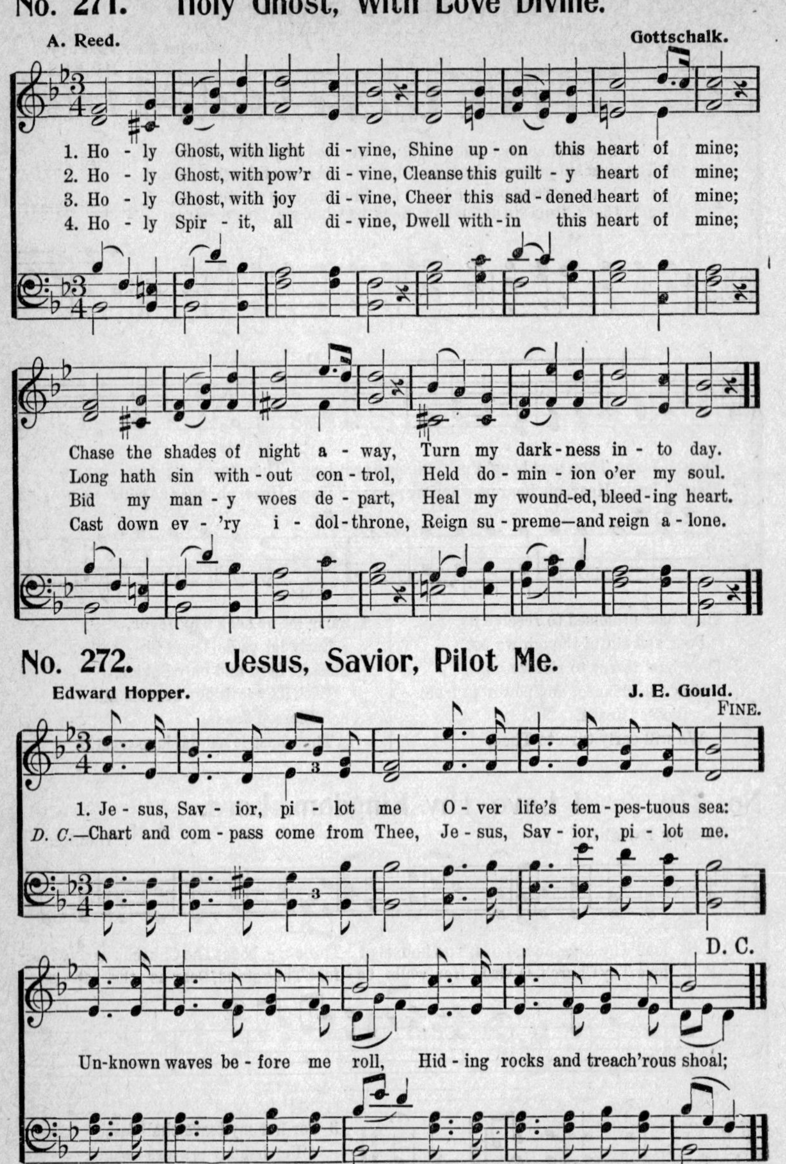
A. Reed.
Gottschalk.
1. Ho - ly Ghost, with light di - vine, Shine up - on this heart of mine;
2. Ho - ly Ghost, with pow'r di - vine, Cleanse this guilt - y heart of mine;
3. Ho - ly Ghost, with joy di - vine, Cheer this sad - dened heart of mine;
4. Ho - ly Spir - it, all di - vine, Dwell with - in this heart of mine;
Chase the shades of night a - way, Turn my dark - ness in - to day.
Long hath sin with - out con - trol, Held do - min - ion o'er my soul.
Bid my man - y woes de - part, Heal my wound-ed, bleed - ing heart.
Cast down ev - 'ry i - dol - throne, Reign su - preme—and reign a - lone.
Edward Hopper.
J. E. Gould.
FINE.
1. Je - sus, Sav - ior, pi - lot me O - ver life's tem - pes-tuous sea:
D. C.—Chart and com - pass come from Thee, Je - sus, Sav - ior, pi - lot me.
D. C.
Un-known waves be - fore me roll, Hid - ing rocks and treach'rous shoal;

2 As a mother stills her child,
Thou canst hush the ocean wild;
Boisterous waves obey Thy will
When Thou say'st to them "Be still!"
Wondrous Sovereign of the sea,
Jesus, Savior, pilot me.

3 When at last I near the shore,
And the fearful breakers roar
'Twixt me and the peaceful rest,
Then, while leaning on Thy breast,
May I hear Thee say to me,
"Fear not, I will pilot thee."

No. 273. Rock of Ages.

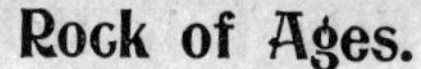

A. M. Toplady. Thomas Hastings.

FINE.

1. Rock of A - ges, cleft for me, Let me hide my - self in Thee;
D. C.—Be of sin the doub - le cure, Save from wrath and make me pure.

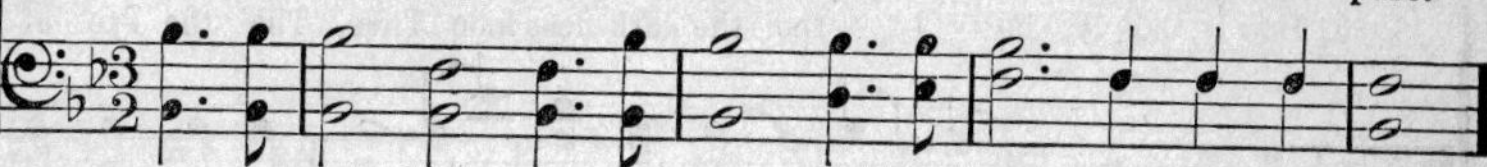

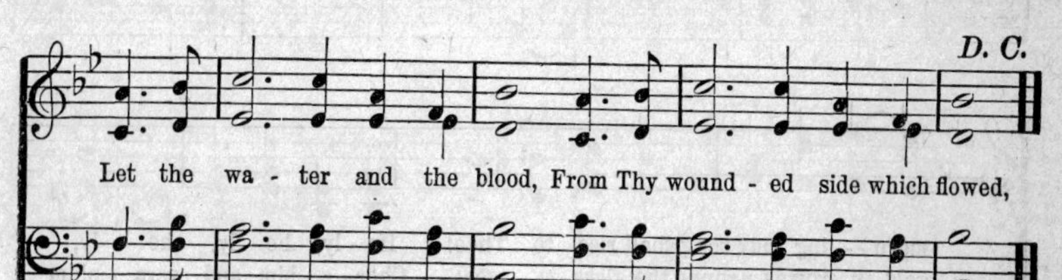
D. C.

Let the wa - ter and the blood, From Thy wound - ed side which flowed,

2 Could my tears forever flow,
Could my zeal no languor know,
These for sin could not atone,
Thou must save, and Thou alone:
In my hand no price I bring,
Simply to Thy cross I cling.

3 While I draw this fleeting breath,
When my eyes shall close in death,
When I rise to worlds unknown,
And behold Thee on Thy throne,
Rock of Ages, cleft for me,
Let me hide myself in Thee.

No. 274. 'T is Midnight; and On Olive's Brow.

William B. Tappan. William B. Bradbury.

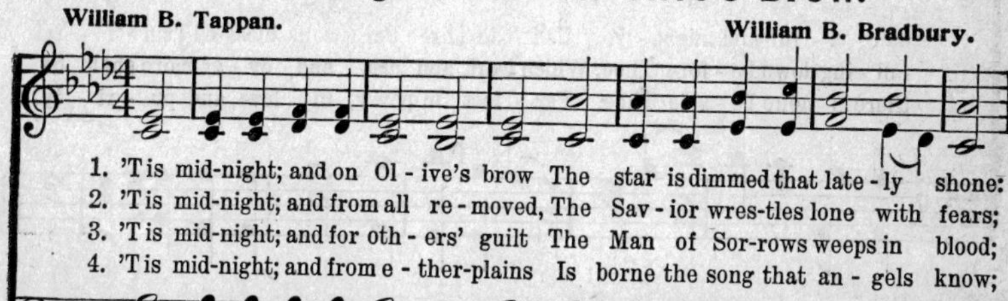

1. 'T is mid-night; and on Ol - ive's brow The star is dimmed that late - ly shone:
2. 'T is mid-night; and from all re - moved, The Sav - ior wres-tles lone with fears;
3. 'T is mid-night; and for oth - ers' guilt The Man of Sor-rows weeps in blood;
4. 'T is mid-night; and from e - ther-plains Is borne the song that an - gels know;

'T is mid-night; in the gar - den, now, The suf-f'ring Sav-ior prays a - lone.
E'en that dis - ci - ple whom He loved Heeds not His Mas-ter's grief and tears.
Yet he that hath in an-guish knelt, Is not for-sak-en by his God.
Un-heard by mor-tals are the strains That sweet-ly soothe the Sav - ior's woe.

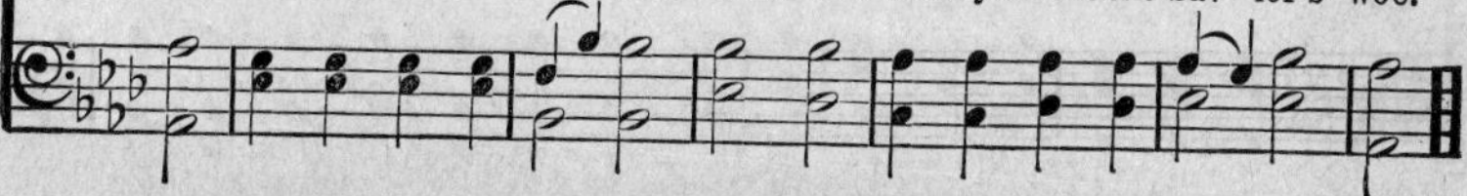

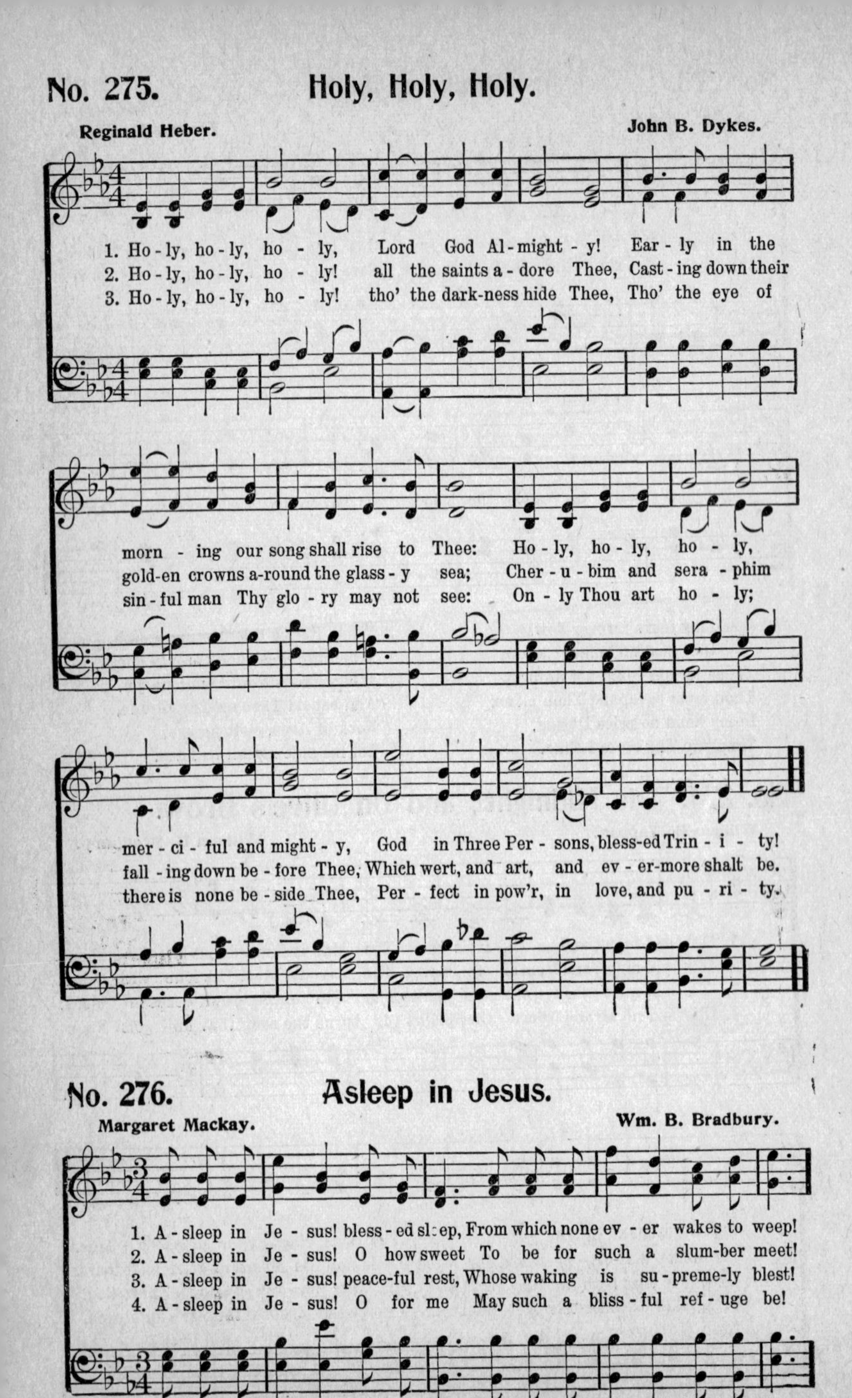
No. 275. Holy, Holy, Holy.
Reginald Heber.
John B. Dykes.
1. Ho-ly, ho-ly, ho-ly, Lord God Al-might-y! Ear-ly in the morn-ing our song shall rise to Thee: Ho-ly, ho-ly, ho-ly, mer-ci-ful and might-y, God in Three Per-sons, bless-ed Trin-i-ty!
2. Ho-ly, ho-ly, ho-ly! all the saints a-dore Thee, Cast-ing down their gold-en crowns a-round the glass-y sea; Cher-u-bim and sera-phim fall-ing down be-fore Thee, Which wert, and art, and ev-er-more shalt be.
3. Ho-ly, ho-ly, ho-ly! tho' the dark-ness hide Thee, Tho' the eye of sin-ful man Thy glo-ry may not see: On-ly Thou art ho-ly; there is none be-side Thee, Per-fect in pow'r, in love, and pu-ri-ty.
No. 276. Asleep in Jesus.
Margaret Mackay.
Wm. B. Bradbury.
1. A-sleep in Je-sus! bless-ed sleep, From which none ev-er wakes to weep!
2. A-sleep in Je-sus! O how sweet To be for such a slum-ber meet!
3. A-sleep in Je-sus! peace-ful rest, Whose waking is su-preme-ly blest!
4. A-sleep in Je-sus! O for me May such a bliss-ful ref-uge be!

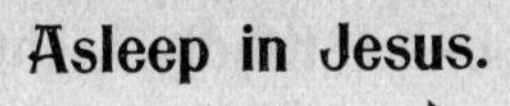
Asleep in Jesus.

A calm and un - dis-turbed re - pose, Un - bro - ken by the last of foes.
With ho - ly con - fi - dence to sing, That Death hath lost his ven-omed sting.
No fear, no woe, shall dim that hour That man - i - fests the Sav - ior's pow'r.
Se - cure - ly shall my ash - es lie, Wait - ing the sum-mons from on high.
No. 277.
Abide With Me.
H. F. Lyte.
W. H. Monk.
1. A - bide with me: fast falls the e - ven - tide; The dark - ness
2. Swift to its close ebbs out life's lit - tle day; Earth's joys grow
3. I need Thy pres - ence ev - 'ry pass - ing hour; What but Thy
4. Hold Thou Thy cross be - fore my clos - ing eyes; Shine thro' the
deep - ens; Lord, with me a - bide! When oth - er help - ers
dim, its glo - ries pass a - way; Change and de - cay in
grace can foil the tempt-er's pow'r? Who, like Thy - self, my
gloom, and point me to the skies; Heav'n's morn - ing breaks, and
fail, and com - forts flee, Help of the help - less, oh, a - bide with me!
all a - round I see; O Thou who chang - est not, a - bide with me!
guide and stay can be? Thro' cloud and sun - shine, oh, a - bide with me!
earth's vain shadows flee; In life, in death, O Lord, a - bide with me!

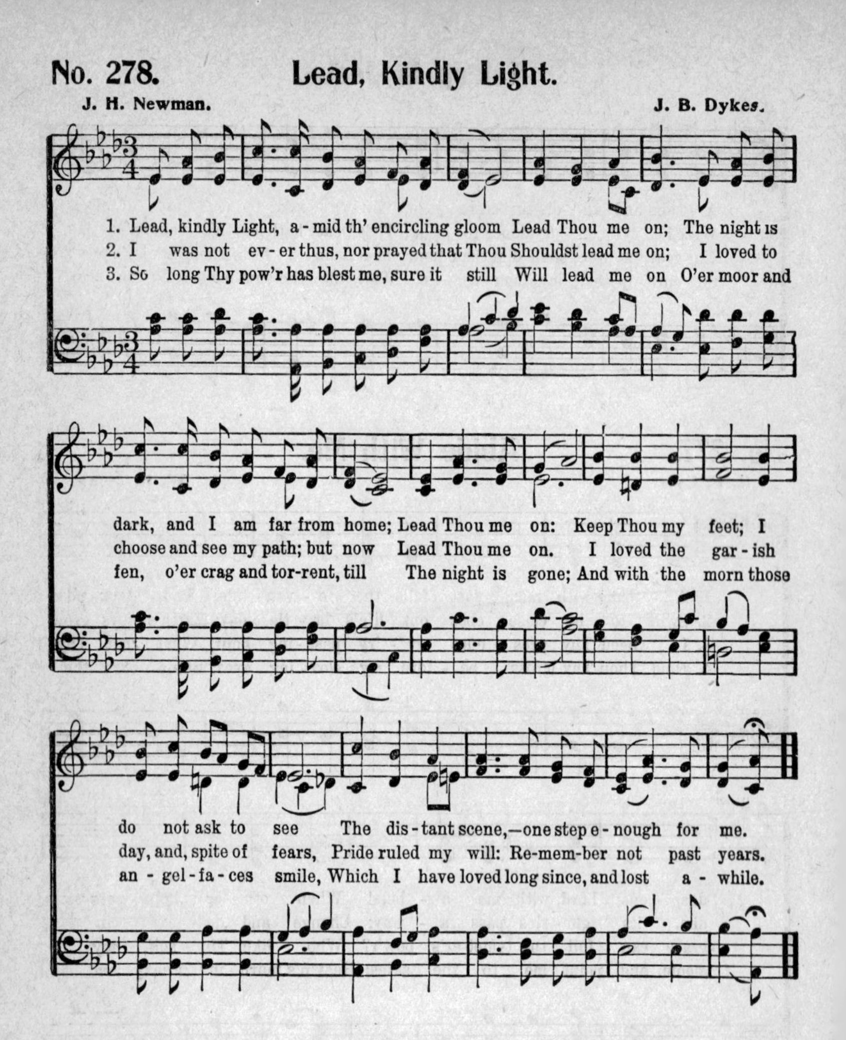
No. 278. Lead, Kindly Light.
J. H. Newman.
J. B. Dykes.
1. Lead, kindly Light, a-mid th' encircling gloom Lead Thou me on; The night is
2. I was not ev-er thus, nor prayed that Thou Shouldst lead me on; I loved to
3. So long Thy pow'r has blest me, sure it still Will lead me on O'er moor and
dark, and I am far from home; Lead Thou me on: Keep Thou my feet; I
choose and see my path; but now Lead Thou me on. I loved the gar-ish
fen, o'er crag and tor-rent, till The night is gone; And with the morn those
do not ask to see The dis-tant scene,—one step e-nough for me.
day, and, spite of fears, Pride ruled my will: Re-mem-ber not past years.
an-gel-fa-ces smile, Which I have loved long since, and lost a-while.

No. 279. Majestic Sweetness Sits Enthroned.

Samuel Stennett. Thomas Hastings.

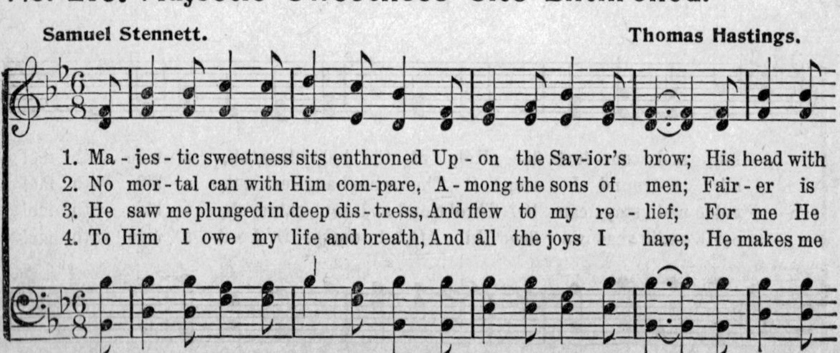
1. Ma-jes-tic sweetness sits enthroned Up-on the Sav-ior's brow; His head with
2. No mor-tal can with Him com-pare, A-mong the sons of men; Fair-er is
3. He saw me plunged in deep dis-tress, And flew to my re-lief; For me He
4. To Him I owe my life and breath, And all the joys I have; He makes me

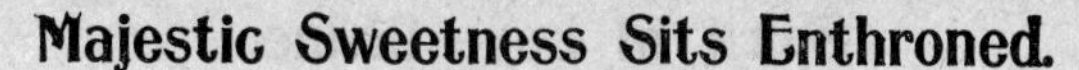

Majestic Sweetness Sits Enthroned.

ra - diant glories crowned, His lips with grace o'erflow, His lips with grace o'er-flow.
He than all the fair That fill the heav'nly train, That fill the heav'nly train.
bore the shameful cross, And car - ried all my grief, And car-ried all my grief.
tri-umph o - ver death, And saves me from the grave, And saves me from the grave.

No. 280. O Sacred Head, Now Wounded.

James W. Alexander, tr. Samuel S. Wesley.

1. O sa-cred Head, now wounded, With grief and shame weighed down, Now scornfully sur-
2. What Thou, my Lord, hast suffered Was all for sinners' gain: Mine, mine was the trans-
3. What language shall I bor - row, To thank Thee, dearest Friend, For this, Thy dy-ing
4. Be near when I am dy - ing, O show Thy cross to me, And for my suc-cor

round - ed With thorns, Thine only crown; O sa - cred Head, what glo - ry, What
gres - sion, But Thine the dead - ly pain. Lo, here I fall, my Sav - ior, 'T is
sor - row, Thy pit - y with - out end? Lord, make me Thine for - ev - er, Nor
fly - ing, Come, Lord, and set me free. These eyes, new faith re - ceiv - ing, From

bliss, till now was Thine! Yet, tho' despised and go - ry, I joy to call Thee mine.
I de-serve Thy place; Look on me with Thy fa - vor, Vouchsafe to me Thy grace.
let me faithless prove: O let me nev - er, nev - er, A - buse such dy - ing love.
Je - sus shall not move; For he who dies be - liev - ing, Dies safe - ly, thro' Thy love.

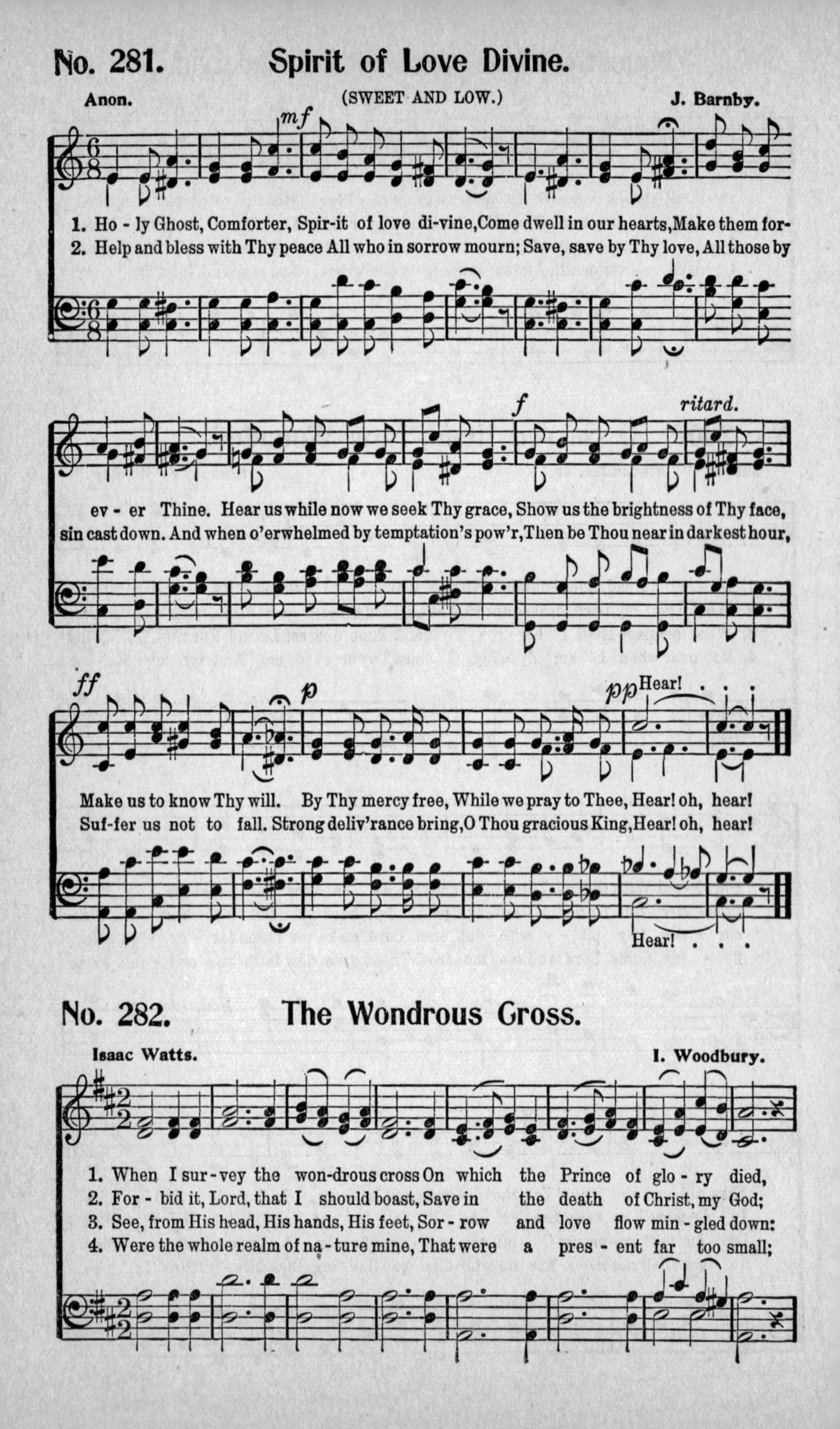
No. 281. Spirit of Love Divine.
Anon.
(SWEET AND LOW.)
J. Barnby.
mf
1. Ho - ly Ghost, Comforter, Spir-it of love di-vine, Come dwell in our hearts, Make them for-
2. Help and bless with Thy peace All who in sorrow mourn; Save, save by Thy love, All those by
f
ritard.
ev - er Thine. Hear us while now we seek Thy grace, Show us the brightness of Thy face,
sin cast down. And when o'erwhelmed by temptation's pow'r, Then be Thou near in darkest hour,
ff
p
pp
Hear! . . .
Make us to know Thy will. By Thy mercy free, While we pray to Thee, Hear! oh, hear!
Suf-fer us not to fall. Strong deliv'rance bring, O Thou gracious King, Hear! oh, hear!
Hear! . . .
No. 282. The Wondrous Cross.
Isaac Watts.
I. Woodbury.
1. When I sur-vey the won-drous cross On which the Prince of glo - ry died,
2. For - bid it, Lord, that I should boast, Save in the death of Christ, my God;
3. See, from His head, His hands, His feet, Sor - row and love flow min - gled down:
4. Were the whole realm of na - ture mine, That were a pres - ent far too small;

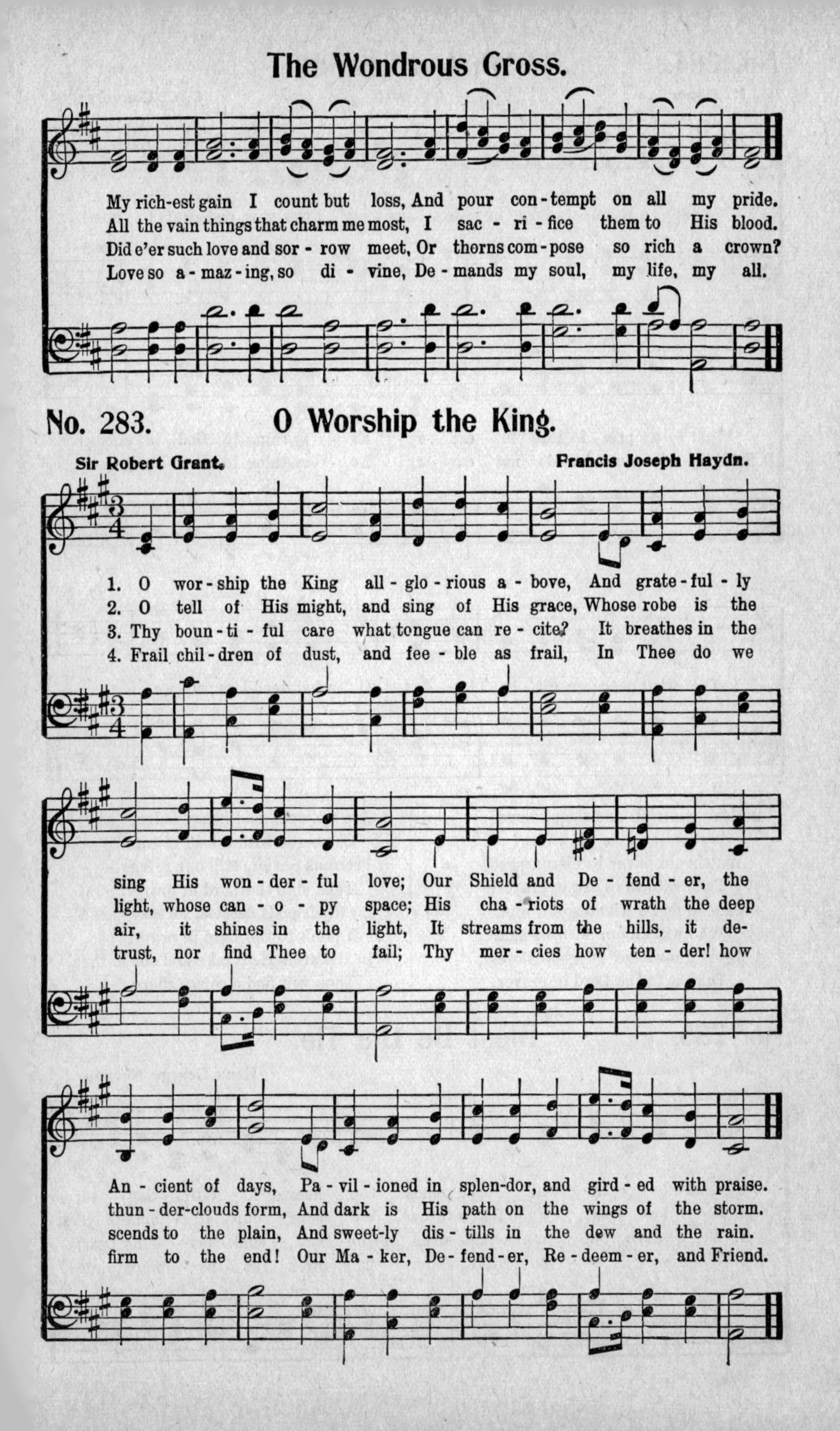
The Wondrous Cross.
My rich-est gain I count but loss, And pour con-tempt on all my pride.
All the vain things that charm me most, I sac - ri - fice them to His blood.
Did e'er such love and sor - row meet, Or thorns com-pose so rich a crown?
Love so a - maz - ing, so di - vine, De - mands my soul, my life, my all.
No. 283. O Worship the King.
Sir Robert Grant.
Francis Joseph Haydn.
1. O wor - ship the King all - glo - rious a - bove, And grate - ful - ly sing His won - der - ful love; Our Shield and De - fend - er, the An - cient of days, Pa - vil - ioned in splen-dor, and gird - ed with praise.
2. O tell of His might, and sing of His grace, Whose robe is the light, whose can - o - py space; His cha - riots of wrath the deep thun - der-clouds form, And dark is His path on the wings of the storm.
3. Thy boun - ti - ful care what tongue can re - cite? It breathes in the air, it shines in the light, It streams from the hills, it de - scends to the plain, And sweet-ly dis - tills in the dew and the rain.
4. Frail chil - dren of dust, and fee - ble as frail, In Thee do we trust, nor find Thee to fail; Thy mer - cies how ten - der! how firm to the end! Our Ma - ker, De - fend - er, Re - deem - er, and Friend.

No. 284. What a Friend.

H. Bonar. C. C. Converse.

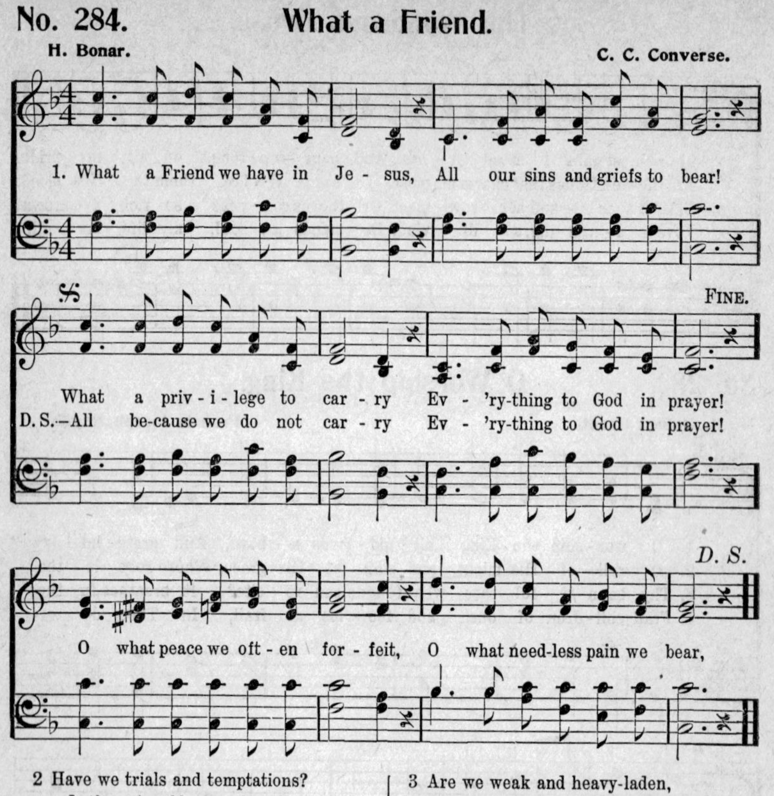
1. What a Friend we have in Je - sus, All our sins and griefs to bear!
What a priv - i - lege to car - ry Ev - 'ry-thing to God in prayer!
D. S.—All be-cause we do not car - ry Ev - 'ry-thing to God in prayer!
FINE.
O what peace we oft - en for - feit, O what need-less pain we bear,
D. S.

2 Have we trials and temptations?
Is there trouble anywhere?
We should never be discouraged,
Take it to the Lord in prayer.
Can we find a friend so faithful,
Who will all our sorrows share?
Jesus knows our every weakness,
Take it to the Lord in prayer.

3 Are we weak and heavy-laden,
Cumbered with a load of care?—
Precious Savior, still our refuge,—
Take it to the Lord in prayer.
Do thy friends despise, forsake thee?
Take it to the Lord in prayer;
In His arms He'll take and shield thee,
Thou wilt find a solace there.

No. 285. Blest Be the Tie.

John Fawcett. Hans George Naegeli.

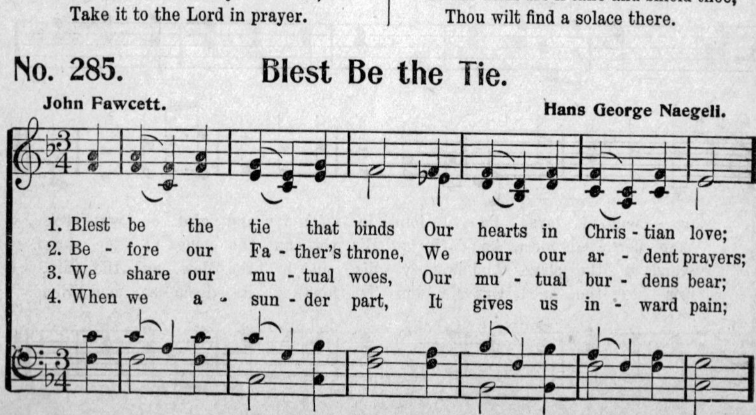
1. Blest be the tie that binds Our hearts in Chris - tian love;
2. Be - fore our Fa - ther's throne, We pour our ar - dent prayers;
3. We share our mu - tual woes, Our mu - tual bur - dens bear;
4. When we a - sun - der part, It gives us in - ward pain;

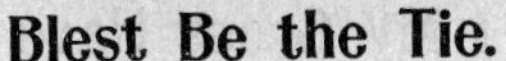
Blest Be the Tie.

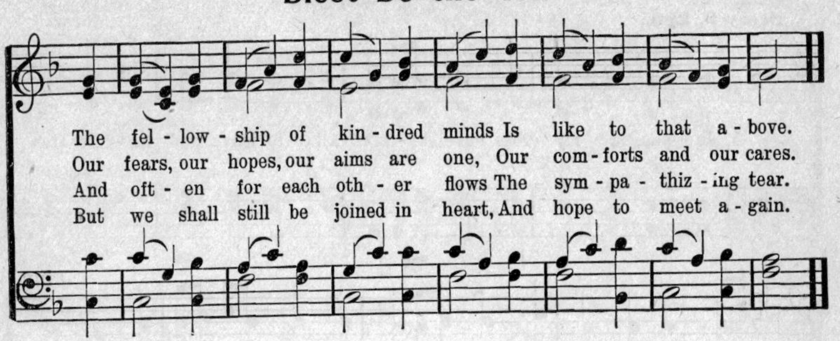
The fel - low - ship of kin - dred minds Is like to that a - bove.
Our fears, our hopes, our aims are one, Our com - forts and our cares.
And oft - en for each oth - er flows The sym - pa - thiz - ing tear.
But we shall still be joined in heart, And hope to meet a - gain.

No. 286. O Little Town of Bethlehem.

Phillip Brooks. Lewis H. Redner.

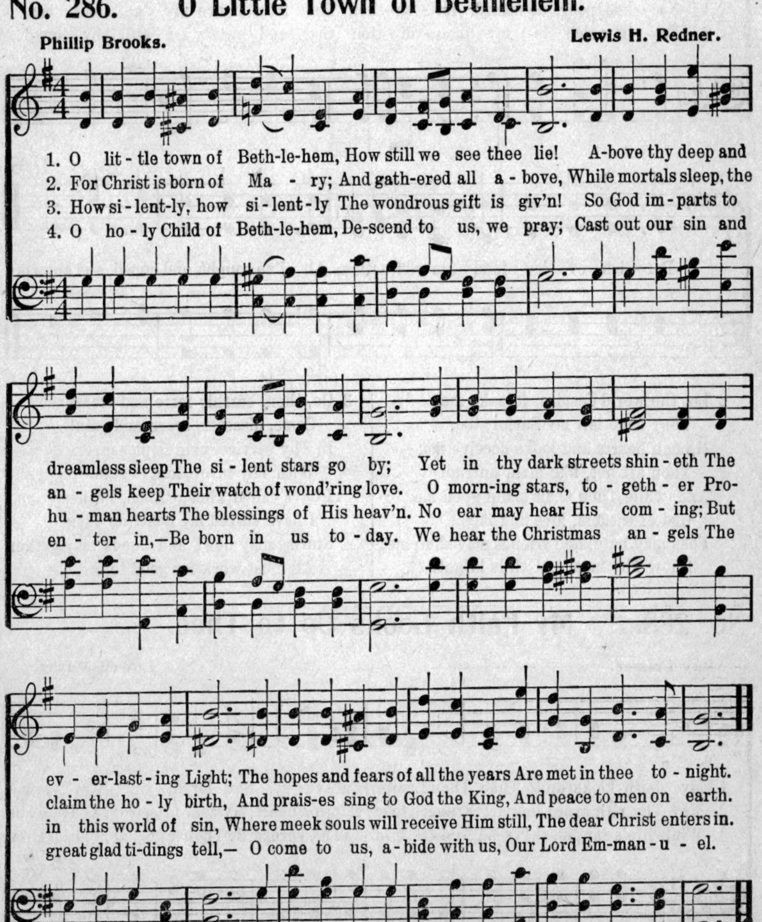
1. O lit - tle town of Beth-le-hem, How still we see thee lie! A-bove thy deep and
2. For Christ is born of Ma - ry; And gath-ered all a - bove, While mortals sleep, the
3. How si - lent-ly, how si - lent - ly The wondrous gift is giv'n! So God im - parts to
4. O ho - ly Child of Beth-le-hem, De-scend to us, we pray; Cast out our sin and
dreamless sleep The si - lent stars go by; Yet in thy dark streets shin - eth The
an - gels keep Their watch of wond'ring love. O morn-ing stars, to - geth - er Pro-
hu - man hearts The blessings of His heav'n. No ear may hear His com - ing; But
en - ter in,—Be born in us to - day. We hear the Christmas an - gels The
ev - er-last - ing Light; The hopes and fears of all the years Are met in thee to - night.
claim the ho - ly birth, And prais-es sing to God the King, And peace to men on earth.
in this world of sin, Where meek souls will receive Him still, The dear Christ enters in.
great glad ti-dings tell,— O come to us, a - bide with us, Our Lord Em-man - u - el.

No. 287. Jesus, I My Cross Have Taken.

Henry F. Lyte.
Mozart.
1. Je - sus, I my cross have ta - ken, All to leave, and fol - low Thee;
Na - ked, poor, de-spised, for - sa - ken, Thou from hence my all shalt be:
D. S.—Yet how rich is my con - di - tion, God and heav'n are still my own!
Fine.
Per - ish ev - 'ry fond am - bi - tion, All I've sought, and hoped, and known;
D. S.

2 Let the world despise, forsake me,
They have left my Savior, too;
Human hearts and looks deceive me;
Thou art not, like man, untrue:
And, while Thou shalt smile upon me,
God of wisdom, love and might,
Foes may hate, and friends may shun me;
Show Thy face, and all is bright.

3 Go, then, earthly fame and treasure!
Come, disaster, scorn and pain!
In Thy service, pain is pleasure;
With Thy favor, loss is gain.
I have called Thee, "Abba, Father,"
I have stayed my heart on Thee;
Storms may howl, and clouds may gather,
All must work for good to me.

No. 288. My Faith Looks Up to Thee.

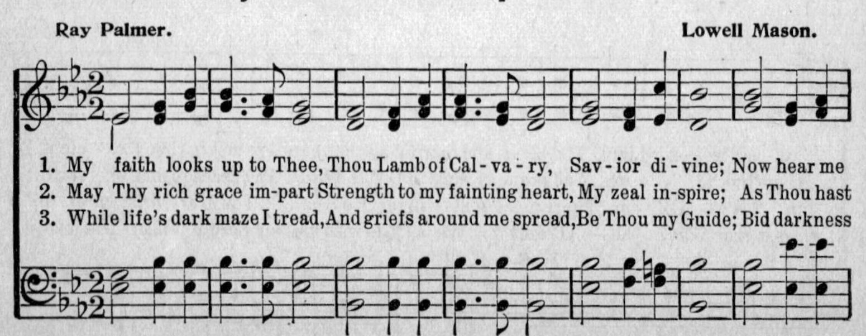
Ray Palmer.
Lowell Mason.
1. My faith looks up to Thee, Thou Lamb of Cal - va - ry, Sav - ior di - vine; Now hear me
2. May Thy rich grace im-part Strength to my fainting heart, My zeal in-spire; As Thou hast
3. While life's dark maze I tread, And griefs around me spread, Be Thou my Guide; Bid darkness

My Faith Looks Up To Thee.

while I pray, Take all my sin a-way, O let me from this day Be whol-ly Thine!
died for me, O may my love to Thee, Pure, warm, and changeless be,—A liv-ing fire!
turn to day, Wipe sorrow's tears a-way, Nor let me ev-er stray From Thee a-side.
No. 289. We Plough the Fields.
Tr. Jane M. Campbell.
J. A. P. Schulz.
1. We plough the fields, and scatter The good seed on the land, But it is fed and watered
2. We thank Thee then, O Father, For all things bright and good, The seed-time and the harvest,
By God's al-might-y hand; He sends the snow in win-ter, The warmth to swell the grain,
Our life, our health, our food. No gifts have we to of - fer For all Thy love im-parts,
Refrain.
The breezes, and the sunshine, And soft, re-fresh-ing rain. All good gifts a-round us
But that which Thou de-sir-est, Our humble, thankful hearts.
Are sent from Heav'n above, Then thank the Lord, O thank the Lord, For all His love.

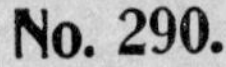

No. 290. O Could I Speak.

S. Medley.
Dr. Lowell Mason.
1. O could I speak the match - less worth, O could I sound the glo - ries forth
Which in my Sav - ior shine,
I'd soar and touch the heav'n-ly strings,
And vie with Ga - briel while he sings
In notes al - most di - vine, In notes al - most di - vine.

2 I'd sing the precious blood He spilt,
My ransom from the dreadful guilt
Of sin, and wrath divine!
I'd sing His glorious righteousness,
In which all-perfect heavenly dress
My soul shall ever shine.

3 Well—the delightful day will come,
When my dear Lord will bring me home,
And I shall see His face:
Then with my Savior, Brother, Friend,
A blest eternity I'll spend,
Triumphant in His grace.

No. 291. Silent Night, Holy Night.

(CHRISTMAS CAROL.)

Hutchinson S. S. Hymnal. Michael Haydn.

pp

1. Si-lent night, holy night, All is calm, all is bright Round yon Virgin Mother and Child;
2. Si-lent night, holy night, Shepherds quake at the sight, Glories stream from Heaven afar,
3. Si-lent night, holy night, Son of God, love's pure light Radiant beams from Thy holy face,

Silent Night, Holy Night.
Ho-ly Infant so tender and mild, Sleep in heavenly peace, Sleep in heavenly peace!
Heav'nly hosts sing Al-le-lu-ia; Christ, the Savior, is born! Christ, the Savior, is born!
With the dawn of redeeming grace, Jesus, Lord, at Thy birth, Je-sus, Lord, at Thy birth.
No. 292. We're Marching to Zion.
Rev. I. Watts.
COPYRIGHT PROPERTY OF MARY RUNYAN LOWRY.
USED BY PERMISSION.
Rev. Robert Lowry.
1. Come, we that love the Lord, And let our joys be known; Join in a song with sweet accord,
2. Let those re - fuse to sing Who never knew our God; But children of the Heav'nly King,
Join in a song with sweet accord, And thus surround the throne, And thus surround the throne.
But children of the Heav'nly King May speak their joys abroad, May speak their joys abroad.
And thus surround the throne, And thus surround the throne.
CHORUS.
We're march-ing to Zi - on, Beau-ti-ful, beau-ti-ful Zi-on; We're marching upward to
We're marching on to Zi - on,
Zi - on, The beau-ti-ful Cit-y of God.
Zi-on, Zi-on,
3 The hill of Zion yields
A thousand sacred sweets,
Before we reach the heav'nly fields,
Or walk the golden streets.
4 Then let our songs abound,
And ev'ry tear be dry; [ground,
We're marching through Immanuel's
To fairer worlds on high.

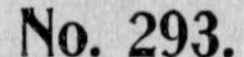

No. 293. Sweet Hour of Prayer.

W. W. Walford. **Wm. B. Bradbury.**

1. Sweet hour of prayer, sweet hour of prayer, That calls me from a world of care,
FINE.
And bids me, at my Father's throne, Make all my wants and wish - es known!
D. S.—And oft es-caped the tempt-er's snare, By thy re - turn, sweet hour of prayer.
D. S.
In sea - sons of dis - tress and grief, My soul has oft - en found re - lief,

2 Sweet hour of prayer, sweet hour of prayer,
The joys I feel, the bliss I share,
Of those whose anxious spirits burn
With strong desires for thy return!
With such I hasten to the place
Where God, my Savior, shows His face,
And gladly take my station there,
And wait for thee, sweet hour of prayer.

3 Sweet hour of prayer, sweet hour of prayer,
Thy wings shall my petition bear
To Him, whose truth and faithfulness
Engage the waiting soul to bless:
And since He bids me seek His face,
Believe His word, and trust His grace,
I'll cast on Him my every care,
And wait for thee, sweet hour of prayer.

No. 294. O Happy Day.

Philip Doddridge. **E. F. Rimbault.**

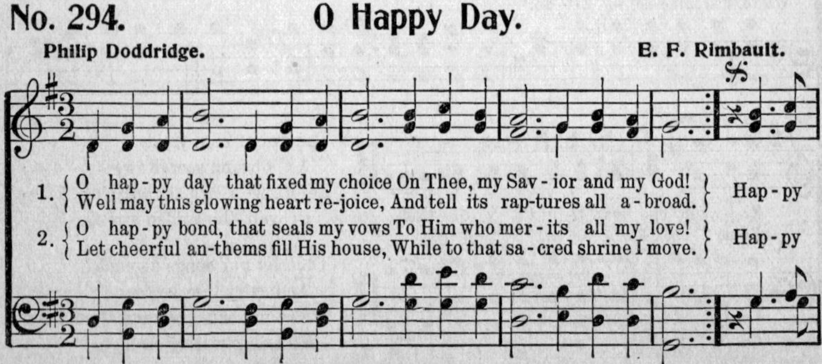

1. { O hap - py day that fixed my choice On Thee, my Sav - ior and my God!
Well may this glowing heart re - joice, And tell its rap - tures all a - broad. } Hap - py
2. { O hap - py bond, that seals my vows To Him who mer - its all my love!
Let cheerful an - thems fill His house, While to that sa - cred shrine I move. } Hap - py

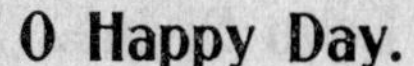

O Happy Day.

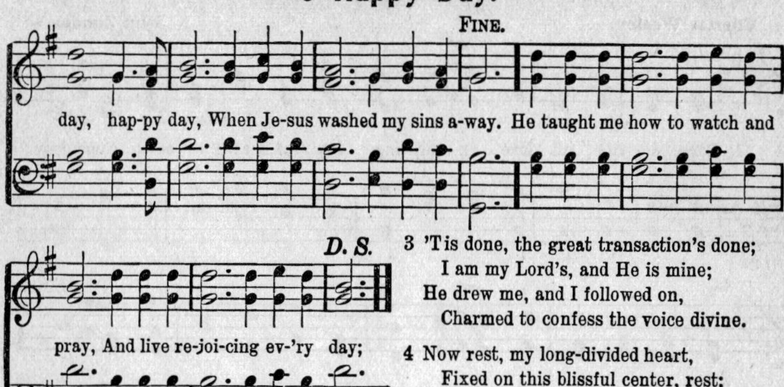

Fine.
day, hap-py day, When Je-sus washed my sins a-way. He taught me how to watch and
D. S.
pray, And live re-joi-cing ev-'ry day;

3 'Tis done, the great transaction's done;
I am my Lord's, and He is mine;
He drew me, and I followed on,
Charmed to confess the voice divine.

4 Now rest, my long-divided heart,
Fixed on this blissful center, rest;
Nor ever from thy Lord depart,
With Him of every good possessed.

No. 295. Sweet By-and-By.

S. Fillmore Bennett. BY PERMISSION. **Jos. P. Webster.**

1. There's a land that is fair-er than day, And by faith we can see it a-far;
For the Fa-ther waits o-ver the way, To pre- [Omit ....]
pare us a dwelling-place there. In the sweet by-and-by, We shall meet on that
Chorus.
In the sweet by-and-by,
beau-ti-ful shore; by-and-by, We shall meet on that beautiful shore.
by-and-by; by-and-by,

2 We shall sing on that beautiful shore
The melodious songs of the blest,
And our spirits shall sorrow no more,
Not a sigh for the blessing of rest.

3 To our bountiful Father above,
We will offer our tribute of praise,
For the glorious gift of His love,
And the blessings that hallow our days.

No. 296. Love Divine.

Charles Wesley. John Zundel.

1. Love di - vine, all love ex - cell - ing, Joy of heav'n, to earth come down!
FINE.
Fix in us Thy hum - ble dwell - ing; All Thy faith - ful mer - cies crown.
D. S.—Vis - it us with Thy sal - va - tion, En - ter ev - 'ry trem - bling heart!
D. S.
Je - sus, Thou art all com - pas - sion, Pure, un - bound - ed love Thou art;

2 Breathe, oh, breathe Thy loving Spirit
Into every troubled breast!
Let us all in Thee inherit,
Let us find the promised rest.
Take away the love of sinning;
Alpha and Omega be;
End of faith, as its beginning,
Set our hearts at liberty!

3 Come, Almighty to deliver,
Let us all Thy grace receive;
Suddenly return, and never,
Never more Thy temples leave:
Thee we would be always blessing.
Serve Thee as Thy hosts above,
Pray, and praise Thee without ceasing,
Glory in Thy perfect love!

No. 297. Guide Me.

W. Williams. Thomas Hastings.

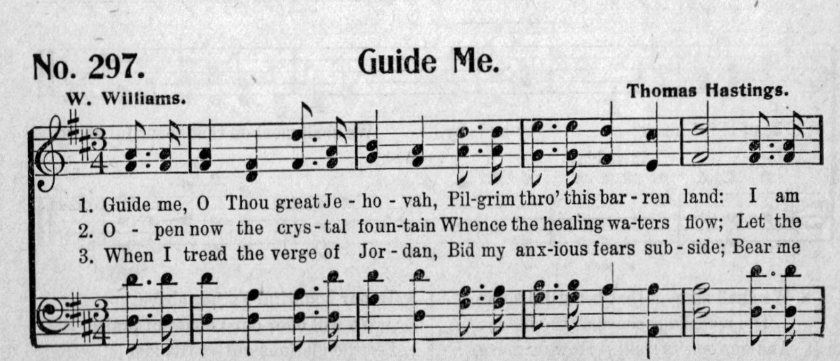
1. Guide me, O Thou great Je - ho - vah, Pil - grim thro' this bar - ren land: I am
2. O - pen now the crys - tal foun - tain Whence the heal - ing wa - ters flow; Let the
3. When I tread the verge of Jor - dan, Bid my anx - ious fears sub - side; Bear me

Guide Me.
weak but Thou art might-y, Hold me with Thy pow'r-ful hand; Bread of Heav - en,
fier - y, cloud - y pil - lar Lead me all my jour - ney thro'; Strong De-liv - 'rer,
thro' the swell-ing cur - rent; Land me safe on Ca - naan's side; Songs of prais - es
Feed me till I want no more; Bread of Heav-en, Feed me till I want no more.
Be Thou still my strength and shield; Strong Deliv'rer, Be Thou still my strength and shield.
I will ev - er give to Thee; Songs of prais-es I will ev - er give to Thee.
No. 298. My Hope is Built.
Edward Mote.
Wm. B. Bradbury.
1. My hope is built on noth-ing less Than Je - sus' blood and right-eous-ness;
I dare not trust the sweet-est frame, But whol - ly lean on Je - sus' name.
2. When darkness veils His love - ly face, I rest on His un-chang-ing grace;
In ev - 'ry high and storm - y gale, My an-chor holds with - in the veil.
Refrain.
On Christ, the sol - id rock, I stand; All oth - er ground is sink - ing sand, All
oth - er ground is sink - ing sand.
3 His oath, His covenant, His blood
Support me in the whelming flood;
When all around my soul gives way,
He then is all my hope and stay.
4 When He shall come with trumpet sound,
Oh, may I then in Him be found;
Dressed in His righteousness alone,
Faultless to stand before the throne.

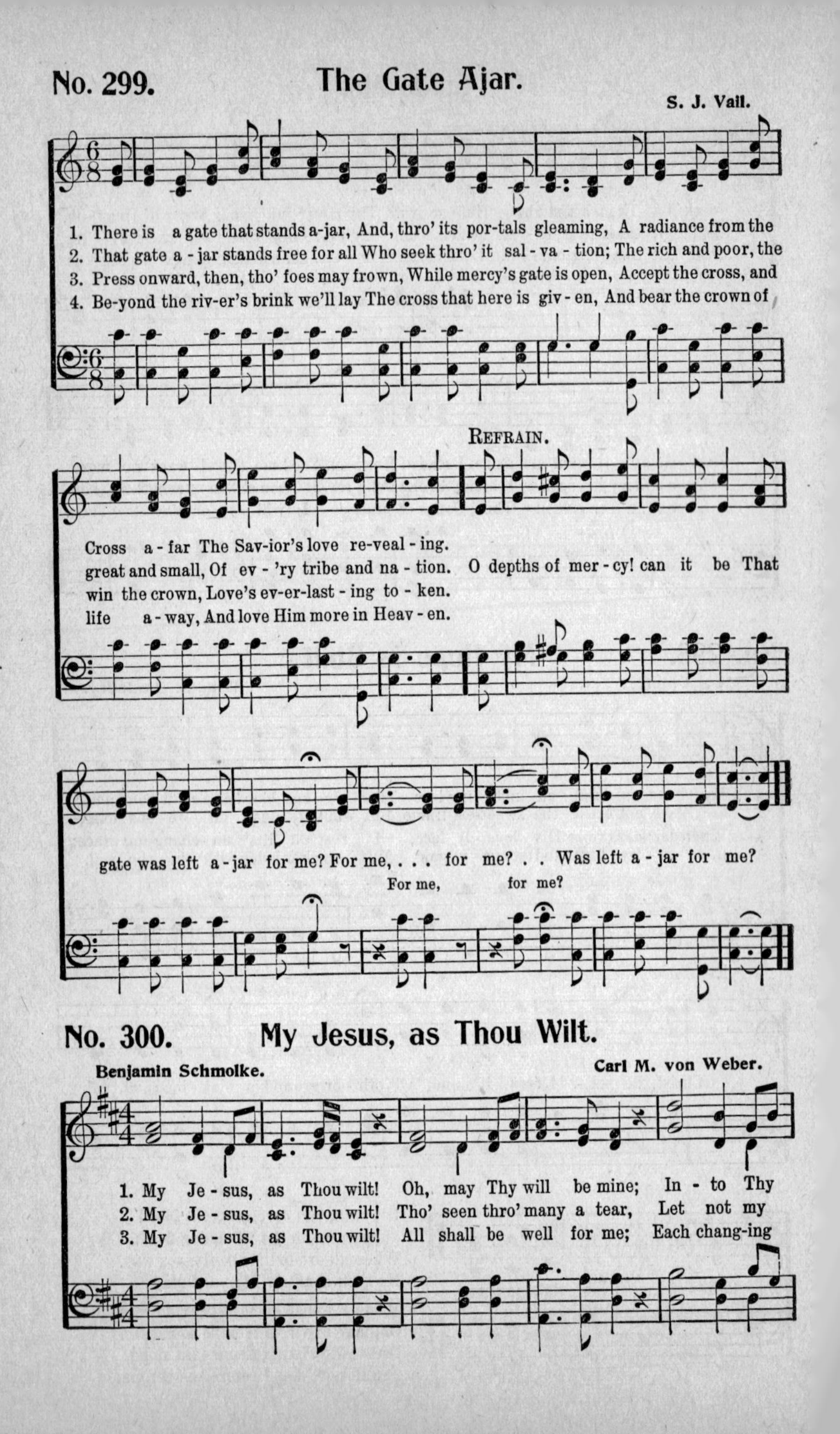
No. 299.
The Gate Ajar.
S. J. Vail.
1. There is a gate that stands a-jar, And, thro' its por-tals gleaming, A radiance from the
2. That gate a - jar stands free for all Who seek thro' it sal - va - tion; The rich and poor, the
3. Press onward, then, tho' foes may frown, While mercy's gate is open, Accept the cross, and
4. Be-yond the riv-er's brink we'll lay The cross that here is giv - en, And bear the crown of
Refrain.
Cross a - far The Sav-ior's love re-veal - ing.
great and small, Of ev - 'ry tribe and na - tion. O depths of mer - cy! can it be That
win the crown, Love's ev-er-last - ing to - ken.
life a - way, And love Him more in Heav - en.
gate was left a - jar for me? For me, . . . for me? . . Was left a - jar for me?
For me, for me?
No. 300.
My Jesus, as Thou Wilt.
Benjamin Schmolke.
Carl M. von Weber.
1. My Je - sus, as Thou wilt! Oh, may Thy will be mine; In - to Thy
2. My Je - sus, as Thou wilt! Tho' seen thro' many a tear, Let not my
3. My Je - sus, as Thou wilt! All shall be well for me; Each chang-ing

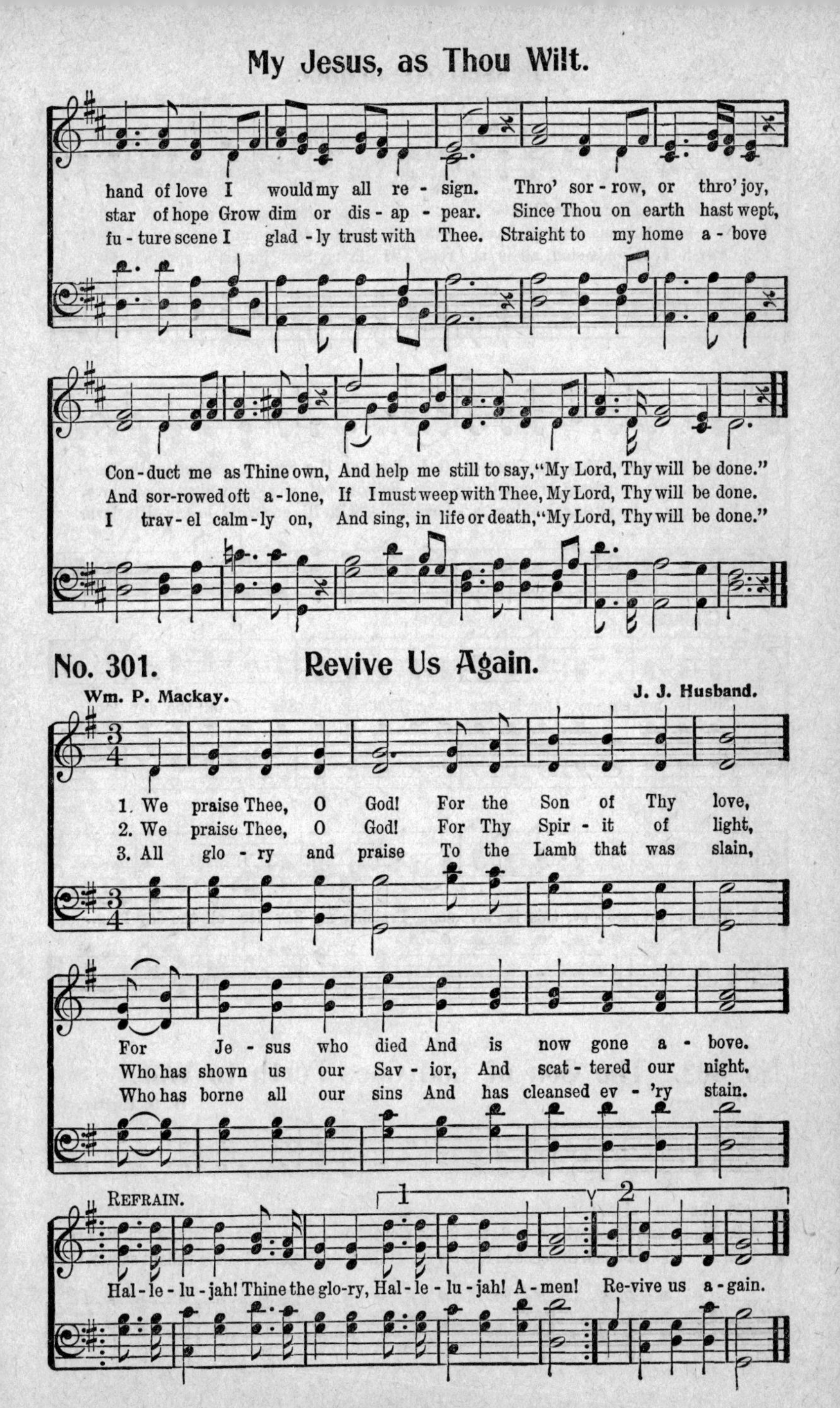
My Jesus, as Thou Wilt.
hand of love I would my all re - sign. Thro' sor - row, or thro' joy,
star of hope Grow dim or dis - ap - pear. Since Thou on earth hast wept,
fu - ture scene I glad - ly trust with Thee. Straight to my home a - bove
Con - duct me as Thine own, And help me still to say, "My Lord, Thy will be done."
And sor-rowed oft a - lone, If I must weep with Thee, My Lord, Thy will be done.
I trav - el calm - ly on, And sing, in life or death, "My Lord, Thy will be done."
No. 301. Revive Us Again.
Wm. P. Mackay.
J. J. Husband.
3
4
1. We praise Thee, O God! For the Son of Thy love,
2. We praise Thee, O God! For Thy Spir - it of light,
3. All glo - ry and praise To the Lamb that was slain,
For Je - sus who died And is now gone a - bove.
Who has shown us our Sav - ior, And scat - tered our night.
Who has borne all our sins And has cleansed ev - 'ry stain.
Refrain.
1
2
Hal - le - lu - jah! Thine the glo-ry, Hal - le - lu - jah! A - men! Re-vive us a - gain.

No. 302. Blessed Assurance.
Fanny J. Crosby.
COPYRIGHT, 1873, BY JOS. F. KNAPP.
Mrs. J. F. Knapp.
1. Bless-ed as-sur-ance, Je-sus is mine! Oh, what a fore-taste of glo-ry di - vine!
2. Per-fect sub-mis-sion, perfect de - light, Vi-sions of rapture now burst on my sight;
3. Per-fect sub-mis-sion, all is at rest, I in my Sav-ior am happy and blest;
Heir of sal - va-tion, purchase of God, Born of His Spir - it, washed in His blood.
An-gels de-scend-ing, bring from a - bove Ech-oes of mer - cy, whispers of love.
Watching and wait-ing, looking a - bove, Filled with His goodness, lost in His love.
CHORUS.
This is my sto - ry, this is my song, Praising my Sav-ior all the day long;
This is my sto - ry, this is my song, Praising my Sav - ior all the day long.
No. 303. The Son of God Goes Forth to War.
R. Heber.
H. S. Cutler.
1. The Son of God goes forth to war, A king-ly crown to gain; His blood - red ban-ner
2. That martyr first, whose eagle eye Could pierce beyond the grave; Who saw his Mas-ter
3. A no - ble band, the chosen few On whom the Spir-it came; Twelve valiant saints, their

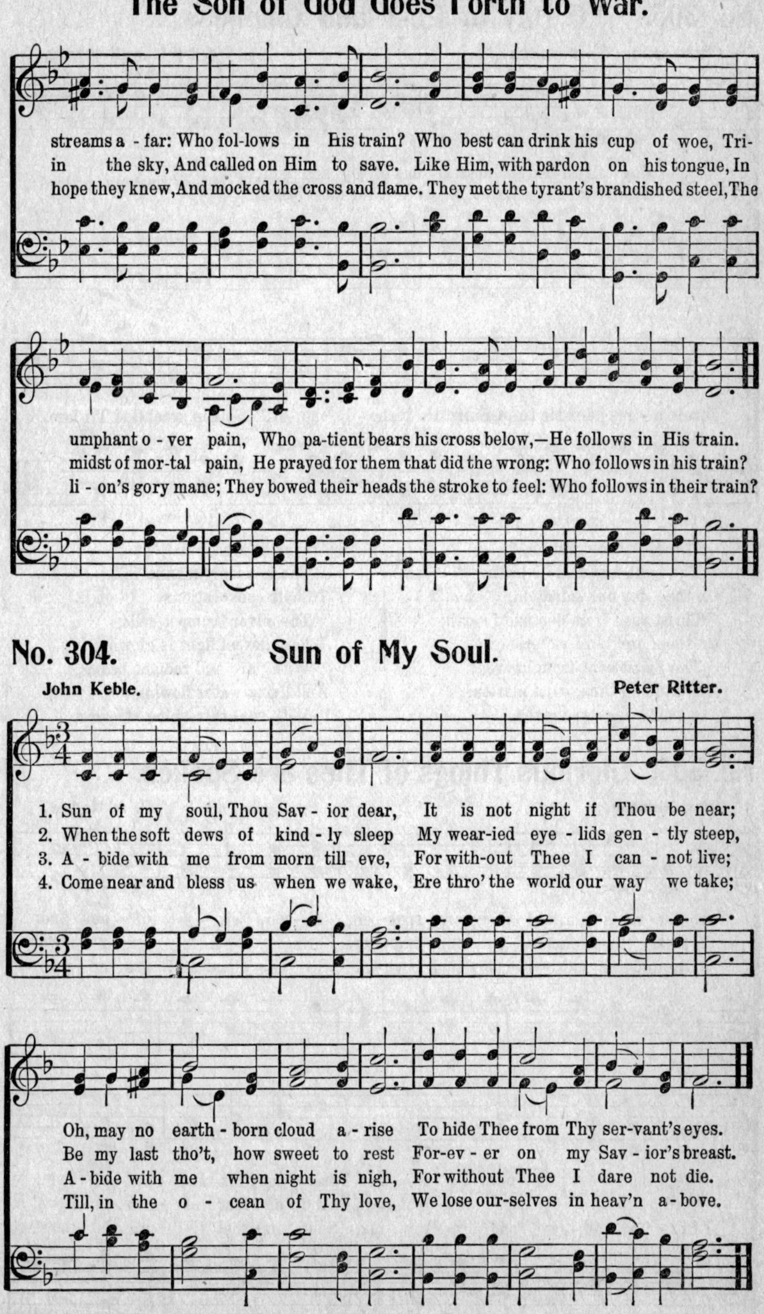
The Son of God Goes Forth to War.
streams a - far: Who fol-lows in His train? Who best can drink his cup of woe, Tri-
in the sky, And called on Him to save. Like Him, with pardon on his tongue, In
hope they knew, And mocked the cross and flame. They met the tyrant's brandished steel, The
umphant o - ver pain, Who pa-tient bears his cross below,—He follows in His train.
midst of mor-tal pain, He prayed for them that did the wrong: Who follows in his train?
li - on's gory mane; They bowed their heads the stroke to feel: Who follows in their train?
No. 304. Sun of My Soul.
John Keble.
Peter Ritter.
1. Sun of my soul, Thou Sav - ior dear, It is not night if Thou be near;
2. When the soft dews of kind - ly sleep My wear-ied eye - lids gen - tly steep,
3. A - bide with me from morn till eve, For with-out Thee I can - not live;
4. Come near and bless us when we wake, Ere thro' the world our way we take;
Oh, may no earth - born cloud a - rise To hide Thee from Thy ser-vant's eyes.
Be my last tho't, how sweet to rest For-ev - er on my Sav - ior's breast.
A - bide with me when night is nigh, For without Thee I dare not die.
Till, in the o - cean of Thy love, We lose our-selves in heav'n a - bove.

No. 305. O Day of Rest and Gladness.

Christopher Wordsworth. Arr. by Lowell Mason.

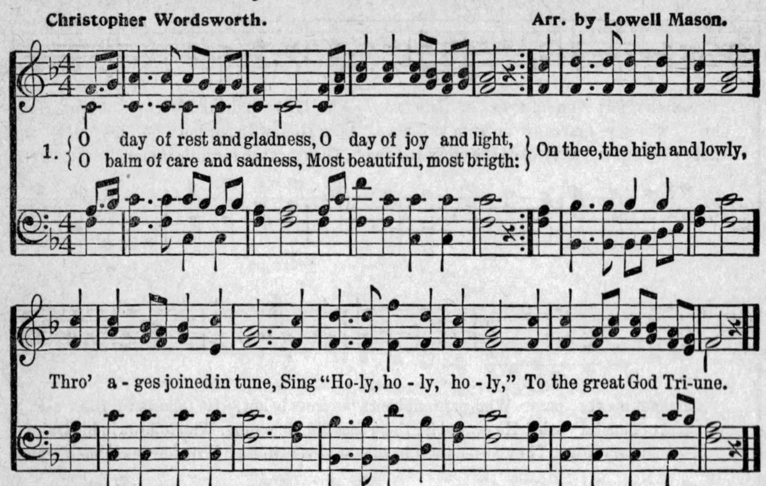
1. { O day of rest and gladness, O day of joy and light,
O balm of care and sadness, Most beautiful, most brigth: } On thee, the high and lowly,
Thro' a - ges joined in tune, Sing "Ho-ly, ho - ly, ho - ly," To the great God Tri-une.

2 On thee, at the creation,
The light first had its birth;
On thee, for our salvation,
Christ rose from depths of earth;
On thee, our Lord victorious,
The Spirit sent from heaven;
And thus on thee, most glorious,
A triple light was given.

3 To-day on weary nations
The heavenly manna falls;
To holy convocations
The silver trumpet calls,
Where gospel light is glowing
With pure and radiant beams,
And living water flowing
With soul-refreshing streams.

No. 306. Glorious Things of Thee are Spoken.

John Newton. F. J. Hadyn.

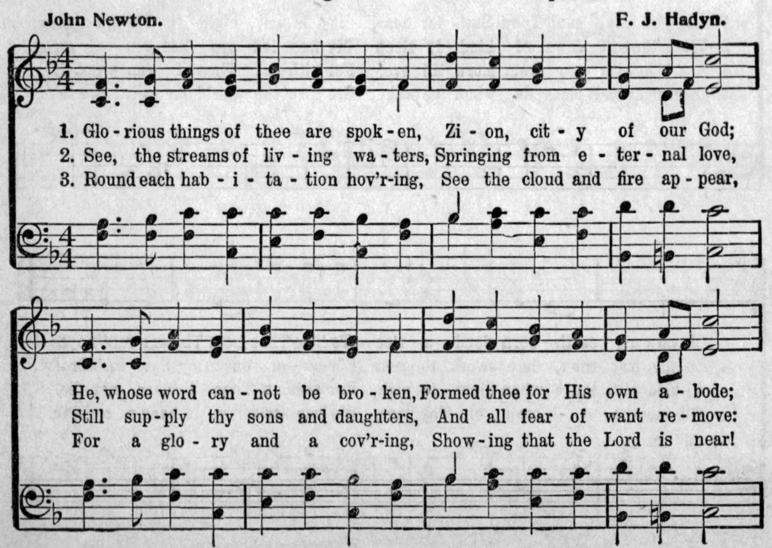
1. Glo - rious things of thee are spok - en, Zi - on, cit - y of our God;
2. See, the streams of liv - ing wa - ters, Springing from e - ter - nal love,
3. Round each hab - i - ta - tion hov'r-ing, See the cloud and fire ap - pear,
He, whose word can - not be bro - ken, Formed thee for His own a - bode;
Still sup - ply thy sons and daughters, And all fear of want re - move:
For a glo - ry and a cov'r-ing, Show - ing that the Lord is near!

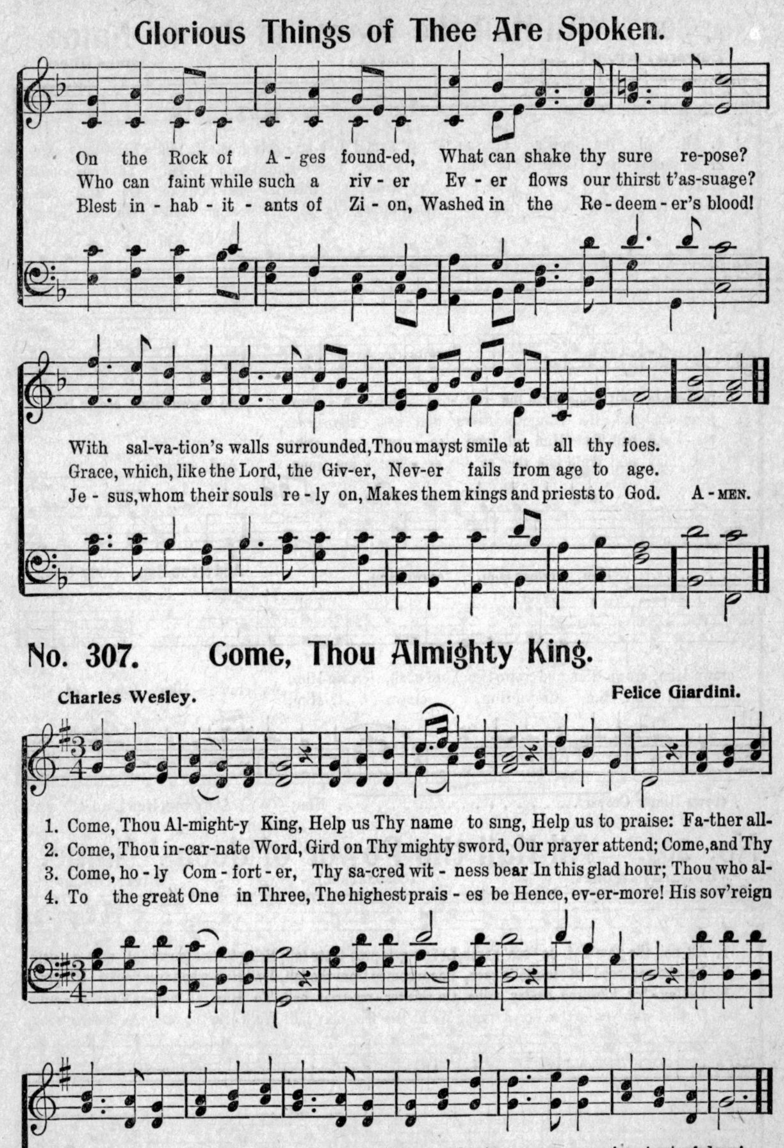
Glorious Things of Thee Are Spoken.
On the Rock of A - ges found-ed, What can shake thy sure re-pose?
Who can faint while such a riv - er Ev - er flows our thirst t'as-suage?
Blest in - hab - it - ants of Zi - on, Washed in the Re - deem - er's blood!
With sal-va-tion's walls surrounded, Thou mayst smile at all thy foes.
Grace, which, like the Lord, the Giv-er, Nev-er fails from age to age.
Je - sus, whom their souls re - ly on, Makes them kings and priests to God. A - MEN.
No. 307. Come, Thou Almighty King.
Charles Wesley.
Felice Giardini.
1. Come, Thou Al-might-y King, Help us Thy name to sing, Help us to praise: Fa-ther all-
2. Come, Thou in-car-nate Word, Gird on Thy mighty sword, Our prayer attend; Come, and Thy
3. Come, ho - ly Com - fort - er, Thy sa-cred wit - ness bear In this glad hour; Thou who al-
4. To the great One in Three, The highest prais - es be Hence, ev-er-more! His sov'reign
glo - ri-ous, O'er all vic - to - ri-ous, Come, and reign o - ver us, An-cient of days!
peo - ple bless, And give Thy word success: Spir-it of ho - li-ness, On us de-scend!
might-y art, Now rule in ev - 'ry heart, And ne'er from us de-part, Spir - it of pow'r!
maj - es - ty May we in glo - ry see, And to e - ter - ni - ty Love and a - dore!

No. 308. All Hail the Power of Jesus' Name.
Edward Perronet.
(DIADEM.)
James Ellor.
1. All hail the pow'r of Je - sus' name! Let an - gels prostrate fall, Let an - gels
2. Ye cho - sen seed of Is - rael's race, Ye ran-somed from the fall, Ye ran-somed
3. Let ev - 'ry kin - dred, ev - 'ry tribe, On this ter-res - trial ball, On this ter-
4. O that with yon - der sa - cred throng We at His feet may fall, We at His
And crown . . . .
pros-trate fall; Bring forth the roy - al di - a - dem, And crown Him, crown Him,
from the fall, Hail Him who saves you by His grace,
res - trial ball, To Him all maj - es - ty as - cribe,
feet may fall! We'll join the ev - er - last - ing song, And crown . . . .
. . . . Him, crown Him, crown Him,
And crown Him, crown Him,
crown Him, crown Him, And crown Him Lord of all, crown Him;
. . . . Him, Crown Him, crown . . . . Him;
And crown Him Lord of all!
crown Him Crown . . . . Him;
And crown Him Lord of all!
No. 309. All Hail the Power of Jesus' Name.
Edward Perronet.
(CORONATION.)
Oliver Holden.
1. All hail the pow'r of Je - sus' name, Let an-gels pros-trate fall; Bring forth the roy - al di - a - dem,
2. Ye cho-sen seed of Is-rael's race, Ye ransomed from the fall, Hail Him who saves you by His grace,
3. Let ev-'ry kin-dred, ev-'ry tribe, On this ter - res-trial ball, To Him all maj-es - ty as-cribe,
4. O that with yon-der sa - cred throng We at His feet may fall! We'll join the ev - er - last-ing song,
And crown Him Lord of all; Bring forth the roy - al di - a - dem, And crown Him Lord of all!
And crown Him Lord of all; Hail Him who saves you by His grace, And crown Him Lord of all!
And crown Him Lord of all; To Him all maj - es - ty as - cribe, And crown Him Lord of all!
And crown Him Lord of all; We'll join the ev - er-last - ing song, And crown Him Lord of all!

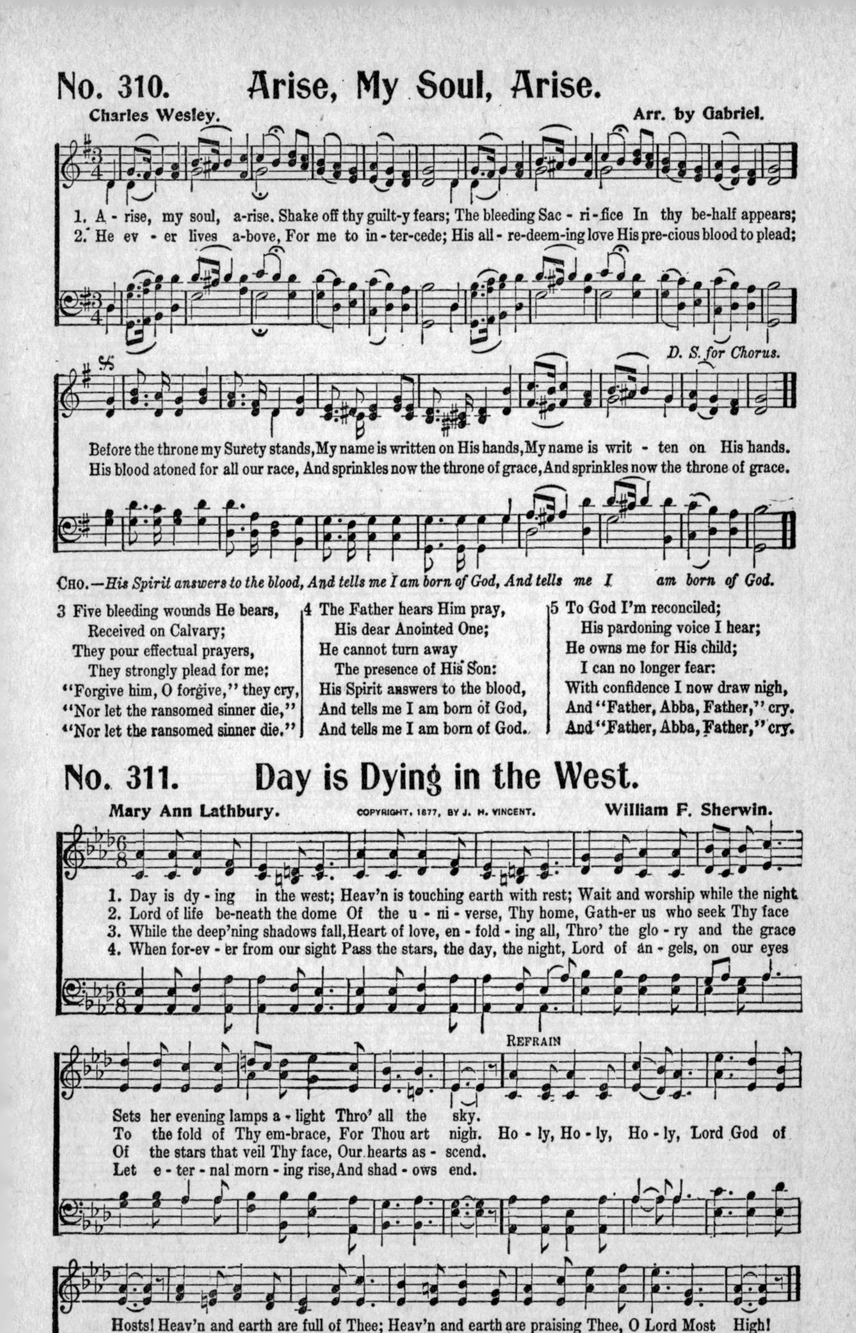
No. 310. Arise, My Soul, Arise.
Charles Wesley.
Arr. by Gabriel.
1. A - rise, my soul, a-rise. Shake off thy guilt-y fears; The bleeding Sac - ri - fice In thy be-half appears;
2. He ev - er lives a-bove, For me to in - ter-cede; His all - re-deem-ing love His pre-cious blood to plead;
D. S. for Chorus.
Before the throne my Surety stands, My name is written on His hands, My name is writ - ten on His hands.
His blood atoned for all our race, And sprinkles now the throne of grace, And sprinkles now the throne of grace.
Cho.—His Spirit answers to the blood, And tells me I am born of God, And tells me I am born of God.
3 Five bleeding wounds He bears,
Received on Calvary;
They pour effectual prayers,
They strongly plead for me;
"Forgive him, O forgive," they cry,
"Nor let the ransomed sinner die,"
"Nor let the ransomed sinner die."
4 The Father hears Him pray,
His dear Anointed One;
He cannot turn away
The presence of His Son:
His Spirit answers to the blood,
And tells me I am born of God,
And tells me I am born of God.
5 To God I'm reconciled;
His pardoning voice I hear;
He owns me for His child;
I can no longer fear:
With confidence I now draw nigh,
And "Father, Abba, Father," cry.
And "Father, Abba, Father," cry.
No. 311. Day is Dying in the West.
Mary Ann Lathbury.
COPYRIGHT, 1877, BY J. H. VINCENT.
William F. Sherwin.
1. Day is dy - ing in the west; Heav'n is touching earth with rest; Wait and worship while the night
2. Lord of life be-neath the dome Of the u - ni - verse, Thy home, Gath-er us who seek Thy face
3. While the deep'ning shadows fall, Heart of love, en - fold - ing all, Thro' the glo - ry and the grace
4. When for-ev - er from our sight Pass the stars, the day, the night, Lord of an - gels, on our eyes
Sets her evening lamps a - light Thro' all the sky.
To the fold of Thy em-brace, For Thou art nigh.
Of the stars that veil Thy face, Our hearts as - cend.
Let e - ter - nal morn - ing rise, And shad - ows end.
Refrain
Ho - ly, Ho - ly, Ho - ly, Lord God of
Hosts! Heav'n and earth are full of Thee; Heav'n and earth are praising Thee, O Lord Most High!

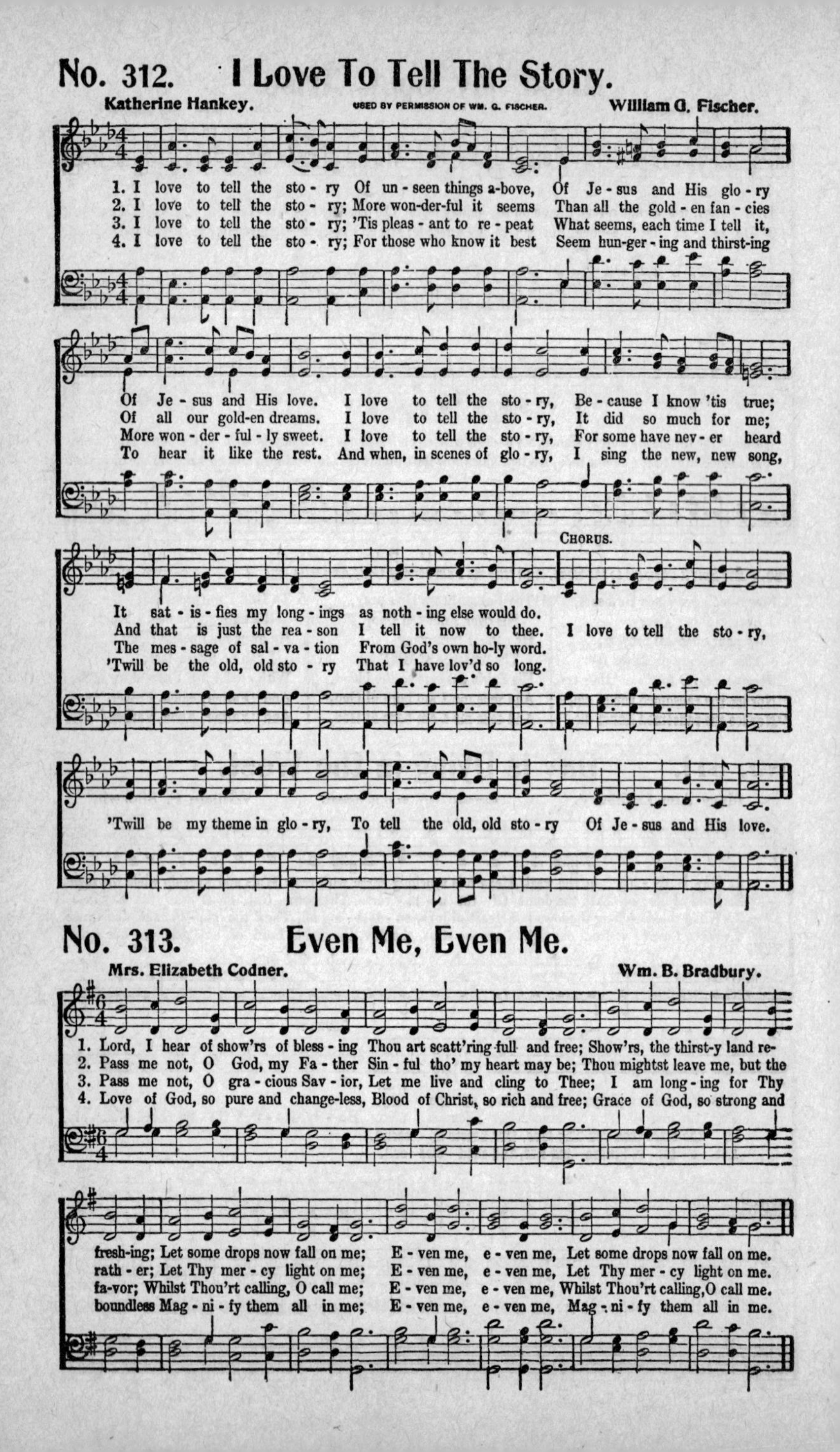
No. 312. I Love To Tell The Story.
Katherine Hankey.
USED BY PERMISSION OF WM. G. FISCHER.
William G. Fischer.
1. I love to tell the sto - ry Of un - seen things a-bove, Of Je - sus and His glo - ry
2. I love to tell the sto - ry; More won-der-ful it seems Than all the gold - en fan - cies
3. I love to tell the sto - ry; 'Tis pleas - ant to re - peat What seems, each time I tell it,
4. I love to tell the sto - ry; For those who know it best Seem hun-ger - ing and thirst-ing
Of Je - sus and His love. I love to tell the sto - ry, Be - cause I know 'tis true;
Of all our gold-en dreams. I love to tell the sto - ry, It did so much for me;
More won - der - ful - ly sweet. I love to tell the sto - ry, For some have nev - er heard
To hear it like the rest. And when, in scenes of glo - ry, I sing the new, new song,
CHORUS.
It sat - is - fies my long - ings as noth - ing else would do.
And that is just the rea - son I tell it now to thee. I love to tell the sto - ry,
The mes - sage of sal - va - tion From God's own ho-ly word.
'Twill be the old, old sto - ry That I have lov'd so long.
'Twill be my theme in glo - ry, To tell the old, old sto - ry Of Je - sus and His love.
No. 313. Even Me, Even Me.
Mrs. Elizabeth Codner.
Wm. B. Bradbury.
1. Lord, I hear of show'rs of bless - ing Thou art scatt'ring full and free; Show'rs, the thirst-y land re-
2. Pass me not, O God, my Fa - ther Sin - ful tho' my heart may be; Thou mightst leave me, but the
3. Pass me not, O gra - cious Sav - ior, Let me live and cling to Thee; I am long - ing for Thy
4. Love of God, so pure and change-less, Blood of Christ, so rich and free; Grace of God, so strong and
fresh-ing; Let some drops now fall on me; E - ven me, e - ven me, Let some drops now fall on me.
rath - er; Let Thy mer - cy light on me; E - ven me, e - ven me, Let Thy mer - cy light on me.
fa-vor; Whilst Thou'rt calling, O call me; E - ven me, e - ven me, Whilst Thou'rt calling, O call me.
boundless Mag - ni - fy them all in me; E - ven me, e - ven me, Mag - ni - fy them all in me.

No. 314.
All For Jesus.
Rev. J. B. Atchinson.
COPYRIGHT, 1889, BY E. O. EXCELL.
WORDS AND MUSIC.
E. O. Excell.
1
2
FINE.
1. All, yes, all I give to Je-sus, It be-longs to Him;
All my heart I give to Je-sus, It be-longs to [Omit . . . .] Him;
D. C.—Ev er-more His good-ness tell-ing, It be-longs to [Omit . . . .] Him.
D. C.
Ev-er-more to be His dwell-ing, Ev-er-more His prais-es swell-ing,
2 All, yes, all I give to Jesus,
It belongs to Him;
All my voice I give to Jesus,
It belongs to Him;
Pleading for the young and hoary,
Telling of His power and glory,
Singing o'er and o'er the story,
It belongs to Him.
3 All, yes, all I give to Jesus,
It belongs to Him;
All my love I give to Jesus,
It belongs to Him;
Loving Him for love unceasing,
For His mercy e'er increasing,
For His watch-care never ceasing,
It belongs to Him.
4 All, yes, all I give to Jesus,
It belongs to Him;
All my life I give to Jesus,
It belongs to Him;
Hour by hour I'll live for Jesus,
Day by day I'll work for Jesus,
Evermore I'll honor Jesus,
It belongs to Him.
No. 315.
He Leadeth Me.
J. H. Gilmore.
Wm. B. Bradbury.
1. He lead-eth me! O bless-ed tho't! O words with heav'nly com-fort fraught! What-e'er I do, wher-e'er I be, Still 'tis God's hand that lead-eth me.
2. Sometimes 'mid scenes of deepest gloom, Sometimes where Eden's bowers bloom, By waters still, o'er troub-led sea, Still 'tis God's hand that lead-eth me.
3. Lord, I would clasp Thy hand in mine, Nor ev-er mur-mur or re-pine, Con-tent, what-ev-er lot I see, Since 'tis God's hand that lead-eth me.
4. And when my task on earth is done, When, by Thy grace, the vict'ry's won, E'en death's cold wave I will not flee, Since God thro' Jor-dan lead-eth me.
CHORUS.
He lead-eth me, He lead-eth me, By His own hand He lead-eth me; His faith-ful fol-low'r I would be, For by His hand He lead-eth me.

No. 316. Gently, Lord, O Gently Lead Us.

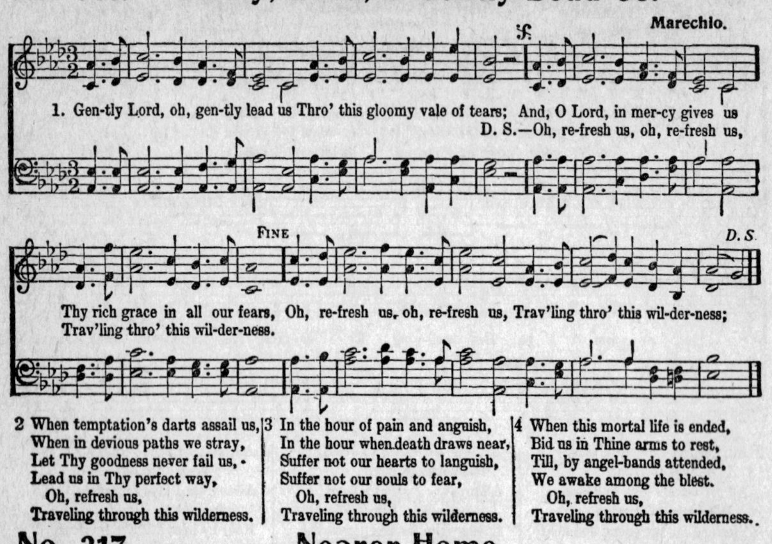
Marechio.
FINE
D. S.
1. Gen-tly Lord, oh, gen-tly lead us Thro' this gloomy vale of tears; And, O Lord, in mer-cy gives us Thy rich grace in all our fears, Oh, re-fresh us, oh, re-fresh us, Trav'ling thro' this wil-der-ness;
D. S.—Oh, re-fresh us, oh, re-fresh us, Trav'ling thro' this wil-der-ness.
2 When temptation's darts assail us,
When in devious paths we stray,
Let Thy goodness never fail us,
Lead us in Thy perfect way,
Oh, refresh us,
Traveling through this wilderness.
3 In the hour of pain and anguish,
In the hour when death draws near,
Suffer not our hearts to languish,
Suffer not our souls to fear,
Oh, refresh us,
Traveling through this wilderness.
4 When this mortal life is ended,
Bid us in Thine arms to rest,
Till, by angel-bands attended,
We awake among the blest.
Oh, refresh us,
Traveling through this wilderness.

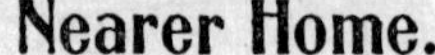

No. 317. Nearer Home.

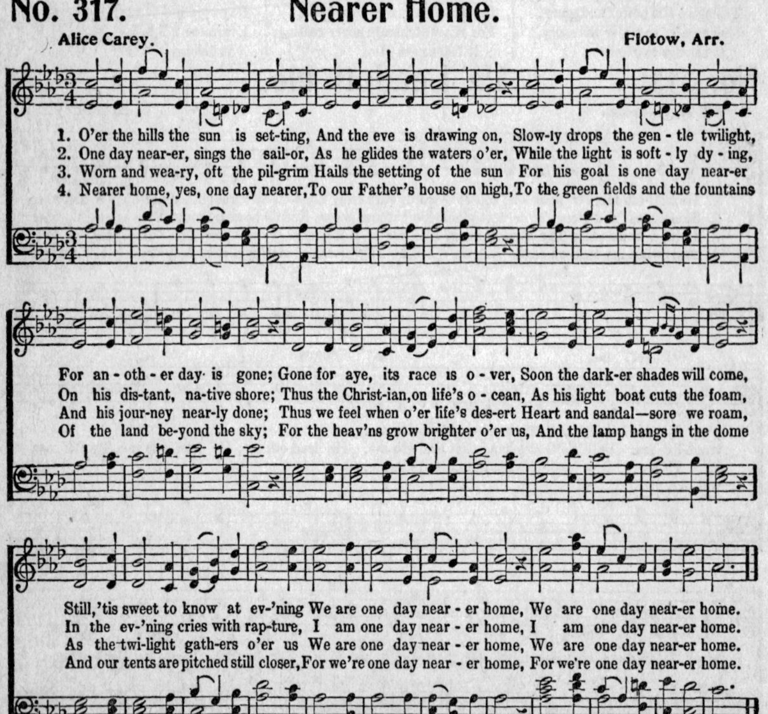
Alice Carey.
Flotow, Arr.
1. O'er the hills the sun is set-ting, And the eve is drawing on, Slow-ly drops the gen-tle twilight, For an-oth-er day is gone; Gone for aye, its race is o-ver, Soon the dark-er shades will come, Still, 'tis sweet to know at ev-'ning We are one day near-er home, We are one day near-er home.
2. One day near-er, sings the sail-or, As he glides the waters o'er, While the light is soft-ly dy-ing, On his dis-tant, na-tive shore; Thus the Christ-ian, on life's o-cean, As his light boat cuts the foam, In the ev-'ning cries with rap-ture, I am one day near-er home, I am one day near-er home.
3. Worn and wea-ry, oft the pil-grim Hails the setting of the sun For his goal is one day near-er And his jour-ney near-ly done; Thus we feel when o'er life's des-ert Heart and sandal—sore we roam, As the twi-light gath-ers o'er us We are one day near-er home, We are one day near-er home.
4. Nearer home, yes, one day nearer, To our Father's house on high, To the green fields and the fountains Of the land be-yond the sky; For the heav'ns grow brighter o'er us, And the lamp hangs in the dome And our tents are pitched still closer, For we're one day near-er home, For we're one day near-er home.

No. 318. God Be With You.
J. E. Rankin, D. D.
COPYRIGHT, BY J. E. RANKIN, D. D. USED BY PER.
W. G. Tomer.
1. God be with you till we meet again, By His counsels guide, uphold you, With His sheep securely fold you,
2. God be with you till we meet again, 'Neath His wings securely hide you, Daily manna still di - vide you,
God be with you till we meet a-gain.
CHORUS.
Till we meet.... till we meet, Till we meet at Je - sus' feet;
Till we meet, till we meet a-gain, till we meet;
God be with you till we meet a - gain.
3 God be with you till we meet again,
When life's perils thick confound you,
Put His arms unfailing round you,
God be with you till we meet again.
4 God be with you till we meet again,
Keep love's banner floating o'er you,
Smite death's threat'ning wave before you,
God be with you till we meet again.
No. 319. Rest for the Weary.
William Hunter.
J. W. Dadmun.
1. In the Chris-tian's home in glo - ry, There re-mains a land of rest; There my Sav-ior's gone be-fore me, To ful-fill my soul's re-quest.
2. He is fit - ting up my man - sion, Which e - ter - nal - ly shall stand, For my stay shall not be tran-sient, In that ho - ly, hap-py land.
3. Pain and sick-ness ne'er shall en - ter, Grief nor woe my lot shall share; But, in that ce-les - tial cen - ter, I a crown of life shall wear.
4. Death it - self shall then be van-quished, And his sting shall be with-drawn; Shout for glad-ness, oh, ye ran-somed! Hail with joy the ris-ing morn.
CHORUS.
There is rest for the wear - y, There is rest for the wear - y, There is rest for the wear - y, There is rest for you;
On the oth - er side of Jor - dan, In the sweet fields of E - den, Where the tree of life is bloom-ing, There is rest for you.

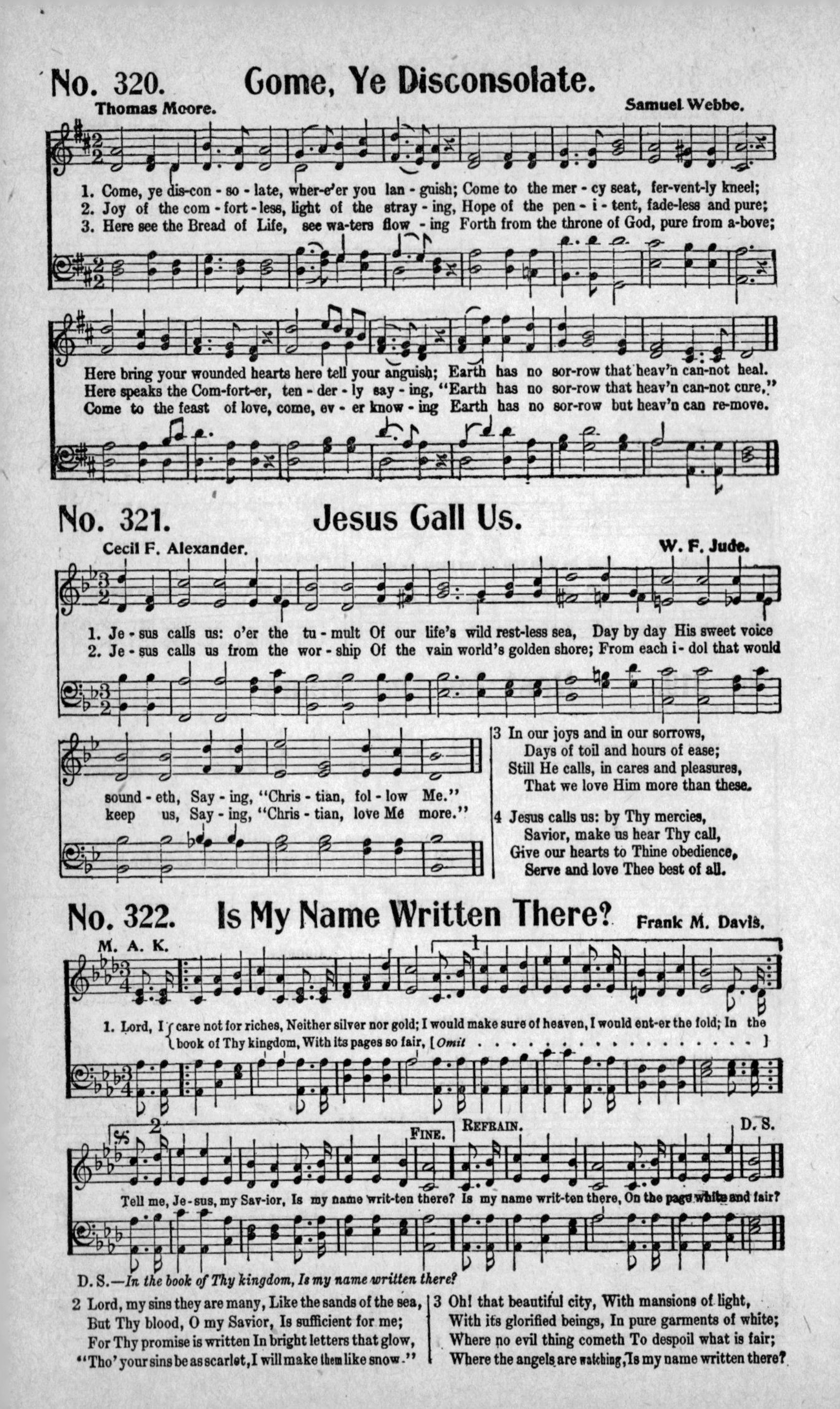
No. 320. Come, Ye Disconsolate.
Thomas Moore.
Samuel Webbe.
1. Come, ye dis-con - so - late, wher-e'er you lan - guish; Come to the mer - cy seat, fer-vent-ly kneel;
2. Joy of the com - fort - less, light of the stray - ing, Hope of the pen - i - tent, fade-less and pure;
3. Here see the Bread of Life, see wa-ters flow - ing Forth from the throne of God, pure from a-bove;
Here bring your wounded hearts here tell your anguish; Earth has no sor-row that heav'n can-not heal.
Here speaks the Com-fort-er, ten - der - ly say - ing, "Earth has no sor-row that heav'n can-not cure."
Come to the feast of love, come, ev - er know - ing Earth has no sor-row but heav'n can re-move.
No. 321. Jesus Call Us.
Cecil F. Alexander.
W. F. Jude.
1. Je - sus calls us: o'er the tu - mult Of our life's wild rest-less sea, Day by day His sweet voice
2. Je - sus calls us from the wor - ship Of the vain world's golden shore; From each i - dol that would
sound - eth, Say - ing, "Chris - tian, fol - low Me."
keep us, Say - ing, "Chris - tian, love Me more."
3 In our joys and in our sorrows,
Days of toil and hours of ease;
Still He calls, in cares and pleasures,
That we love Him more than these.
4 Jesus calls us: by Thy mercies,
Savior, make us hear Thy call,
Give our hearts to Thine obedience,
Serve and love Thee best of all.
No. 322. Is My Name Written There?
Frank M. Davis.
M. A. K.
1. Lord, I { care not for riches, Neither silver nor gold; I would make sure of heaven, I would ent-er the fold; In the
book of Thy kingdom, With its pages so fair, [Omit . . . .]
Fine.
Refrain.
D. S.
Tell me, Je-sus, my Sav-ior, Is my name writ-ten there? Is my name writ-ten there, On the page white and fair?
D. S.—In the book of Thy kingdom, Is my name written there?
2 Lord, my sins they are many, Like the sands of the sea,
But Thy blood, O my Savior, Is sufficient for me;
For Thy promise is written In bright letters that glow,
"Tho' your sins be as scarlet, I will make them like snow."
3 Oh! that beautiful city, With mansions of light,
With its glorified beings, In pure garments of white;
Where no evil thing cometh To despoil what is fair;
Where the angels are watching, Is my name written there?

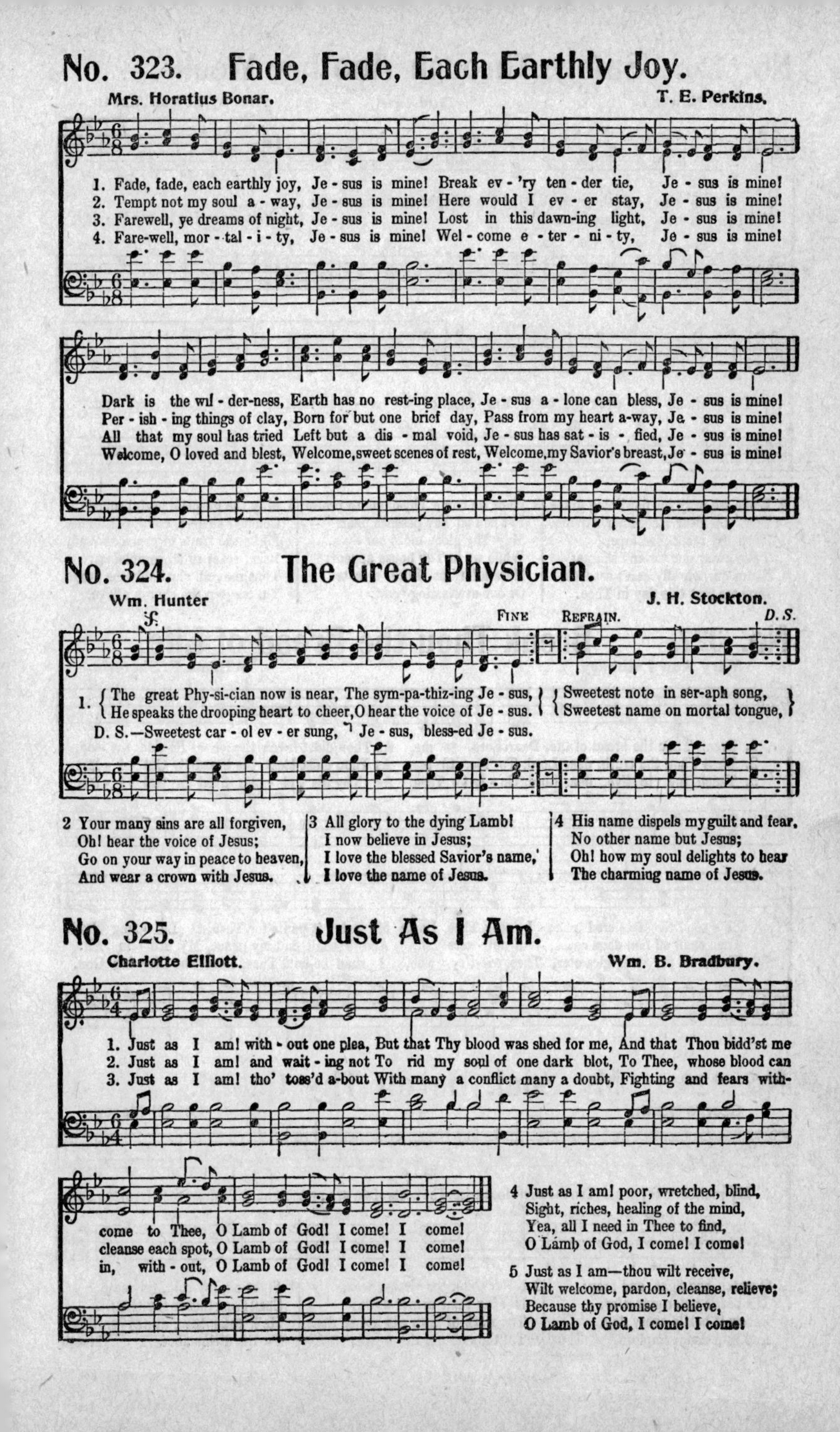
No. 323. Fade, Fade, Each Earthly Joy.
Mrs. Horatius Bonar.
T. E. Perkins.
1. Fade, fade, each earthly joy, Je - sus is mine! Break ev - 'ry ten - der tie, Je - sus is mine!
2. Tempt not my soul a - way, Je - sus is mine! Here would I ev - er stay, Je - sus is mine!
3. Farewell, ye dreams of night, Je - sus is mine! Lost in this dawn-ing light, Je - sus is mine!
4. Fare-well, mor - tal - i - ty, Je - sus is mine! Wel - come e - ter - ni - ty, Je - sus is mine!
Dark is the wil - der-ness, Earth has no rest-ing place, Je - sus a - lone can bless, Je - sus is mine!
Per - ish - ing things of clay, Born for but one brief day, Pass from my heart a-way, Je - sus is mine!
All that my soul has tried Left but a dis - mal void, Je - sus has sat - is - fied, Je - sus is mine!
Welcome, O loved and blest, Welcome,sweet scenes of rest, Welcome,my Savior's breast, Je - sus is mine!
No. 324. The Great Physician.
Wm. Hunter
J. H. Stockton.
Fine
Refrain.
D. S.
1. The great Phy-si-cian now is near, The sym-pa-thiz-ing Je - sus, He speaks the drooping heart to cheer, O hear the voice of Je - sus.
Sweetest note in ser-aph song, Sweetest name on mortal tongue,
D. S.—Sweetest car - ol ev - er sung, Je - sus, bless-ed Je - sus.
2 Your many sins are all forgiven,
Oh! hear the voice of Jesus;
Go on your way in peace to heaven,
And wear a crown with Jesus.
3 All glory to the dying Lamb!
I now believe in Jesus;
I love the blessed Savior's name,
I love the name of Jesus.
4 His name dispels my guilt and fear,
No other name but Jesus;
Oh! how my soul delights to hear
The charming name of Jesus.
No. 325. Just As I Am.
Charlotte Elliott.
Wm. B. Bradbury.
1. Just as I am! with - out one plea, But that Thy blood was shed for me, And that Thou bidd'st me come to Thee, O Lamb of God! I come! I come!
2. Just as I am! and wait - ing not To rid my soul of one dark blot, To Thee, whose blood can cleanse each spot, O Lamb of God! I come! I come!
3. Just as I am! tho' toss'd a-bout With many a conflict many a doubt, Fighting and fears with-in, with - out, O Lamb of God! I come! I come!
4 Just as I am! poor, wretched, blind,
Sight, riches, healing of the mind,
Yea, all I need in Thee to find,
O Lamb of God, I come! I come!
5 Just as I am—thou wilt receive,
Wilt welcome, pardon, cleanse, relieve;
Because thy promise I believe,
O Lamb of God, I come! I come!

No. 326. Safely Through Another Week.

John Newton. *Third Tune.* Arr. by Lowell Mason.

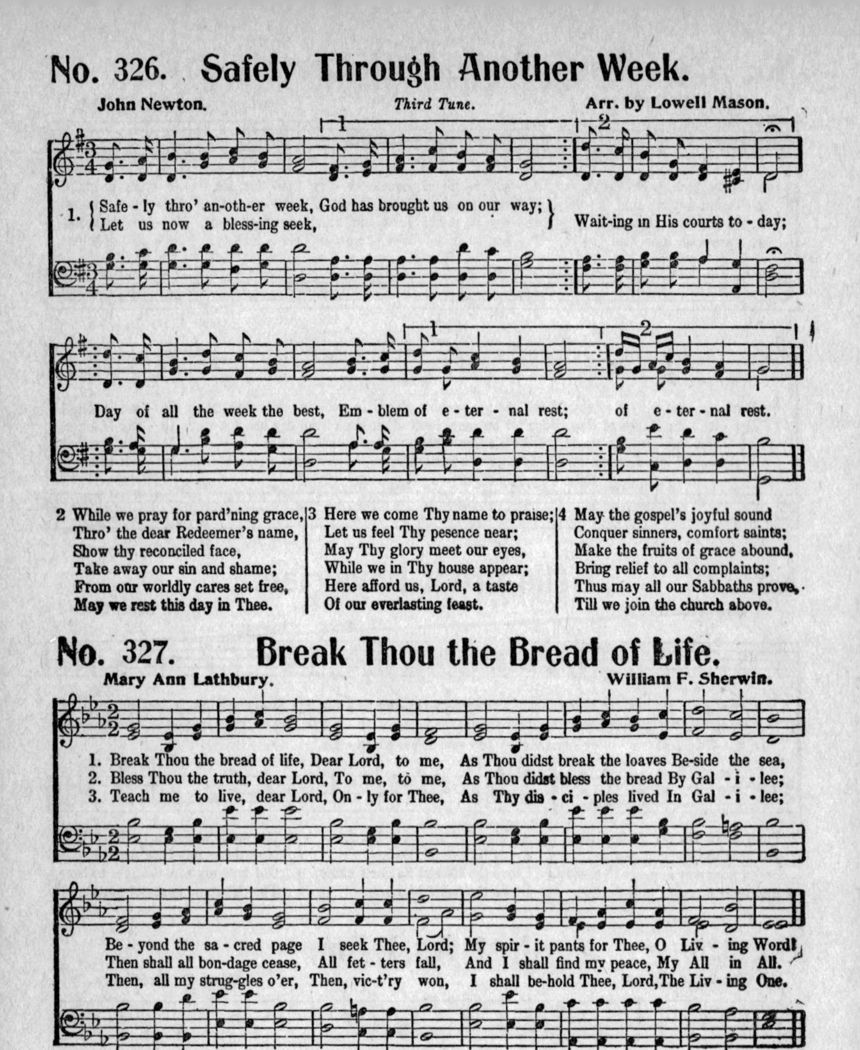

1. { Safe - ly thro' an-oth-er week, God has brought us on our way; }
{ Let us now a bless-ing seek, Wait-ing in His courts to - day; }
Day of all the week the best, Em - blem of e - ter - nal rest; of e - ter - nal rest.

2 While we pray for pard'ning grace,
Thro' the dear Redeemer's name,
Show thy reconciled face,
Take away our sin and shame;
From our worldly cares set free,
May we rest this day in Thee.

3 Here we come Thy name to praise;
Let us feel Thy pesence near;
May Thy glory meet our eyes,
While we in Thy house appear;
Here afford us, Lord, a taste
Of our everlasting feast.

4 May the gospel's joyful sound
Conquer sinners, comfort saints;
Make the fruits of grace abound,
Bring relief to all complaints;
Thus may all our Sabbaths prove,
Till we join the church above.

No. 327. Break Thou the Bread of Life.

Mary Ann Lathbury. William F. Sherwin.

1. Break Thou the bread of life, Dear Lord, to me, As Thou didst break the loaves Be-side the sea,
Be - yond the sa - cred page I seek Thee, Lord; My spir - it pants for Thee, O Liv - ing Word!

2. Bless Thou the truth, dear Lord, To me, to me, As Thou didst bless the bread By Gal - i - lee;
Then shall all bon-dage cease, All fet - ters fall, And I shall find my peace, My All in All.

3. Teach me to live, dear Lord, On - ly for Thee, As Thy dis - ci - ples lived In Gal - i - lee;
Then, all my strug-gles o'er, Then, vic-t'ry won, I shall be-hold Thee, Lord, The Liv - ing One.

No. 328. My Soul, Be on Thy Guard.

George Heath. Lowell Mason.

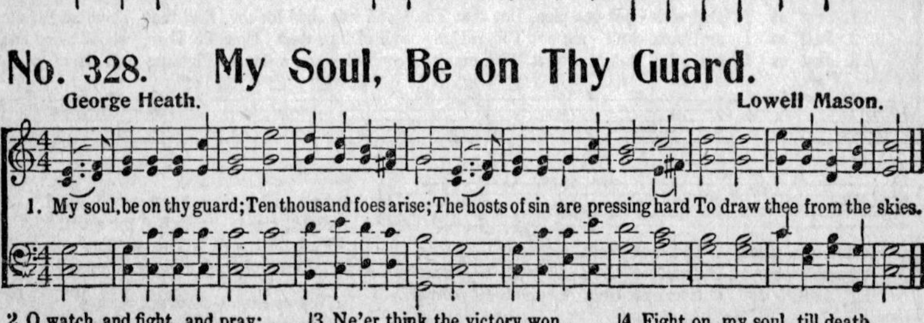

1. My soul, be on thy guard; Ten thousand foes arise; The hosts of sin are pressing hard To draw thee from the skies.

2 O watch, and fight, and pray;
The battle ne'er give o'er;
Renew it boldly every day,
And help divine implore.

3 Ne'er think the victory won,
Nor lay thine armor down:
The work of faith will not be done,
Till thou obtain the crown.

4 Fight on, my soul, till death
Shall bring thee to thy God:
He'll take thee, at thy parting breath,
To His divine abode.

No. 329. O Sing of His Mighty Love.
Frank Bottome.
Wm. B. Bradbury.
1. { Oh, bliss of the pur-i-fied, bliss of the free, I plunge in the crim-son tide o-pen'd for me;
O'er sin and un-clean-ness ex-ult-ing I stand, And point to the print of the nails in His hand. }
2. { Oh, bliss of the pur-i-fied, Je-sus is mine, No long-er in dread-con-dem-na-tion I pine;
In con-scious sal-va-tion I sing of His grace, Who lift-eth up-on me the light of His face. }
Chorus.
rit.
Oh, sing of His might-y love, Sing of His might-y love, Sing of His might-y love, Might-y to save.
3 Oh, bliss of the purified! bliss of the pure!
No wound hath the soul that His blood cannot cure;
No sorrow-bowed head but may sweetly find rest,
No tears but may dry them on Jesus' breast.
4 O Jesus the crucified! Thee will I sing,
My blessed Redeemer, my God and my King;
My soul, filled with rapture, shall shout o'er the grave,
And triumph in death in the "Mighty to Save."
No. 330. Only Trust Him.
J. H. S.
J. H. Stockton.
1. Come ev-'ry soul by sin oppress'd, There's mercy with the Lord, And He will surely give you rest By trust-ing in His word.
2. For Je-sus shed His precious blood, Rich bless-ings to bestow; Plunge now in-to the crimson flood That wash-es white as snow.
3. Yes, Je-sus is the Truth, the Way, That leads you in-to rest; Be-lieve in Him with-out de-lay, And you are ful-ly blest.
4. Come, then, and join this ho-ly band, And on to glo-ry go, To dwell in that ce-les-tial land, Where joys im-mor-tal flow.
{ On-ly trust Him, on-ly trust Him, On-ly trust Him now;
He will save you, He will save you, He will.......... save you now. }
1
2
No. 331. Did Christ O'er Sinners Weep?
Benj. Beddome.
Lowell Mason.
1. Did Christ o'er sinners weep? And shall our tears be dry? Let tears of penitential grief Flow forth from ev'ry eye.
1 Did Christ o'er sinners weep?
And shall our tears be dry?
Let tears of penitential grief
Flow forth from every eye.
2 The Son of God in tears
The wondering angels see;
Be thou astonished, O my soul;
He shed those tears for thee.
3 He wept that we might weep—
Each sin demands a tear;
In heaven alone no sin is found,
And there's no weeping there.

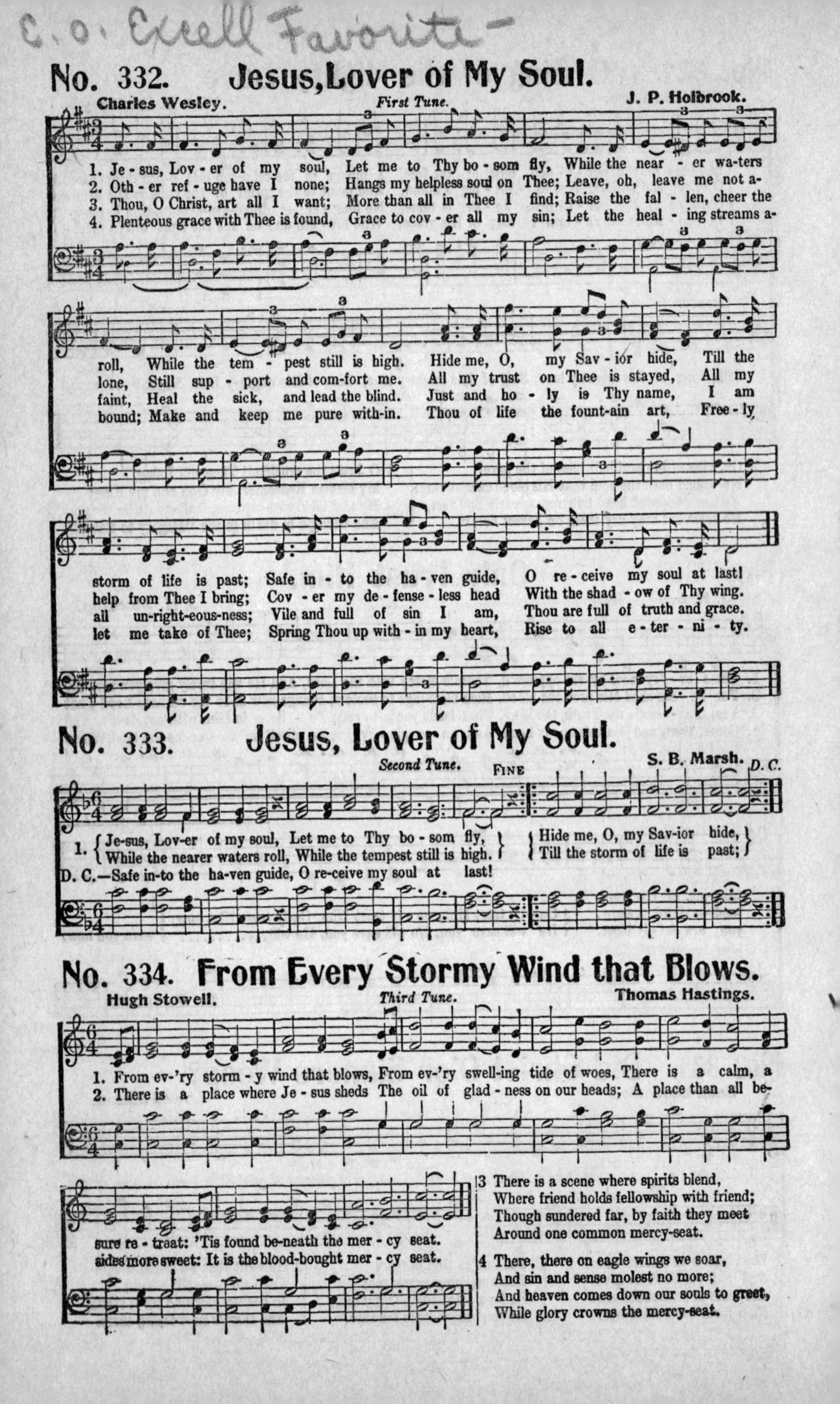
C. O. Excell Favorite -
No. 332. Jesus, Lover of My Soul.
Charles Wesley.
First Tune.
J. P. Holbrook.
1. Je - sus, Lov - er of my soul, Let me to Thy bo - som fly, While the near - er wa - ters
2. Oth - er ref - uge have I none; Hangs my helpless soul on Thee; Leave, oh, leave me not a-
3. Thou, O Christ, art all I want; More than all in Thee I find; Raise the fal - len, cheer the
4. Plenteous grace with Thee is found, Grace to cov - er all my sin; Let the heal - ing streams a-
roll, While the tem - pest still is high. Hide me, O, my Sav - ior hide, Till the
lone, Still sup - port and com-fort me. All my trust on Thee is stayed, All my
faint, Heal the sick, and lead the blind. Just and ho - ly is Thy name, I am
bound; Make and keep me pure with-in. Thou of life the fount-ain art, Free - ly
storm of life is past; Safe in - to the ha - ven guide, O re - ceive my soul at last!
help from Thee I bring; Cov - er my de - fense - less head With the shad - ow of Thy wing.
all un-right-eous-ness; Vile and full of sin I am, Thou are full of truth and grace.
let me take of Thee; Spring Thou up with - in my heart, Rise to all e - ter - ni - ty.
No. 333. Jesus, Lover of My Soul.
Second Tune.
S. B. Marsh.
Fine
D. C.
1. Je-sus, Lov-er of my soul, Let me to Thy bo - som fly,
While the nearer waters roll, While the tempest still is high.
Hide me, O, my Sav-ior hide,
Till the storm of life is past;
D. C.—Safe in-to the ha-ven guide, O re-ceive my soul at last!
No. 334. From Every Stormy Wind that Blows.
Hugh Stowell.
Third Tune.
Thomas Hastings.
1. From ev-'ry storm - y wind that blows, From ev-'ry swell-ing tide of woes, There is a calm, a
2. There is a place where Je - sus sheds The oil of glad - ness on our heads; A place than all be-
sure re - treat: 'Tis found be-neath the mer - cy seat.
sides more sweet: It is the blood-bought mer - cy seat.
3 There is a scene where spirits blend,
Where friend holds fellowship with friend;
Though sundered far, by faith they meet
Around one common mercy-seat.
4 There, there on eagle wings we soar,
And sin and sense molest no more;
And heaven comes down our souls to greet,
While glory crowns the mercy-seat.

No. 335. Wash Me in the Blood.
COPYRIGHT, 1887, BY E. O. EXCELL.
W. Cowper.
First Tune.
E. O. Excell.
CHORUS.
There is a fountain filled with blood, Drawn from Immanuel's veins,
And sinners, plung'd beneath that flood, Lose all their guilty stains.
Savior wash...... me in the blood,
Savior, wash me in the blood, in the blood, the blood of the Lamb,
Sav-ior wash.......... me in the blood,
Sav - ior wash me in the blood, in the blood, the blood of the Lamb, Oh.
Oh, And I shall be whit-er than the snow.
No. 336. There is a Fountain.
W. Cowper
Second Tune.
Lowell Mason.
1. There is a fountain filled with blood, Drawn from Immanuel's veins,
And sinners, plung'd beneath that flood, Lose all their
D.S. And sinners, plung'd beneath that flood, Lose all their
FINE
D.C.
guilty stains; Lose all their guilty stains, Lose all their guilty stains;
guilty stains;
2 The dying thief rejoiced to see
That fountain in his day;
And there may I, tho' vile as he,
Wash all my sins away.
3 Thou dying Lamb, Thy precious blood
Shall never lose its power,
Till all the ransomed Church of God
Be saved, to sin no more
4 E'er since by faith I saw the stream
Thy flowing wounds supply
Redeeming love has been my theme,
And shall be till I die.
5 Then in a nobler, sweeter song,
I'll sing Thy power to save,
When this poor lisping, stammering tongue
Lies silent in the grave.
No. 337. Holy Spirit, Faithful Guide.
M. M. W.
FINE
M. M. Wells.
1. Ho - ly Spir - it, faith - ful Guide, Ev-er near the Chris-tian's side, Gen - tly lead us by the hand,
2. Ev - er pres-ent, tru - est Friend, Ev-er near Thine aid to lend, Leave us not to doubt and fear,
3. When our days of toil shall cease, Waiting still for sweet re-lease, Nothing left but heav'n and pray'r,

D.C.—Whisper soft-ly, "Wand'rer, come, Follow me, I'll guide thee home."

D. C.

Pil-grims in a des-ert land; Wea - ry souls for - e'er re-joice, While they hear that sweetest voice,
Grop-ing on in dark-ness drear; When the storms are rag-ing sore, Hearts grow faint, and hopes give o'er,
Wondering if our names are there; Wad - ing deep the dis - mal flood, Plead-ing naught but Je - sus blood;

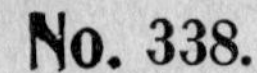

No. 338. My Jesus I Love Thee.

English. *First Tune.* **A. J. Gordon.**

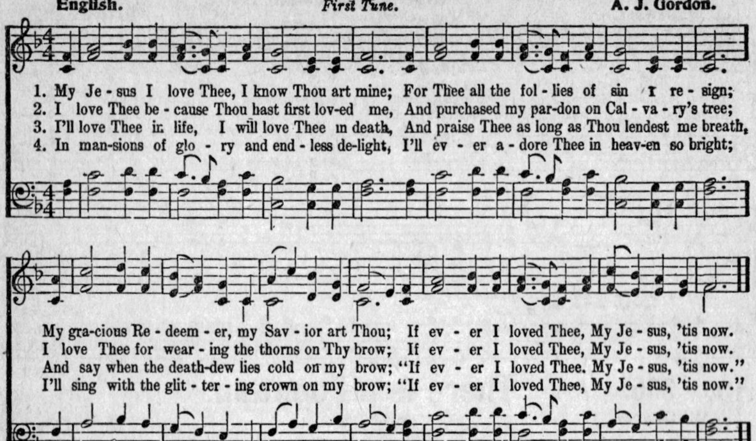
1. My Je - sus I love Thee, I know Thou art mine; For Thee all the fol - lies of sin I re - sign;
2. I love Thee be - cause Thou hast first lov-ed me, And purchased my par-don on Cal - va - ry's tree;
3. I'll love Thee in life, I will love Thee in death, And praise Thee as long as Thou lendest me breath,
4. In man-sions of glo - ry and end - less de-light, I'll ev - er a - dore Thee in heav-en so bright;
My gra-cious Re - deem - er, my Sav - ior art Thou; If ev - er I loved Thee, My Je - sus, 'tis now.
I love Thee for wear - ing the thorns on Thy brow; If ev - er I loved Thee, My Je - sus, 'tis now.
And say when the death-dew lies cold on my brow; "If ev - er I loved Thee, My Je - sus, 'tis now."
I'll sing with the glit - ter - ing crown on my brow; "If ev - er I loved Thee, My Je - sus, 'tis now."

No. 339. O Turn Ye.

First or Second Tune.

1 O turn ye, O turn ye, for why will ye die,
When God in great mercy is coming so nigh?
Now Jesus invites you, the Spirit says, "Come,"
And angels are waiting to welcome you home.

2 And now Christ is ready your souls to receive,
O how can you question, if you will believe?
If sin is your burden, why will you not come?
'Tis you He bids welcome; He bids you come home.

3 In riches, in pleasures, what can you obtain,
To soothe your affliction, or banish your pain?
To bear up your spirit when summoned to die,
Or waft you to mansions of glory on high?

4 Why will you be starving, and feeding on air?
There's mercy in Jesus, enough and to spare;
If still you are doubting, make trial and see,
And prove that His mercy is boundless and free.

No. 340. Look to Jesus.

First or Second Tune.

1 O eyes that are weary, and hearts that are sore,
Look off unto Jesus, now sorrow no more;
The light of His countenance shineth so bright,
That here, as in Heaven, there need be no night.

2 While looking to Jesus, my heart cannot fear,
I tremble no more when I see Jesus near,
I know that His presence my safe-guard will be,
For, "Why are ye troubled?" He saith unto me.

3 Still looking to Jesus, oh, may I be found,
When Jordan's dark waters encompass me round;
They bear me away in His presence to be
I see Him still nearer whom always I see.

Then, then shall I know the full beauty and grace
Of Jesus, my Lord, when I stand face to face
Shall know how His love went before me each day,
And wonder that ever my eyes turned away.

No. 341. Expostulation.

Josiah Hopkins. *Second Tune.* **Koschat.**

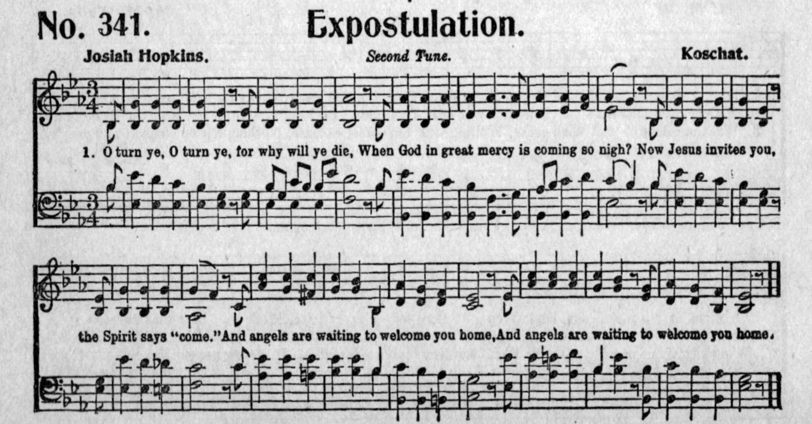
1. O turn ye, O turn ye, for why will ye die, When God in great mercy is coming so nigh? Now Jesus invites you,
the Spirit says "come." And angels are waiting to welcome you home, And angels are waiting to welcome you home.

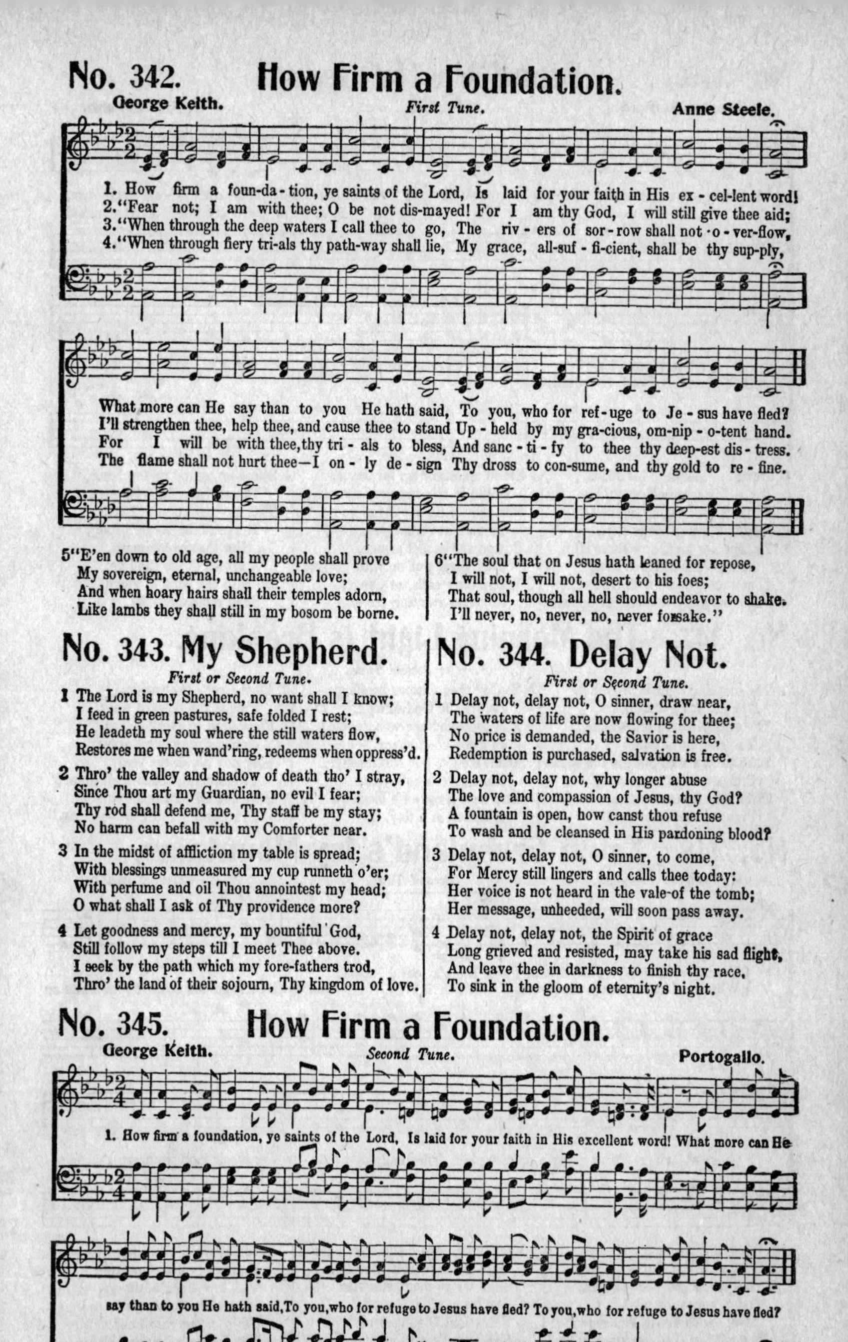

No. 342. How Firm a Foundation.

George Keith. *First Tune.* Anne Steele.

1. How firm a foun-da-tion, ye saints of the Lord, Is laid for your faith in His ex-cel-lent word! What more can He say than to you He hath said, To you, who for ref-uge to Je-sus have fled?
2. "Fear not; I am with thee; O be not dis-mayed! For I am thy God, I will still give thee aid; I'll strengthen thee, help thee, and cause thee to stand Up-held by my gra-cious, om-nip-o-tent hand.
3. "When through the deep waters I call thee to go, The riv-ers of sor-row shall not o-ver-flow, For I will be with thee, thy tri-als to bless, And sanc-ti-fy to thee thy deep-est dis-tress.
4. "When through fiery tri-als thy path-way shall lie, My grace, all-suf-fi-cient, shall be thy sup-ply, The flame shall not hurt thee—I on-ly de-sign Thy dross to con-sume, and thy gold to re-fine.

5 "E'en down to old age, all my people shall prove
My sovereign, eternal, unchangeable love;
And when hoary hairs shall their temples adorn,
Like lambs they shall still in my bosom be borne.

6 "The soul that on Jesus hath leaned for repose,
I will not, I will not, desert to his foes;
That soul, though all hell should endeavor to shake.
I'll never, no, never, no, never forsake."

No. 343. My Shepherd.

First or Second Tune.

1 The Lord is my Shepherd, no want shall I know;
I feed in green pastures, safe folded I rest;
He leadeth my soul where the still waters flow,
Restores me when wand'ring, redeems when oppress'd.

2 Thro' the valley and shadow of death tho' I stray,
Since Thou art my Guardian, no evil I fear;
Thy rod shall defend me, Thy staff be my stay;
No harm can befall with my Comforter near.

3 In the midst of affliction my table is spread;
With blessings unmeasured my cup runneth o'er;
With perfume and oil Thou annointest my head;
O what shall I ask of Thy providence more?

4 Let goodness and mercy, my bountiful God,
Still follow my steps till I meet Thee above.
I seek by the path which my fore-fathers trod,
Thro' the land of their sojourn, Thy kingdom of love.

No. 344. Delay Not.

First or Second Tune.

1 Delay not, delay not, O sinner, draw near,
The waters of life are now flowing for thee;
No price is demanded, the Savior is here,
Redemption is purchased, salvation is free.

2 Delay not, delay not, why longer abuse
The love and compassion of Jesus, thy God?
A fountain is open, how canst thou refuse
To wash and be cleansed in His pardoning blood?

3 Delay not, delay not, O sinner, to come,
For Mercy still lingers and calls thee today:
Her voice is not heard in the vale of the tomb;
Her message, unheeded, will soon pass away.

4 Delay not, delay not, the Spirit of grace
Long grieved and resisted, may take his sad flight,
And leave thee in darkness to finish thy race,
To sink in the gloom of eternity's night.

No. 345. How Firm a Foundation.

George Keith. *Second Tune.* Portogallo.

1. How firm a foundation, ye saints of the Lord, Is laid for your faith in His excellent word! What more can He say than to you He hath said, To you, who for refuge to Jesus have fled? To you, who for refuge to Jesus have fled?

No. 346. Stand Up for Jesus.

George Duffield. *First Tune.* G. J. Webb.

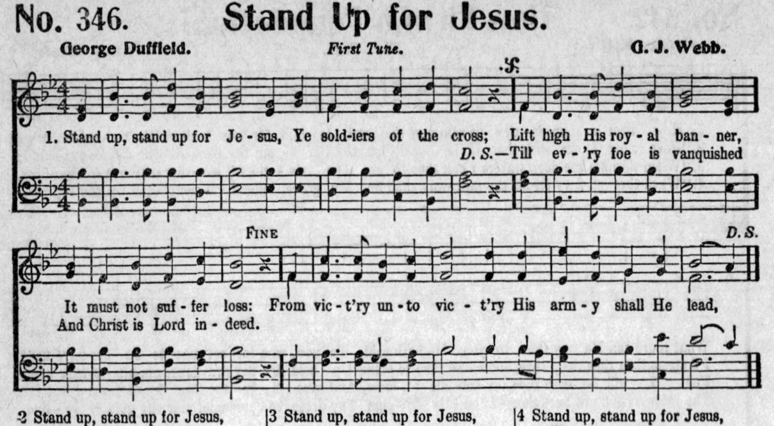

FINE
D. S.
1. Stand up, stand up for Je - sus, Ye sold-iers of the cross; Lift high His roy - al ban - ner,
D. S.—Till ev - 'ry foe is vanquished
It must not suf - fer loss: From vic - t'ry un - to vic - t'ry His arm - y shall He lead,
And Christ is Lord in - deed.

2 Stand up, stand up for Jesus,
The trumpet call obey;
Forth to the mighty conflict,
In this His glorious day,
'Ye that are men, now serve Him,"
Against unnumbered foes;
Your courage rise with danger,
And strength to strength oppose.

3 Stand up, stand up for Jesus,
Stand in His strength alone;
The arm of flesh will fail you;
Ye dare not trust your own,
Put on the gospel armor,
Each piece put on with prayer;
Where duty calls, or danger,
Be never wanting there.

4 Stand up, stand up for Jesus,
The strife will not be long;
This day the noise of battle,
The next the victor's song;
To Him that overcometh,
A crown of life shall be;
He with the King of glory
Shall reign eternally.

No. 347. The Morning Light is Breaking.

First or Second Tune.

1 The morning light is breaking,
The darkness disappears,
The sons of earth are waking,
To penitential tears;
Each breeze that sweeps the ocean
Brings tidings from afar,
Of nations in commotion,
Prepared for Zion's war.

2 See heathen nations bending
Before the God of love,
And thousand hearts ascending
In gratitude above;
While sinners now confessing,
The gospel's call obey,
And seek a Savior's blessing,
A nation in a day.

3 Blest river of salvation,
Pursue thy onward way;
Flow thou to every nation,
Nor in thy richness stay;
Stay not till all the lowly,
Triumphant, reach their home;
Stay not till all the holy
Proclaim, "The Lord is come."

No. 348. From Greenland's Icy Mountains.

R. Heber. *Second Tune.* Lowell Mason.

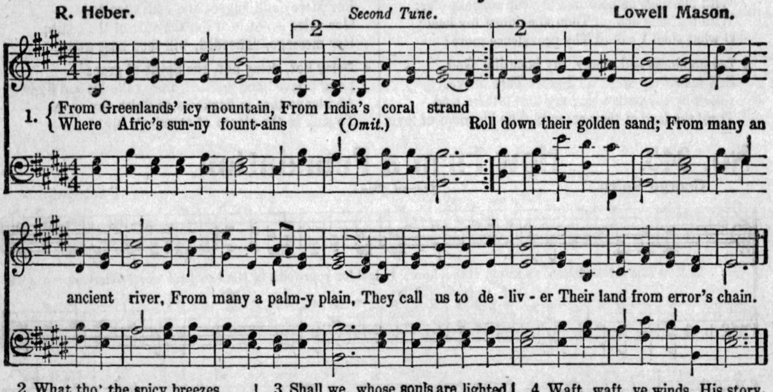

2
2
1. { From Greenlands' icy mountain, From India's coral strand
Where Afric's sun-ny fount-ains (Omit.) Roll down their golden sand; From many an
ancient river, From many a palm-y plain, They call us to de - liv - er Their land from error's chain.

2 What tho' the spicy breezes,
Blow soft o'er Ceylon's isle;
Tho' every prospect pleases,
And only man is vile?
In vain with lavish kindness
The gifts of God are strown,
The heathen in his blindness,
Bow down to wood and stone.

3 Shall we, whose souls are lighted
With wisdom from on high,
Shall we to men benighted
The lamp of life deny?
Salvation! O salvation!
The joyful sound proclaim,
Till earth's remotest nation
Has learned Messiah's name.

4 Waft, waft, ye winds, His story,
And you, ye waters, roll,
Till, like a sea of glory,
It spreads from pole to pole:
Till o'er our ransomed nature
The Lamb for sinners slain,
Redeemer, King, Creator,
In bliss returns to reign.

Patriotic and Temperance

No. 349. Home, Sweet Home.

John Howard Payne. H. R. Bishop.

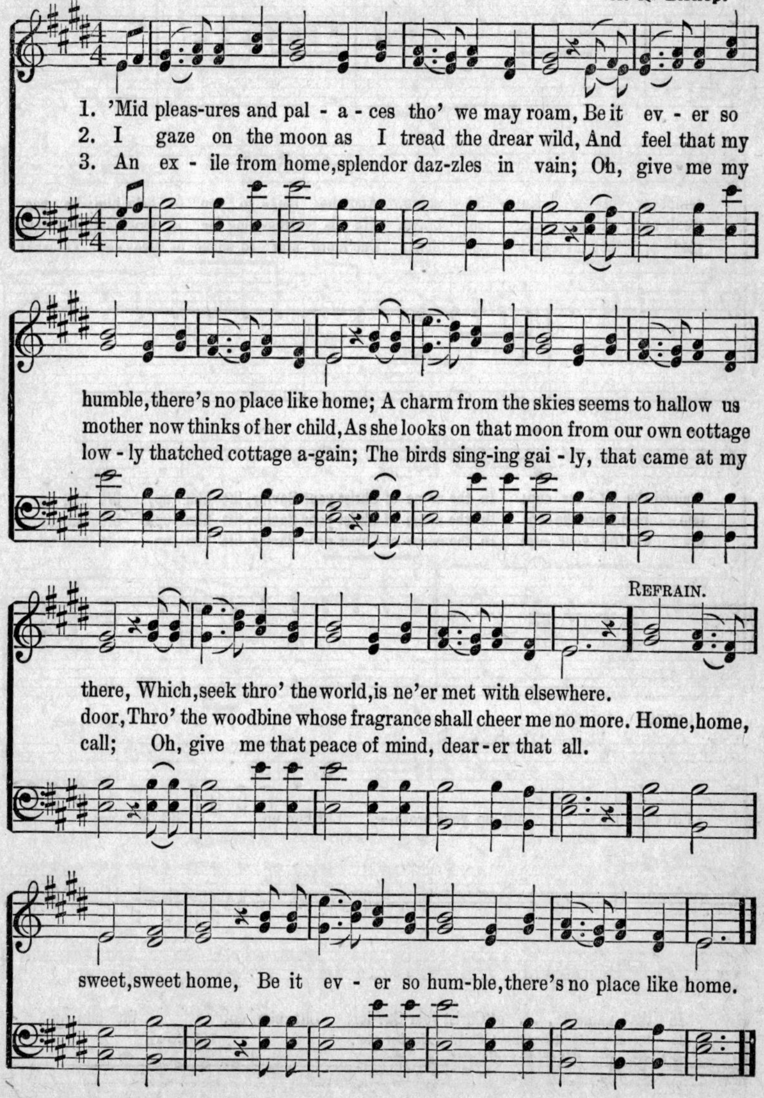

1. 'Mid pleas-ures and pal - a - ces tho' we may roam, Be it ev - er so
2. I gaze on the moon as I tread the drear wild, And feel that my
3. An ex - ile from home, splendor daz-zles in vain; Oh, give me my

humble, there's no place like home; A charm from the skies seems to hallow us
mother now thinks of her child, As she looks on that moon from our own cottage
low - ly thatched cottage a-gain; The birds sing-ing gai - ly, that came at my

there, Which, seek thro' the world, is ne'er met with elsewhere.
door, Thro' the woodbine whose fragrance shall cheer me no more. Home, home,
call; Oh, give me that peace of mind, dear - er that all.

REFRAIN.

sweet, sweet home, Be it ev - er so hum-ble, there's no place like home.

No. 350. Lift Him Up.
S. R. Amy.
WORDS AND MUSIC COPYRIGHT, 1906, BY E. O. EXCELL. INTERNATIONAL COPYRIGHT SECURED.
J. M. Dungan.
1. Your broth-er has a bur-den that is hard to bear; He fell be-fore the tempt-er in a sin-ful snare, And he looks to you to help him; he has drained the bit-ter cup: In the name of Christ your Savior, lift him up, lift him up.
2. In God's own im-age, with a pre-cious soul to save, His strength turned in-to weak-ness, who was once so brave, He is strug-gling for a foot-hold, and would fain re-nounce the cup: In the name of Christ your Savior, lift him up, lift him up.
3. If you will give him cour-age and his soul is won, Your heart will leap with glad-ness when the work is done; One more star to shine in Heav-en, O what joy will fill your cup! In the name of Christ your Savior, lift him up, lift him up.
Chorus or Quartet.
Lift him up, ... lift up your broth-er, Lift him up, lift him up;
Lift him up, Lift him up, lift him up;
In the name . . . . of Christ your Sav-ior, Lift him up, lift him up.
In the name, in the name of Christ your Sav-ior, Lift him up.

No. 351. The Handwriting On the Wall.

K. Shaw. Knowles Shaw.
Arr. by E. O. Excell.

1. At the feast of Bel-shaz-zar and a thou-sand of his lords, While they drank from gold-en
2. See the brave captive Dan-iel, as he stood be-fore the throng, And re-buked the haught-y
3. See the faith, zeal and courage, that would dare to do the right, Which the Spir-it gave to
4. So our deeds are re-cord-ed, there's a Hand that's writing now, Sin-ner, give your heart to

ves-sels, as the Book of Truth re-cords; In the night, as they rev-el in the
mon-arch for his might-y deeds of wrong; As he read out the writ-ing, 't was the
Dan-iel, this the se-cret of his might; In his home in Ju-de-a, or a
Je-sus, to His roy-al man-date bow; For the day is ap-proach-ing, it must

roy-al pal-ace hall, They were seized with con-ster-na-tion,—'t was the hand up-on the wall.
doom of one and all, For the king-dom now was fin-ished,—said the hand up-on the wall.
cap-tive in the hall— He un-der-stood the writ-ing of his God up-on the wall.
come to one and all, When the sin-ner's con-dem-na-tion will be writ-ten on the wall.

CHORUS OR QUARTET.

'T is the hand of God on the wall, on the wall, 'T is the hand of God on the wall; on the wall; Shall the record be, "Found wanting," or shall it be "Found trusting?" While that hand is writing on the wall.
writing on the wall.

No. 352. 'Twas Rum that Spoiled my Boy.

Rev. L. F. Cole. USED BY PER. OF THE AUTHOR. T. Martin Towne.

With pathos.
1. I have seen a moth-er weep-ing, O'er a lit-tle pal-lid face;
2. I have known a moth-er wait-ing, Wait-ing while the years roll'd by,
3. I have seen a moth-er pac-ing On the shore where breaks the sea,
4. Gaze in-to the eyes cher-u-bic; Rain your kiss-es on his cheek;
rit.
I have seen her kiss the fore-head, Seen the last, sad, fond em-brace;
Start-ing from her dreams at mid-night, Wait-ing, watch-ing ea-ger-ly,
Plead-ing with the storm-y wa-ters, "Give, oh, give my boy to me!"
Clasp him fond-ly to your bos-om, Feel the thrill you can-not speak;
A tempo.
I have seen her heav-y, heart-sore, Turn-ing t'ward her home a-gain;
For her boy, long lost and wand'ring In some strange and dis-tant land,
But by waves by far more cru-el, Waves that drown my sweet-est joy,
Link your-self to God and heav-en, All your moth-er-love em-ploy,
And I've en-vied her her sad-ness, There was much to soothe her pain.
And I've tho't, oh, blest the watch-er! Hop-ing yet to clasp his hand.
I am sit-ting and la-ment-ing, Oh, 'twas rum that spoiled my boy!
That your lips may nev-er fal-ter, Oh, 'twas rum that spoiled my boy!

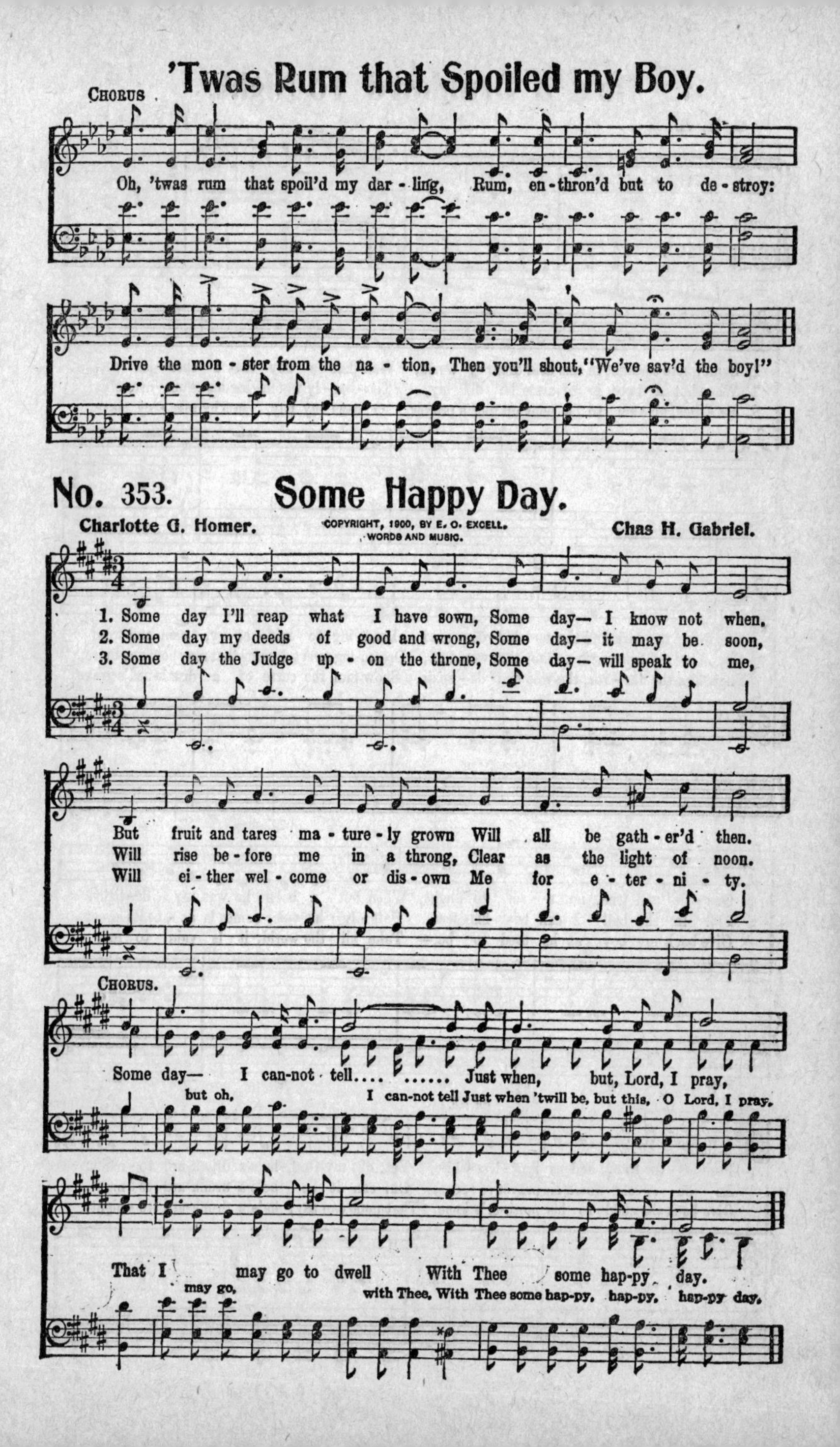
'Twas Rum that Spoiled my Boy.
Chorus
Oh, 'twas rum that spoil'd my dar - ling, Rum, en - thron'd but to de - stroy:
Drive the mon - ster from the na - tion, Then you'll shout, "We've sav'd the boy!"
No. 353. Some Happy Day.
Charlotte G. Homer.
COPYRIGHT, 1900, BY E. O. EXCELL. WORDS AND MUSIC.
Chas H. Gabriel.
1. Some day I'll reap what I have sown, Some day— I know not when,
2. Some day my deeds of good and wrong, Some day— it may be soon,
3. Some day the Judge up - on the throne, Some day— will speak to me,
But fruit and tares ma - ture - ly grown Will all be gath - er'd then.
Will rise be - fore me in a throng, Clear as the light of noon.
Will ei - ther wel - come or dis - own Me for e - ter - ni - ty.
Chorus.
Some day— I can-not tell.... ...... Just when, but, Lord, I pray,
but oh, I can-not tell Just when 'twill be, but this, O Lord, I pray,
That I may go to dwell With Thee some hap-py day.
may go, with Thee, With Thee some hap-py, hap-py, hap-py day.

No. 354. He's a Drunkard To-Night.
C. H. G.
COPYRIGHT, 1889, BY E. O. EXCELL.
Chas. H. Gabriel.
Intro.
1. Somewhere to-night in this cold drear-y world, Wan-ders a boy that I cher-ish so,
2. When but a babe in my arms he did lay, Ten-der-ly watch-ing his slum-bers o'er
3. Fa-ther, give ear to a poor mother's prayer, O save my boy, in Thy mer-cy save,
Tread-ing the dark and the un-bid-den road Lead-ing to mis-er-y, pain and woe;
Oh, how my heart with e-mo-tion would fill, Dream-ing sweet dreams that may come no more;
Show him the ter-ror, the woe and de-spair, Show him the curse of a drunk-ard's grave;
Gen-tle and true, not a sin to blight, When but a babe he was my de-light,
Still in the hall I can hear his feet, Soft-ly his voice comes in ac-cents sweet,
Give back my boy as he used to be,— Take all the world, it is vain to me,
ad lib.
Pure as the snow, and as spot-less white, Yet, oh, my God, he's a drunk-ard to-night.
As he of old would his prayer re-peat, Oh, can it be he's a drunk-ard to-night.
Give back the child to his moth-er's knee, That none can say, he's a drunk-ard to-night.

He's a Drunkard To-Night.
Chorus or Quartet.
p
cres.
rit. e dim.
Pit-y the boy! Pit-y the boy! An-gels might weep at be-hold-ing the sight;
m
rit.
Oh! how I loved him, the child of my heart, Yet, oh, my God, he's a drunk-ard to-night.
No. 355. Look to Jesus.
Harriet E. Jones.
Copyright, 1893, by Chas. H. Gabriel. E. O. Excell, owner.
Chas. H. Gabriel.
1. Tho' your sins be red like crim-son, And your soul be steeped in woe,
2. Lo, He came the lost to gath-er, Lo, He came for such to die,
3. Hear the prom-ise; oh, be-lieve Him; Lo! His grace is free and full;
You may look in faith to Je-sus, And be washed as white as snow.
Broad and deep is mer-cy's foun-tain, It can all the world sup-ply.
Tho' your sins may be like scar-let, He will make them white as wool.
Chorus or Quartet.
Then look up, look up to Je-sus, Oh, look up and He will save;
He will par-don your trans-gres-sions, Look to Je-sus, He will save.

No. 356. A Mother is Lonely To-Night.

P. D. B.

P. Douglas Bird.

mf Moderato.
1. A moth-er is lone-ly to - night, Watch-ing the hours as they go, . . . From
2. A moth-er with snow-white hair, Rocks gen-tly as night's shadows fall, . . .
mp
rall.
twi-light to shadow, from shadow to dark, And the light flutters dim-ly and low; . . See the
Humming a lull-a - by, think-ing of him, The boy she had watched thro' it all; . . And
mp
rall.
tears on the cheeks that are wasted with sorrow, Think of the sadness that comes with the morrow, Her
O, what a joy in the sim - ple to-mor-row, The dawning for her is so sweet aft-er sor - row;
rall.
boy in the grasp of the de-mon of sin, And a mother's heart, yearn-ing, yearning for him.
Think of a world of moth-ers like this, With God in the home, and a reign of bliss.
rall.

A Mother is Lonely To-Night.

mf Refrain. A tempo.
O ye, who are men with the pow'r, . . O ye, who are men who will fight, . . Stand
mp
up, and in this sol-emn hour . . Tell God you will do what is right. . .
rall.
poco lento.
mp
No. 357. Wonderful Savior.
J. W. MacGill.
Copyright, 1909, by E. O Excell.
Arr. by E. O. E.
1. Je-sus has loved me—won-der-ful Savior! Je-sus has loved me, I can-not tell why; . . .
2. Je-sus has saved me—won-der-ful Sav-ior! Je-sus has saved me, I can-not tell how; . . .
3. Je-sus will lead me—won-der-ful Sav-ior! Je-sus will lead me, I can-not tell where; . .
4. Je-sus will crown me—won-der-ful Sav-ior! Je-sus will crown me, I can-not tell when; . .
He came to res-cue sin-ners un-wor-thy, My heart He conquered, for Him I would die.
But this I do know, He came, my ran-som, Dy-ing on Cal-v'ry, with thorns on His brow.
So I will fol-low, thro' joy or sor-row, Sun-shine or tempest, since He leads me there.
White throne of splendor hail I with glad-ness, Crowned in the presence of an-gels and men.

No. 358. Touch Not, Taste Not.

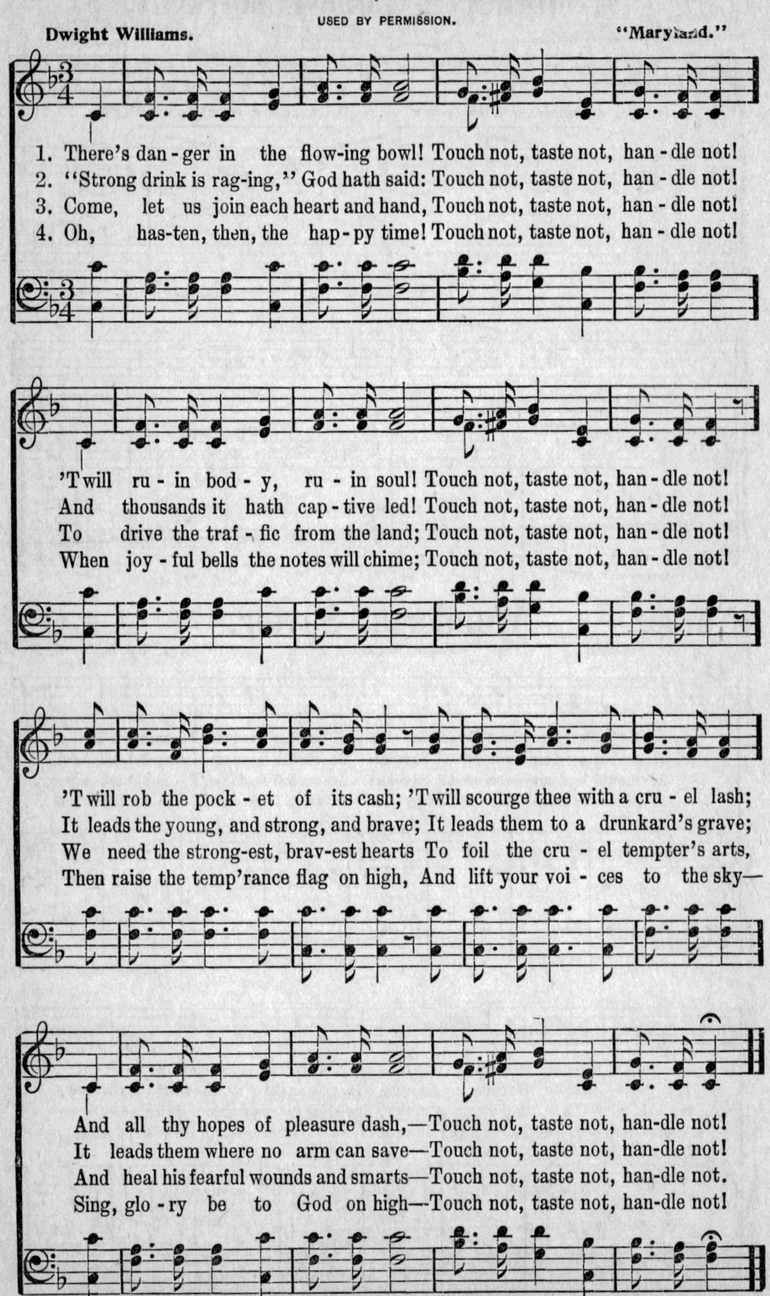

USED BY PERMISSION.
Dwight Williams.
"Maryland."
1. There's dan-ger in the flow-ing bowl! Touch not, taste not, han-dle not!
2. "Strong drink is rag-ing," God hath said: Touch not, taste not, han-dle not!
3. Come, let us join each heart and hand, Touch not, taste not, han-dle not!
4. Oh, has-ten, then, the hap-py time! Touch not, taste not, han-dle not!
'Twill ru-in bod-y, ru-in soul! Touch not, taste not, han-dle not!
And thousands it hath cap-tive led! Touch not, taste not, han-dle not!
To drive the traf-fic from the land; Touch not, taste not, han-dle not!
When joy-ful bells the notes will chime; Touch not, taste not, han-dle not!
'Twill rob the pock-et of its cash; 'Twill scourge thee with a cru-el lash;
It leads the young, and strong, and brave; It leads them to a drunkard's grave;
We need the strong-est, brav-est hearts To foil the cru-el tempter's arts,
Then raise the temp'rance flag on high, And lift your voi-ces to the sky—
And all thy hopes of pleasure dash,—Touch not, taste not, han-dle not!
It leads them where no arm can save—Touch not, taste not, han-dle not!
And heal his fearful wounds and smarts—Touch not, taste not, han-dle not.
Sing, glo-ry be to God on high—Touch not, taste not, han-dle not!

No. 359. Yield Not to Temptation.
H. R. P.
USED BY PERMISSION OF DR. H. R. PALMER, OWNER OF COPYRIGHT.
Dr. H. R. Palmer.
1. Yield not to temp-ta - tion, For yield-ing is sin; Each vic-t'ry will help you Some oth - er to win; Fight man-ful - ly on - ward, Dark passions sub - due; Look ev - er to Je - sus, He'll car-ry you thro'.
2. Shun e - vil com-pan - ions, Bad language dis - dain; God's name hold in rev - 'rence, Nor take it in vain; Be thought-ful and ear - nest, Kind-heart-ed and true; Look ev - er to Je - sus, He'll car-ry you thro'.
3. To him that o'er-com-eth, God giv - eth a crown; Thro' faith we will con - quer, Tho' oft - en cast down; He who is our Sav - ior, Our strength will re-new; Look ev - er to Je - sus, He'll car-ry you thro'.
CHORUS.
Ask the Sav - ior to help you, Com-fort, strengthen, and keep you;
He is will - ing to aid you, He will car - ry you thro'.

No. 360. Was It You?

C. D. Martin.
COPYRIGHT, 1905, BY CHAS. H. GABRIEL.
E. O EXCELL, OWNER.
Chas. H. Gabriel.
1. Some-bod - y vot - ed to ru - in my boy, Was that somebody you?
2. Some-bod - y ar - gued in fa - vor of wrong. Was that somebody you?
3. Some-bod - y turned all my day in - to night, Was that somebody you?
4. Some-bod - y li-censed an-oth-er to sell, Was that somebody you?
Some-bod - y helped his pure life to de - stroy, Was that some-bod-y you?
Some-bod - y hushed in my life a sweet song, Was that some-bod-y you?
Some-bod - y vot - ed to throt-tle the right, Was that some-bod-y you?
That which could turn Par-a-dise in - to hell, Was that some-bod-y you?
CHORUS.
Was that some-bod-y you?....... Was that some-bod-y you?.......
was it you? was it you?
Some-bod-y vot-ed to ru - in my boy, Was that some-bod-y you?.......
was it you?

No. 361. Somebody's Boy.

Floy S. Armstrong. Chas. H. Gabriel.

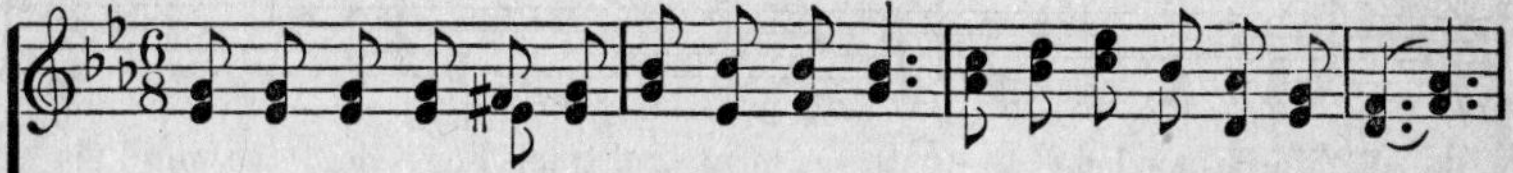

1. Homeless and friendless he wan-ders to-day In-to the pathways of shame;
2. Somewhere it may be a moth-er in prayer Whispers the wanderer's name;
3. See how the tempt-er, destructive and bold, Ev-er is seek-ing for prey;
4. Spurn then the gold from the dramseller's hand Buying your sanction to vice;

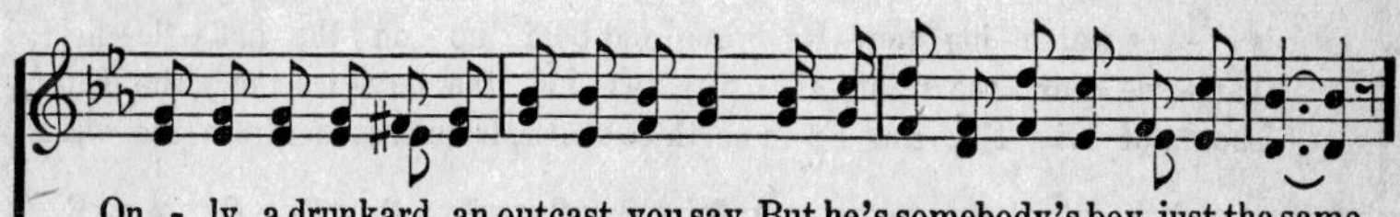

On - ly a drunkard, an outcast, you say, But he's somebody's boy, just the same.
Tho' he has spurned both her counsel and care He is some mother's boy, just the same.
Tales of wrecked manhood and ruin are told–Of the boys that are ruined each day.
Banish the dramshops that darken our land, For your boy and my boy pays the price.

CHORUS.

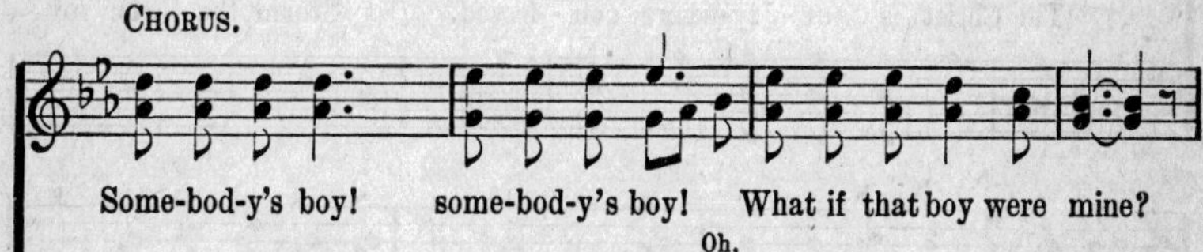

Some-bod-y's boy! some-bod-y's boy! What if that boy were mine?
Oh,

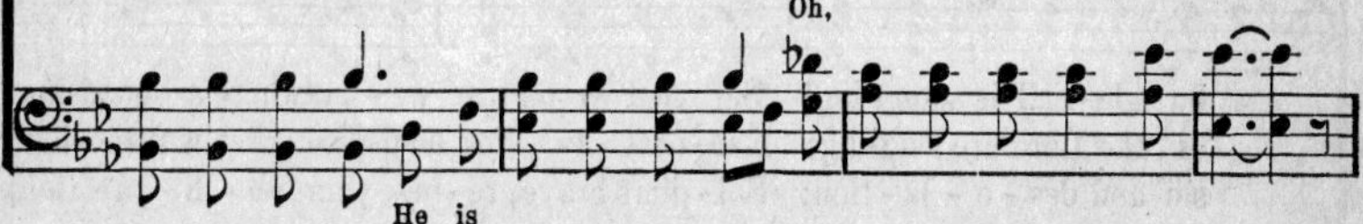

He is

Some-bod-y's boy, some-bod-y's boy, What if that boy were thine?
He is

No. 362.
The Temperance Army.
Charlotte G. Homer.
COPYRIGHT, 1895, BY CHAS. H. GABRIEL.
E. O. EXCELL, OWNER.
Mrs. Carrie B. Adams.
Cho.–1. March a - long to - geth - er, firm and true, For lo, the world is
2. On we go, with ar - mor shin - ing bright, With sword in hand to
3. True as steel, and loy - al to our King, We'll fight un - til the
ev - er watch - ing you; Be brave and bold up - on the bat - tle - field,
bat - tle for the right; U - ni - ted in the serv - ice of the Lord,
shouts of vic - t'ry ring From north to south, from east and from the west,
Fine.
Unison Solo.
De - ter-mined that the foe shall yield. Long and loud the
We're marching at our Cap - tain's word. Val - iant sol - diers
Till Christ is ev - 'ry-where con - fessed. Storm the forts of
bu - gle - call is sound-ing! Sin and wrong are ev - 'ry-where a-bound-ing;
of the Lord are lead-ing; Ear - nest - ly for help the church is plead-ing;
sin and des - o - la - tion; Sol - diers brave, re - new your ob - li - ga - tion;
D. C. Cho.
"Forward!" all a - long the line resounding, Bids us march a - way.
Slow - ly backward see the foe re - ced - ing; Forward march to - day.
And with earnest prayer and sup-pli-ca-tion Forward march to - day.

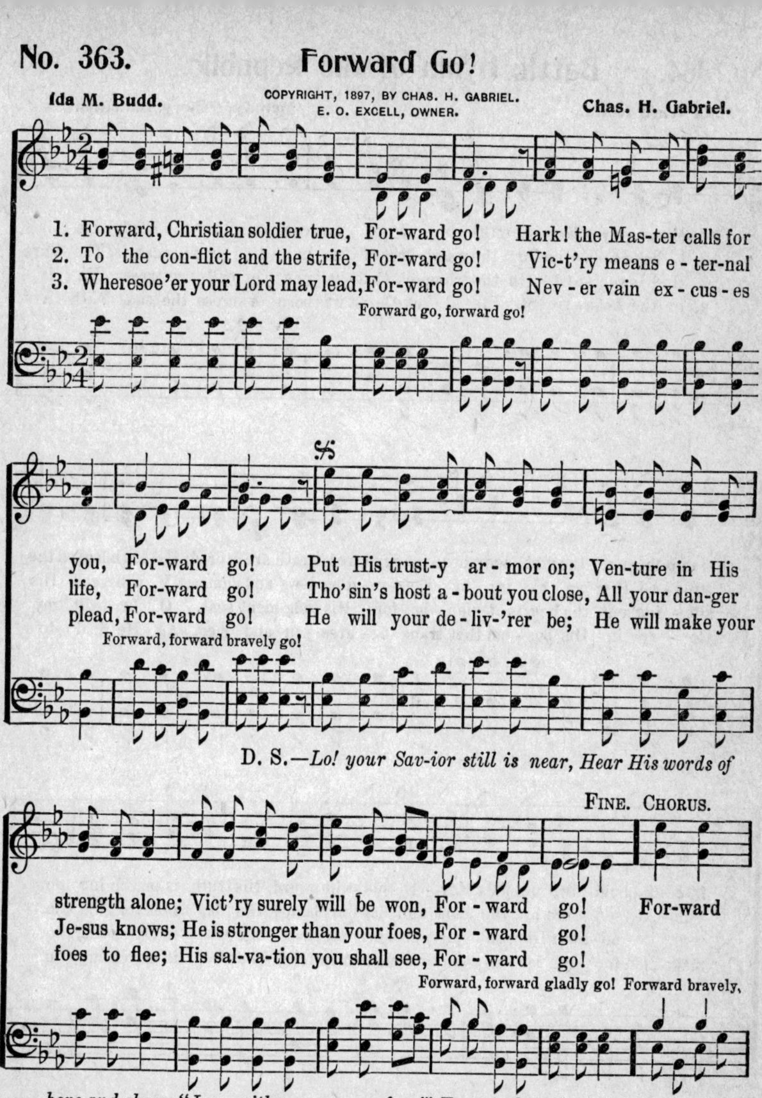
No. 363.
Forward Go!
Ida M. Budd.
COPYRIGHT, 1897, BY CHAS. H. GABRIEL.
E. O. EXCELL, OWNER.
Chas. H. Gabriel.
1. Forward, Christian soldier true, For-ward go! Hark! the Mas-ter calls for
2. To the con-flict and the strife, For-ward go! Vic-t'ry means e - ter-nal
3. Wheresoe'er your Lord may lead, For-ward go! Nev - er vain ex - cus - es
Forward go, forward go!
you, For-ward go! Put His trust-y ar - mor on; Ven-ture in His
life, For-ward go! Tho' sin's host a - bout you close, All your dan-ger
plead, For-ward go! He will your de - liv-'rer be; He will make your
Forward, forward bravely go!
D. S.—Lo! your Sav-ior still is near, Hear His words of
FINE. CHORUS.
strength alone; Vict'ry surely will be won, For - ward go! For-ward
Je-sus knows; He is stronger than your foes, For - ward go!
foes to flee; His sal-va-tion you shall see, For - ward go!
Forward, forward gladly go! Forward bravely,
hope and cheer: "I am with you, nev-er fear!" For-ward go!
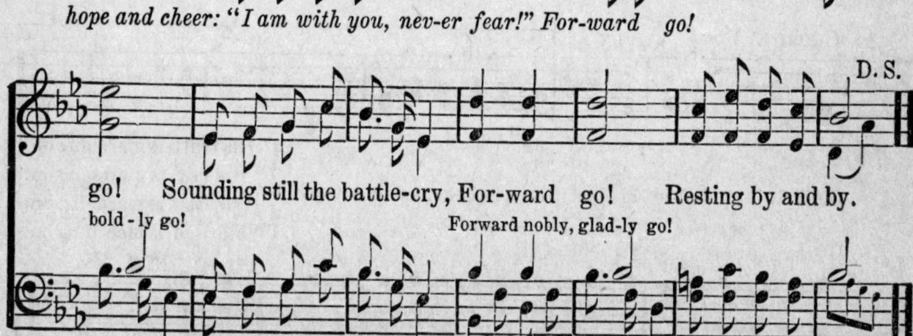
D. S.
go! Sounding still the battle-cry, For-ward go! Resting by and by.
bold - ly go!
Forward nobly, glad-ly go!

No. 364. Battle Hymn of the Republic.

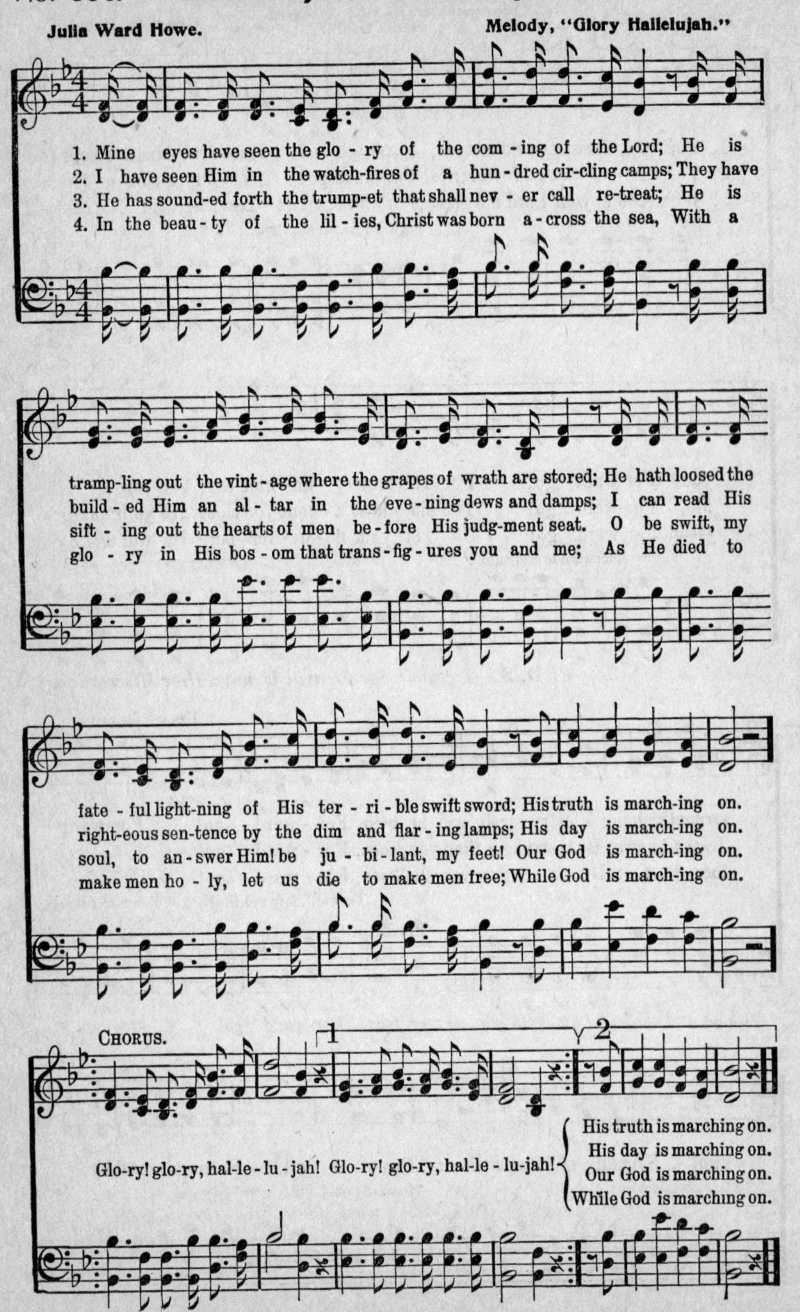
Julia Ward Howe.
Melody, "Glory Hallelujah."
1. Mine eyes have seen the glo - ry of the com - ing of the Lord; He is
2. I have seen Him in the watch-fires of a hun - dred cir-cling camps; They have
3. He has sound-ed forth the trump-et that shall nev - er call re-treat; He is
4. In the beau - ty of the lil - ies, Christ was born a - cross the sea, With a
tramp-ling out the vint - age where the grapes of wrath are stored; He hath loosed the
build - ed Him an al - tar in the eve - ning dews and damps; I can read His
sift - ing out the hearts of men be - fore His judg-ment seat. O be swift, my
glo - ry in His bos - om that trans - fig - ures you and me; As He died to
fate - ful light-ning of His ter - ri - ble swift sword; His truth is march-ing on.
right-eous sen-tence by the dim and flar - ing lamps; His day is march-ing on.
soul, to an - swer Him! be ju - bi - lant, my feet! Our God is march-ing on.
make men ho - ly, let us die to make men free; While God is march-ing on.
CHORUS.
1
2
Glo-ry! glo-ry, hal-le - lu - jah! Glo-ry! glo-ry, hal-le - lu-jah!
His truth is marching on.
His day is marching on.
Our God is marching on.
While God is marching on.

No. 365. The Red, White and Blue.
1. O Co-lum-bia! the gem of the o-cean, The home of the brave and the free;
2. When war winged its wide des-o-la-tion, And threatened the land to de-form,
3. Then, sons of Co-lum-bia, come hither, And join in our na-tion's sweet hymn;
The shrine of each patriot's de-vo-tion, A world offers homage to thee.
The ark then of freedom's foundation, Co - lum-bia rode safe thro' the storm;
May the wreaths they have won never wither, Nor the stars of their glory grow dim!
Thy mandates make heroes assemble, When Lib-er-ty's form stands in view;
With her garlands of vict'ry around her, When so proudly she bore her brave crew,
May the serv-ice, u-ni-ted, ne'er sever, But they to their colors prove true!
Thy ban-ners make tyr-an-ny tremble, When borne by the red, white and blue.
With her flag proudly waving be-fore her, The boast of the red, white and blue.
The Ar-my and Na-vy for-ev - er, Three cheers for the red, white and blue.
FINE.
CHORUS.
When borne by the red, white and blue, When borne by the red, white and blue;
The boast of the red, white and blue, The boast of the red, white and blue;
Three cheers for the red, white and blue, Three cheers for the red, white and blue;
D.S.

No. 366. The Star-Spangled Banner.

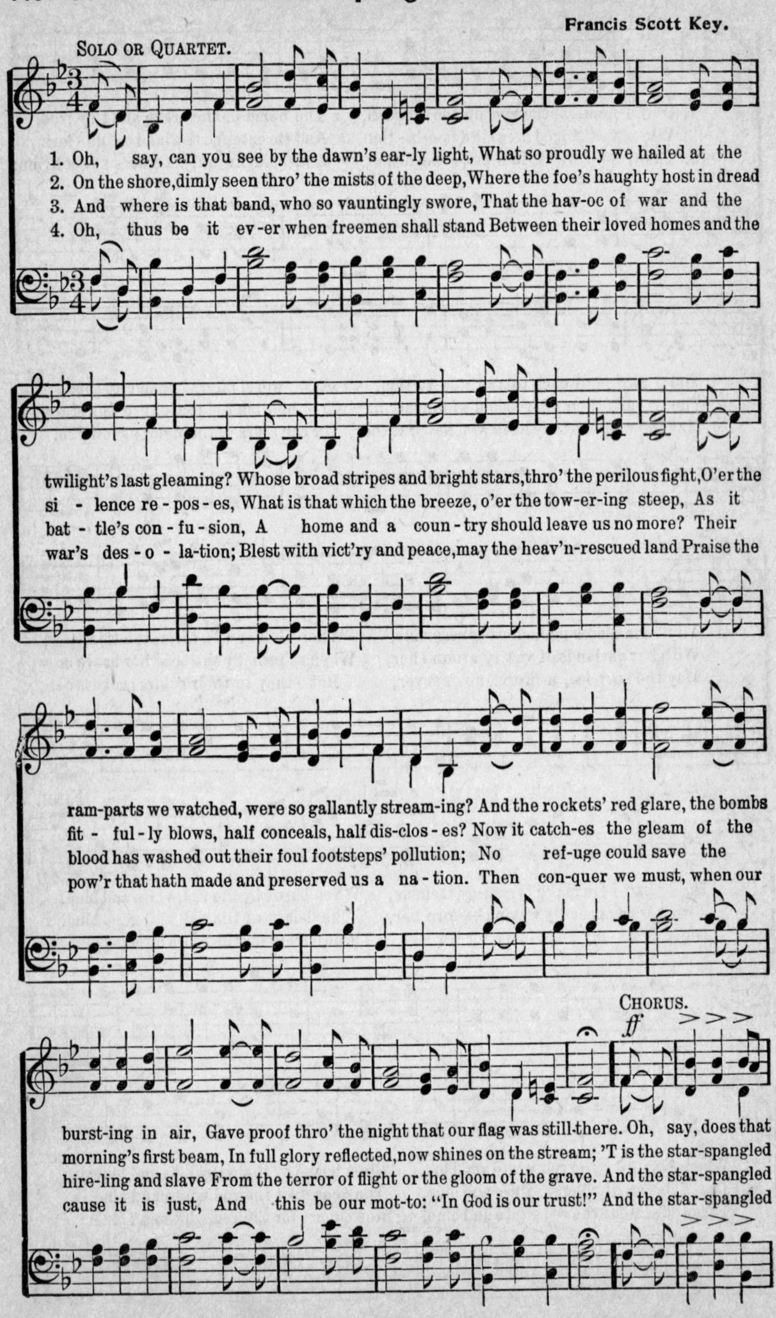
Francis Scott Key.
Solo or Quartet.
1. Oh, say, can you see by the dawn's ear-ly light, What so proudly we hailed at the
2. On the shore, dimly seen thro' the mists of the deep, Where the foe's haughty host in dread
3. And where is that band, who so vauntingly swore, That the hav-oc of war and the
4. Oh, thus be it ev-er when freemen shall stand Between their loved homes and the
twilight's last gleaming? Whose broad stripes and bright stars, thro' the perilous fight, O'er the
si - lence re - pos - es, What is that which the breeze, o'er the tow-er-ing steep, As it
bat - tle's con - fu - sion, A home and a coun - try should leave us no more? Their
war's des - o - la-tion; Blest with vict'ry and peace, may the heav'n-rescued land Praise the
ram-parts we watched, were so gallantly stream-ing? And the rockets' red glare, the bombs
fit - ful - ly blows, half conceals, half dis-clos - es? Now it catch-es the gleam of the
blood has washed out their foul footsteps' pollution; No ref-uge could save the
pow'r that hath made and preserved us a na - tion. Then con-quer we must, when our
Chorus.
ff
burst-ing in air, Gave proof thro' the night that our flag was still there. Oh, say, does that
morning's first beam, In full glory reflected, now shines on the stream; 'T is the star-spangled
hire-ling and slave From the terror of flight or the gloom of the grave. And the star-spangled
cause it is just, And this be our mot-to: "In God is our trust!" And the star-spangled

The Star-Spangled Banner.

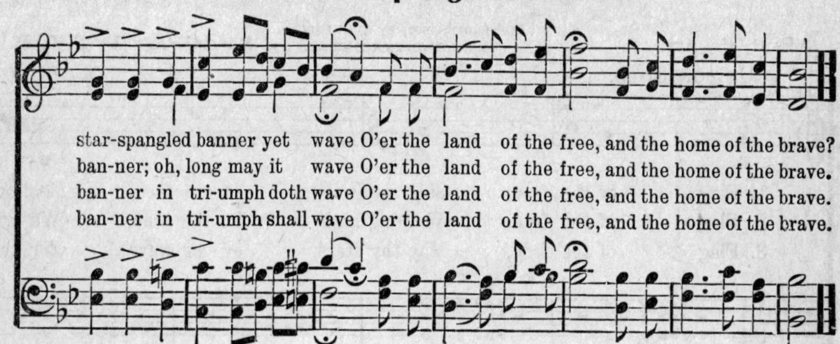

star-spangled banner yet wave O'er the land of the free, and the home of the brave?
ban-ner; oh, long may it wave O'er the land of the free, and the home of the brave.
ban-ner in tri-umph doth wave O'er the land of the free, and the home of the brave.
ban-ner in tri-umph shall wave O'er the land of the free, and the home of the brave.

No. 367. America.

S. F. Smith. The National Song of America. English.

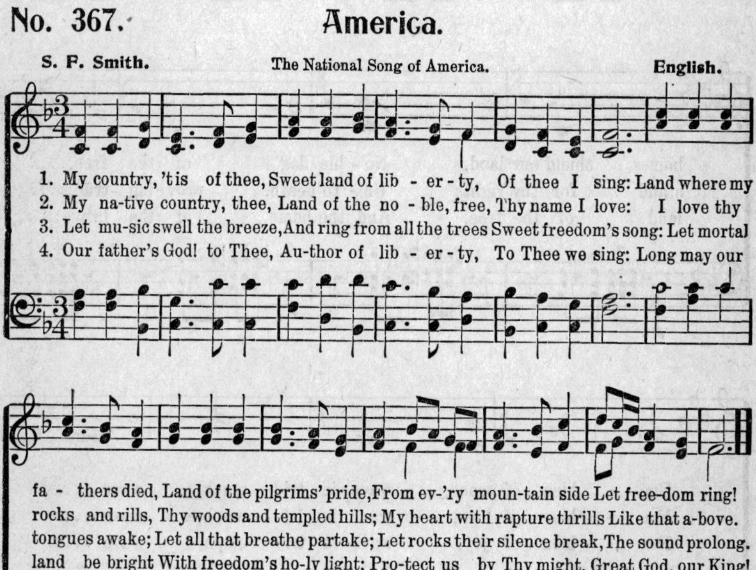

1. My country, 'tis of thee, Sweet land of lib - er - ty, Of thee I sing: Land where my
2. My na-tive country, thee, Land of the no - ble, free, Thy name I love: I love thy
3. Let mu-sic swell the breeze, And ring from all the trees Sweet freedom's song: Let mortal
4. Our father's God! to Thee, Au-thor of lib - er - ty, To Thee we sing: Long may our
fa - thers died, Land of the pilgrims' pride, From ev-'ry moun-tain side Let free-dom ring!
rocks and rills, Thy woods and templed hills; My heart with rapture thrills Like that a-bove.
tongues awake; Let all that breathe partake; Let rocks their silence break, The sound prolong.
land be bright With freedom's ho-ly light; Pro-tect us by Thy might, Great God, our King!

No. 368. God Save the King.

The National Song of Britain.

1.

God save our gracious King,
Long live our noble King,
God save the King:
Send him victorious,
Happy and glorious,
Long to reign over us;
God save the King.

2.

Through every changing scene,
O Lord, preserve our King;
Long may he reign:
His heart inspire and move
With wisdom from above,
And in a nation's love
His throne maintain.

3.

Thy choicest gifts in store,
On him be pleased to pour;
Long may he reign:
May he defend our laws,
And ever give us cause
To sing with heart and voice,
God save the King.

No. 369. Beautiful Flag.

E. O. E. Arr.
COPYRIGHT, 1902, BY E. O. EXCELL. ARR. OF WORDS AND MUSIC.
Rossini. Arr. by E. O. E.
Unison Solo.
1. Flag of the free, Sing we prais - es to thee; Shield our homes, shield our land, No - ble flag of the free;.... Em - blem of peace, wave in tri - umph, wave......
2. Flag of the free, Wav-ing high in the blue, We will stand for thy rights Un - to death, prov - ing true;.... Em - blem of love, wave in tri - umph, wave......
3. Flag of the free, May thy stars ev - er wave O'er the land of the free, And the home of the brave;... Em - blem of joy, wave in tri - umph, wave......
Chorus.
Flag of the free, Sing we prais - - -
Beau-ti-ful flag, beau-ti-ful flag, Prais-es to thee,

Beautiful Flag.
es to thee; Shield our homes, shield our
prais-es to thee; Shielding our homes,
land, No-ble flag of the free............
shielding our land, No-ble our flag, flag of the free.
No. 370. The Flag of the Free.
March from "Lohengrin."
1. Flag of the free, fair-est to see! Borne thro' the strife and the thunder of war;
2. Flag of the brave, long may it wave, Cho-sen of God while His might we a-dore;
Ban-ner so bright, with starry light, Float ev-er proudly from mountain to shore.
In Lib-er-ty's van for manhood of man, Symbol of right thro' the years passing o'er.
FINE.
D. S.—Flag of the free, flag of the brave, Emblem of lib-er-ty, long may it wave!
D. S.
Emblem of freedom, hope to the slave, Spread thy fair folds but to shield and to save;
Pride of our country, honored a-far, Scat-ter each cloud that would darken a star;

No. 371. The Maple Leaf Forever.

THE NATIONAL SONG OF CANADA.

Alexander Muir.

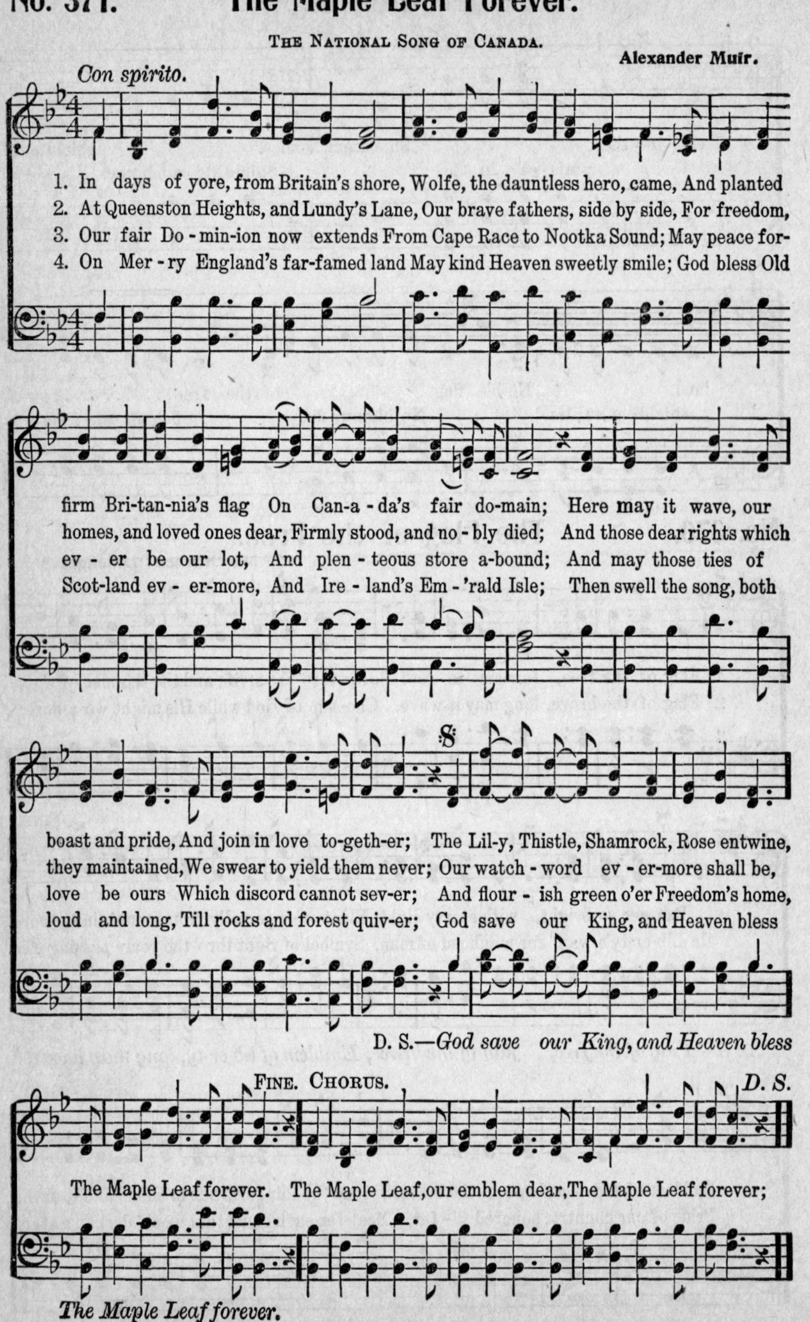
Con spirito.
1. In days of yore, from Britain's shore, Wolfe, the dauntless hero, came, And planted
2. At Queenston Heights, and Lundy's Lane, Our brave fathers, side by side, For freedom,
3. Our fair Do - min-ion now extends From Cape Race to Nootka Sound; May peace for-
4. On Mer - ry England's far-famed land May kind Heaven sweetly smile; God bless Old
firm Bri-tan-nia's flag On Can-a - da's fair do-main; Here may it wave, our
homes, and loved ones dear, Firmly stood, and no - bly died; And those dear rights which
ev - er be our lot, And plen - teous store a-bound; And may those ties of
Scot-land ev - er-more, And Ire - land's Em - 'rald Isle; Then swell the song, both
boast and pride, And join in love to-geth-er; The Lil-y, Thistle, Shamrock, Rose entwine,
they maintained, We swear to yield them never; Our watch - word ev - er-more shall be,
love be ours Which discord cannot sev-er; And flour - ish green o'er Freedom's home,
loud and long, Till rocks and forest quiv-er; God save our King, and Heaven bless
D. S.—God save our King, and Heaven bless
FINE. CHORUS.
D. S.
The Maple Leaf forever. The Maple Leaf, our emblem dear, The Maple Leaf forever;
The Maple Leaf forever.

Selected Psalms

No. 372. PSALM 1.

1 Blessed is the man that walketh not in the counsel of the ungodly, nor standeth in the way of sinners, nor sitteth in the seat of the scornful.

2 But his delight is in the law of the Lord; and in his law doth he meditate day and night.

3 And he shall be like a tree planted by the rivers of water, that bringeth forth his fruit in his season; his leaf also shall not wither, and whatsoever he doeth shall prosper.

4 The ungodly are not so: but are like the chaff which the wind driveth away.

5 Therefore the ungodly shall not stand in the judgment, nor sinners in the congregation of the righteous.

6 For the Lord knoweth the way of the righteous: but the way of the ungodly shall perish.

Sing No. 268.

Walk in the Light.

No. 373. PSALM 5.

1 Give ear to my words, O Lord; consider my meditation.

2 Hearken unto the voice of my cry, my King and my God; for unto thee will I pray.

3 My voice shalt thou hear in the morning, O Lord; in the morning will I direct my prayer unto thee, and will look up.

4 For thou art not a God that hath pleasure in wickedness: neither shall evil dwell with thee.

5 The foolish shall not stand in thy sight: thou hatest all workers of iniquity.

6 Thou shalt destroy them that speak leasing: the Lord will abhor the bloody and deceitful man.

7 But as for me, I will come into thy house in the multitude of thy mercy: and in thy fear will I worship toward thy holy temple.

8 Lead me, O Lord, in thy righteousness because of mine enemies; make thy way straight before my face.

Sing No. 272.

Jesus, Savior, Pilot Me.

No. 374. PSALM 8.

1 O Lord, how excellent is thy name in all the earth! who hast set thy glory above the heavens.

2 Out of the mouths of babes and sucklings hast thou ordained strength, because of thine enemies, that thou mightest still the enemy and the avenger.

3 When I consider thy heavens, the work of thy fingers, the moon and the stars, which thou hast ordained;

4 What is man, that thou art mindful of him? and the son of man, that thou visitest him?

5 For thou hast made him a little lower than the angels, and hast crowned him with glory and honor.

6 Thou madest him to have dominion over the works of thy hands; thou hast put all things under his feet:

7 All sheep and oxen, yea, and the beasts of the field;

8 The fowl of the air, and the fish of the sea, and whatsoever passeth through the paths of the seas.

9 O Lord, our Lord, how excellent is thy name in all the earth!

Sing No. 266.

Oh, for a thousand tongues.

No. 375. PSALM 15.

1 Lord, who shall abide in thy tabernacle? who shall dwell in thy holy hill?

2 He that walketh uprightly, and worketh righteousness, and speaketh the truth in his heart.

3 He that backbiteth not with his tongue, nor doeth evil to his neighbor, nor taketh up a reproach against his neighbor.

4 In whose eyes a vile person is contemned; but he honoreth them that fear the Lord. He that sweareth to his own hurt, and changeth not.

5 He that putteth not out his money to usury, nor taketh reward against the innocent. He that doeth these things shall never be moved.

Sing No. 338.

My Jesus, I love Thee.

Selected Psalms.

No. 376. PSALM 17.

1 Hear the right, O Lord, attend unto my cry; give ear unto my prayer, that goeth not out of feigned lips.

2 Let my sentence come forth from thy presence; let thine eyes behold the things that are equal.

3 Thou hast proved mine heart; thou hast visited me in the night; thou hast tried me, and shalt find nothing: I am purposed that my mouth shall not transgress.

4 Concerning the works of men, by the word of thy lips I have kept me from the paths of the destroyer.

5 Hold up my goings in thy paths, that my footsteps slip not.

6 I have called upon thee, for thou wilt hear me, O God: incline thine ear unto me, and hear my speech.

Sing. No 297.

Guide me, O Thou great Jehovah.

No. 377. PSALM 19.

1 The law of the Lord is perfect, converting the soul: the testimony of the Lord is sure, making wise the simple.

2 The statutes of the Lord are right, rejoicing the heart; the commandment of the Lord is pure, enlightening the eyes.

3 The fear of the Lord is clean, enduring forever: the judgments of the Lord are true and righteous altogether.

4 More to be desired are they than gold, yea, than much fine gold: sweeter also than honey and the honeycomb.

5 Moreover by them is thy servant warned; and in keeping of them there is great reward.

6 Who can understand his errors? cleanse thou me from secret faults.

7 Keep back thy servant also from presumptuous sins; let them not have dominion over me: then shall I be upright, and I shall be innocent from the great transgression.

8 Let the words of my mouth, and the meditation of my heart, be acceptable in thy sight, O Lord, my strength, and my Redeemer.

Sing. No. 410.

How gentle God's commands.

No. 378. PSALM 23.

1 The Lord is my Shepherd; I shall not want.

2 He maketh me to lie down in green pastures: he leadeth me beside the still waters.

3 He restoreth my soul: he leadeth me in the paths of righteousness for his name's sake.

4 Yea, though I walk through the valley of the shadow of death, I will fear no evil: for thou art with me; thy rod and thy staff they comfort me.

5 Thou preparest a table before me in the presence of mine enemies: thou anointest my head with oil; my cup runneth over.

Sing No. 248.

I can hear my Savior calling.

No. 379. PSALM 24.

1 The earth is the Lord's, and the fullness thereof; the world, and they that dwell therein.

2 For he hath founded it upon the seas, and established it upon the floods.

3 Who shall ascend into the hill of the Lord? or who shall stand in his holy place?

4 He that hath clean hands, and a pure heart; who hath not lifted his soul unto vanity, nor sworn deceitfully.

5 He shall receive the blessing from the Lord, and righteousness from the God of his salvation.

6 This is the generation of them that seek him, that seek thy face, O Jacob. Selah.

7 Lift up your heads, O ye gates; and be ye lifted up ye everlasting doors; and the King of glory shall come in.

8 Who is this King of glory? The Lord strong and mighty, the Lord mighty in battle.

9 Lift up your heads, O ye gates; even lift them up, ye everlasting doors; and the King of glory shall come in.

10 Who is this King of glory? The Lord of hosts, he is the King of glory. Selah.

Sing No. 283.

O worship the King, etc.

Selected Psalms.

No. 380. PSALM 27.

1 The Lord is my light and my salvation; whom shall I fear? the Lord is the strength of my life; of whom shall I be afraid?

2 When the wicked, even mine enemies and my foes, came upon me to eat up my flesh, they stumbled and fell.

3 Though a host should encamp against me, my heart shall not fear: though war should rise against me, in this will I be confident.

4 One thing have I desired of the Lord, that will I seek after; that I may dwell in the house of the Lord all the days of my life, to behold the beauty of the Lord, and to inquire in his temple.

5 For in the time of trouble he shall hide me in his pavilion; in the secret of his tabernacle shall he hide me; he shall set me up upon a rock.

6 And now shall mine head be lifted up above mine enemies round about me; therefore will I offer in his tabernacle sacrifices of joy; I will sing, yea, I will sing praises unto the Lord.

7 Hear, O Lord, when I cry with my voice: have mercy also upon me, and answer me.

Sing No 307.

Come Thou Almighty King.

No. 381. PSALM 32.

1 Blessed is he whose transgression is forgiven, whose sin is covered.

2 Blessed is the man unto whom the Lord imputeth not iniquity, and in whose spirit there is no guile.

3 When I kept silence, my bones waxed old through my roaring all the day long.

4 For day and night thy hand was heavy upon me; my moisture is turned into the drought of summer. Selah.

5 I acknowledged my sin unto thee, and mine iniquity have I not hid. I said, I will confess my transgressions unto the Lord; and thou forgavest the iniquity of my sin. Selah.

6 For this shall every one that is godly pray unto thee in a time when thou mayest be found; surely in the floods of great waters they shall not come nigh unto him.

7 Thou art my hiding place; thou shalt preserve me from trouble; thou shalt compass me about with songs of deliverance. Selah.

Sing No. 273.

Rock of Ages.

No. 382. PSALM 34.

1 I will bless the Lord at all times; His praise shall continually be in my mouth.

2 My soul shall make her boast in the Lord: the humble shall hear thereof, and be glad.

3 O magnify the Lord with me, and let us exalt his name together.

4 I sought the Lord, and he heard me, and delivered me from all my fears.

5 They looked unto him, and were lightened: and their faces were not ashamed.

6 This poor man cried, and the Lord heard him, and saved him out of all his troubles.

7 The angel of the Lord encampeth round about them that fear him, and delivereth them.

8 O taste and see that the Lord is good; blessed is the man that trusteth in Him.

Sing No. 288.

My faith looks up to Thee.

No. 383. PSALM 51.

1 Have mercy upon me, O God, according to thy loving-kindness: according unto the multitude of thy tender mercies blot out my transgressions.

2 Wash me thoroughly from mine iniquity, and cleanse me from my sin.

3 For I acknowledge my trangressions: and my sin is ever before me.

4 Against thee, thee only, have I sinned, and done this evil in thy sight: that thou mightest be justified when thou speakest, and be clear when thou judgest.

5 Behold, I was shapen in iniquity; and in sin did my mother conceive me.

6 Behold, thou desireth truth in the inward parts: and in the hidden part thou shalt make me to know wisdom.

7 Purge me with hyssop, and I shall be clean: wash me, and I shall be whiter than snow.

8 Make me to hear joy and gladness, that the bones which thou hast broken may rejoice.

9 Hide thy face from my sins, and blot out all my iniquities.

10 Create in me a clean heart, O God; and renew a right spirit within me.

Sing No. 298.

My Hope Is Built On Nothing Less.

Selected Psalms.

No. 384. PSALM 61.

1 Hear my cry, O God; attend unto my prayer.

2 From the end of the earth will I cry unto thee, when my heart is overwhelmed; lead me to the rock that is higher than I.

3 For thou hast been a shelter for me, and a strong tower from the enemy.

4 I will abide in thy tabernacle forever: I will trust in the covert of thy wings.

5 For thou, O God, hast heard my vows; thou hast given me the heritage of them that fear thy name.

6 Thou wilt prolong the king's life: and his years as many generations.

7 He shall abide before God for ever; O prepare mercy and truth, which may preserve him.

8 So will I sing praise unto Thy name for ever, that I may daily perform my vows.

Sing No. 290.

O Could I Speak the Matchless Worth.

No. 385. PSALM 63.

1 O God, Thou art my God; early will I seek thee; my soul thirsteth for thee, my flesh longeth for thee in a dry and thirsty land, where no water is;

2 To see thy power and thy glory, so as I have seen thee in the sanctuary.

3 Because thy lovingkindness is better than life, my lips shall praise thee.

4 Thus will I bless thee while I live; I will lift up my hands in thy name.

5 My soul shall be satisfied as with marrow and fatness; and my mouth shall praise thee with joyful lips:

6 When I remember thee upon my bed, and meditate on thee in the night watches.

7 Because thou hast been my help, therefore in the shadow of thy wings will I rejoice.

8 My soul followeth hard after thee: thy right hand upholdeth me.

9 But those that seek my soul, to destroy it, shall go into the lower parts of the earth.

10 They shall fall by the sword: they shall be a portion for foxes.

11 But the king shall rejoice in God; every one that sweareth by him shall glory: but the mouth of them that speak lies shall be stopped.

Sing No. 282.

When I Survey the Wondrous Cross.

No. 386. PSALM 65.

1 Praise waiteth for thee, O God, in Zion: and unto thee shall the vow be performed.

2 O thou that hearest prayer, unto thee shall all flesh come.

3 Iniquities prevail against me; as for our transgressions, thou shalt purge them away.

4 Blessed is the man whom thou choosest, and causest to approach unto thee, that he may dwell in thy courts: we shall be satisfied with the goodness of thy house, even thy holy temple.

5 By terrible things in righteousness wilt thou answer us, O God of our salvation; who art the confidence of all the ends of the earth, and of them that are afar off upon the sea:

6 Which by his strength setteth fast the mountains; being girded with power:

7 Which stilleth the noise of the seas, the noise of their waves, and the tumult of the people.

8 They also that dwell in the uttermost parts are afraid at thy tokens: thou makest the outgoings of the morning and evening rejoice.

9 Thou visitest the earth, and waterest it: thou greatly enrichest it with the river of God, which is full of water: thou preparest them corn, when thou hast so provided for it.

Sing No. 332.

Jesus, Lover of My Soul.

No. 387. PSALM 67.

1 God be merciful unto us, and bless us; and cause his face to shine upon us. Selah.

2 That thy way may be known upon earth, thy saving health among all nations.

3 Let the people praise thee, O God; let all the people praise thee.

4 O let the nations be glad and sing for joy: for thou shalt judge the people righteously, and govern the nations upon earth. Selah.

5 Let the people praise thee, O God; let all the people praise thee.

6 Then shall the earth yield her increase; and God, even our own God, shall bless us.

7 God shall bless us; and all the ends of the earth shall fear him.

Sing No. 116.

Count your blessings.

Selected Psalms.

No. 388. PSALM 84.

1 How amiable are thy tabernacles, O Lord of hosts!

2 My soul longeth, yea, even fainteth for the courts of the Lord: my heart and my flesh crieth out for the living God.

3 Yea, the sparrow hath found an house, and the swallow a nest for herself, where she may lay her young, even thine altars, O Lord of hosts, my King, and my God.

4 Blessed are they that dwell in thy house: they will be still praising thee. Selah.

5 Blessed is the man whose strength is in thee; in whose heart are the ways of them.

6 Who passing through the valley of Baca make it a well: the rain also filleth the pools.

7 They go from strength to strength, every one of them in Zion appeareth before God.

8 O Lord God of hosts, hear my prayer: give ear, O God of Jacob. Selah.

9 Behold, O God, our shield, and look upon the face of thine anointed.

10 For a day in thy courts is better than a thousand. I had rather be a doorkeeper in the house of my God, than to dwell in the tents of wickedness.

11 For the Lord God is a sun and shield: the Lord will give grace and glory: no good thing will he withhold from them that walk uprightly.

12 O Lord of hosts, blessed is the man that trusteth in thee.

Sing No. 296.

Love Divine.

No. 389. PSALM 91.

1 He that dwelleth in the secret place of the Most High shall abide under the shadow of the Almighty.

2 I will say of the Lord, he is my refuge and my fortress: my God; in him will I trust.

3 Surely he shall deliver thee from the snare of the fowler, and from the noisome pestilence.

4 He shall cover thee with his feathers, and under his wings shalt thou trust: his truth shall be thy shield and buckler.

5 Thou shalt not be afraid for the terror by night; nor for the arrow that flieth by day;

6 Nor for the pestilence that walketh in the darkness: nor for the destruction that wasteth at noonday.

7 A thousand shall fall at thy side, and ten thousand at thy right hand; but it shall not come nigh thee.

8 Only with thine eyes shalt thou behold and see the reward of the wicked.

9 Because thou hast made the Lord, which is my refuge, even the Most High, thy habitation.

Sing No. 258.

Nearer, my God, to Thee.

No. 390. PSALM 93.

1 The Lord reigneth, he is clothed with majesty; the Lord is clothed with strength, wherewith he hath girded himself: the world also is established, and cannot be moved.

2 Thy throne is established of old; thou art from everlasting.

3 The floods have lifted up, O Lord, the floods have lifted up their voice; the floods lift up their waves.

4 The Lord on high is mightier than the noise of many waters, yea, than the mighty waves of the sea.

5 Thy testimonies are very sure: holiness becometh thine house, O Lord, for ever.

Sing No. 275.

Holy, Holy, Holy.

No. 391. PSALM 95.

1 O come, let us sing unto the Lord; let us make a joyful noise to the Rock of our salvation.

2 Let us come before his presence with thanksgiving, and make a joyful noise unto him with psalms.

3 For the Lord is a great God, and a great King above all gods.

4 In his hand are the deep places of the earth: the strength of the hills is his also.

5 The sea is his, and he made it: and his hand formed the dry land.

6 O come, let us worship and bow down: let us kneel before the Lord, our Maker.

7 For he is our God; and we are the people of his pasture, and the sheep of his hand.

Sing No. 283.

O worship the King.

Selected Psalms.

No. 392. PSALM 98.

1 O sing unto the Lord a new song; for he hath done marvelous things; his right hand, and his holy arm, hath gotten him the victory.

2 The Lord hath made known his salvation: his righteousness hath he openly showed in the sight of the heathen.

3 He hath remembered his mercy and his truths toward the house of Israel: all the ends of the earth have seen the salvation of our God.

4 Make a joyful noise unto the Lord, all the earth; make a loud noise, and rejoice, and sing praise.

5 Sing unto the Lord with the harp; with the harp, and the voice of a psalm.

6 With trumpets and sound of cornet make a joyful noise before the Lord, the King.

7 Let the sea roar, and the fulness thereof; the world, and they that dwell therein.

8 Let the floods clap their hands: let the hills be joyful together

9 Before the Lord; for he cometh to judge the earth: with righteousness shall he judge the world, and the people with equity.

Sing No. 290.

O could I speak.

No. 393. PSALM 103.

1 Bless the Lord, O my soul: and all that is within me, bless his holy name.

2 Bless the Lord, O my soul, and forget not all his benefits.

3 Who forgiveth all thine iniquities; who healeth all thy diseases;

4 Who redeemeth thy life from destruction; who crowneth thee with lovingkindness and tender mercies;

5 Who satisfieth thy mouth with good things; so that thy youth is renewed like the eagle's.

6 The Lord executeth righteousness and judgment of all that are oppressed.

7 He made known his ways unto Moses, his acts unto the children of Israel.

8 The Lord is merciful and gracious, slow to anger, and plenteous in mercy,

9 He will not always chide: neither will he keep his anger forever.

10 He hath not dealt with us after our sins; nor rewarded us according to our iniquities.

11 For as the heaven is high above the earth, so great is his mercy toward them that fear him.

12 As far as the east is from the west, so far hath he removed our transgressions from us.

Sing No. 294.

O happy day.

No. 394. PSALM 119.

1 Blessed are the undefiled in the way, who walk in the law of the Lord.

2 Blessed are they that keep his testimonies, and that seek him with the whole heart.

3 They also do no iniquity: they walk in his ways.

4 Thou hast commanded us to keep thy precepts diligently.

5 O that my ways were directed to keep thy statutes!

6 Then shall I not be ashamed, when I have respect unto all thy commandments.

7 I will praise thee with uprightness of heart, when I shall have learned thy righteous judgments.

8 I will keep thy statutes: O forsake me not utterly.

Sing No. 302.

Blessed Assurance.

No. 395. PSALM 122.

1 I was glad when they said unto me, Let us go into the house of the Lord.

2 Our feet shall stand within thy gates, O Jerusalem.

3 Jerusalem is builded as a city that is compact together.

4 Whither the tribes go up, the tribes of the Lord, unto the testimony of Israel, to give thanks unto the name of the Lord.

5 For there are set thrones of judgment, the thrones of the house of David.

6 Pray for the peace of Jerusalem: they shall prosper that love thee.

7 Peace be within thy walls, and prosperity within thy palaces.

8 For my brethren and companions' sakes, I will now say, Peace be within thee.

9 Because of the house of the Lord our God I will seek thy good.

Sing No. 270.

I Love Thy Kingdom, Lord.

Selected Psalms.

No. 396. PSALM 138.

1 I will praise thee with my whole heart; before the gods will I sing praise unto thee.

2 I will worship toward thy holy temple, and praise thy name for thy lovingkindness and for thy truth; for thou hast magnified thy word above all thy name.

3 In the day when I cried thou answeredst me, and strengthenedst me with strength in my soul.

4 All the kings of the earth shall praise thee, O Lord, when they hear the words of thy mouth.

5 Yea, they shall sing in the way of the Lord: for great is the glory of the Lord.

6 Though the Lord be high, yet hath he respect unto the lowly; but the proud he knoweth afar off.

7 Though I walk in the midst of trouble, thou wilt revive me: thou shalt stretch forth thine hand against the wrath of mine enemies, and thy right hand shall save me.

8 The Lord will perfect that which concerneth me: thy mercy, O Lord, endureth for ever: forsake not the works of thine own hands.

Sing No. 279.

Majestic sweetness.

No. 397. PSALM 142.

1 I cried unto the Lord with my voice; with my voice unto the Lord did I make my supplication.

2 I poured out my complaint before him: I shewed before him my trouble.

3 When my spirit was overwhelmed within me, then thou knewest my path. In the way wherein I walked have they privily laid a snare for me.

4 I looked on my right hand, and beheld, but there was no man that would know me: refuge failed me; no man cared for my soul.

5 I cried unto thee, O Lord: I said, thou art my refuge and my portion in the land of the living.

6 Attend unto my cry: for I am brought very low; deliver me from my persecutors; for they are stronger than I.

7 Bring my soul out of prison, that I may praise thy name; the righteous shall compass me about, for thou shalt deal bountifully with me.

Sing No. 269.

Savior, Like a Shepherd Lead Us.

No. 398. PSALM 149.

1 Praise ye the Lord. Sing un[to the] Lord a new song, and his praise in [the] congregation of saints.

2 Let Israel rejoice in him that made him: let the children of Zion be joyful in their King.

3 Let them praise his name in the dance: let them sing praises unto him with the timbrel and harp.

4 For the Lord taketh pleasure in his people: he will beautify the meek with salvation.

5 Let the saints be joyful in glory: let them sing aloud upon their beds.

6 Let the high praises of God be in their mouth, and a two-edged sword in their hand:

7 To execute vengeance upon the heathen, and punishment upon the people.

8 To bind their kings with chains, and their nobles with fetters of iron;

9 To execute upon them the judgment written: this honor have all his saints. Praise ye the Lord.

Sing No. 307.

Come Thou Almighty King.

No. 399. PSALM 150.

1 Praise ye the Lord. Praise God in his sanctuary: praise him in the firmament of his power.

2 Praise him for his mighty acts: praise him according to his excellent greatness.

3 Praise him with the sound of the trumpet: praise him with the psaltery and harp.

4 Praise him with the timbrel and dance: praise him with stringed instruments and organs.

5 Praise him upon the loud cymbals; praise him upon the high sounding cymbals.

6 Let everything that hath breath praise the Lord. Praise ye the Lord.

Sing No. 309.

All hail the power.

Selected Scripture.

3.

...ot my law; but let
...mandments:
...and long life, and
...thee.

...not mercy and truth forsake thee: bind them about thy neck; write them upon the table of thine heart:

4 So shalt thou find favour and good understanding in the sight of God and men.

5 Trust in the Lord with all thine heart; and lean not unto thine own understanding.

6 In all thy way acknowledge him, and he shall direct thy paths.

7 Be not wise in thine own eyes: fear the Lord and depart from evil.

Sing No. 254.

Who is on the Lord's side?

No. 401. MATT. 5.

1 And seeing the multitudes, he went up into a mountain: and when he was set, his disciples came unto him:

2 And he opened his mouth and taught them, saying,

3 Blessed are the poor in spirit: for theirs is the kingdom of heaven.

4 Blessed are they that mourn: for they shall be comforted.

5 Blessed are the meek: for they shall inherit the earth.

6 Blessed are they which do hunger and thirst after righteousness: for they shall be filled.

7 Blessed are the merciful: for they shall obtain mercy.

8 Blessed are the pure in heart: for they shall see God.

9 Blessed are the peacemakers: for they shall be called the children of God.

10 Blessed are they which are persecuted for righteousness' sake: for theirs is the kingdom of heaven.

11 Blessed are ye, when men shall revile you, and persecute you, and shall say all manner of evil against you falsely, for my sake.

12 Rejoice, and be exceeding glad: for great is your reward in heaven: for so persecuted they the prophets which were before you.

Sing No. 410.

How Gentle God's Commands.

No. 402. The Apostles' Creed.

I believe in God the Father Almighty, Maker of heaven and earth; and in Jesus Christ his only Son, our Lord; who was conceived by the Holy Ghost, born of the Virgin Mary, suffered under Pontius Pilate; was crucified, dead and buried; the third day he rose from the dead; he ascended into heaven, and sitteth on the right hand of God the Father Almighty; from thence he shall come to judge the quick and the dead.

I believe in the Holy Ghost; the Holy Catholic Church, the communion of saints; the forgiveness of sins; the resurrection of the body, and the life everlasting. Amen.

Sing No. 413.

Gloria Patri. No. 2.

No. 403. 1 COR. 13.

1 Though I speak with the tongues of men and of angels, and have not charity, I am become as sounding brass or a tinkling cymbal.

2 And though I have the gift of prophecy and understand all mysteries, and all knowledge; and though I have all faith, so that I could remove mountains, and have not charity, I am nothing.

3 And though I bestow all my goods to feed the poor, and though I give my body to be burned, and have not charity, it profiteth me nothing.

4 Charity suffereth long, and is kind; charity envieth not; charity vaunteth not itself, is not puffed up,

5 Doth not behave itself unseemly, seeketh not her own, is not easily provoked, thinketh no evil;

6 Rejoiceth not in iniquity, but rejoiceth in the truth;

7 Beareth all things, believeth all things, hopeth all things, endureth all things.

8 Charity never faileth: but whether there be prophecies, they shall fail; whether there be tongues, they shall cease; whether there be knowledge, it shall vanish away.

9 For we know in part, and we prophesy in part.

10 But when that which is perfect is come, then that which is in part shall be done away.

Sing No. 255.

Onward Christian Soldiers.

Responsive Readings

Order of Service. No. 1.

Prepared by Marion Lawrance, Chicago, Ill.

No. 404. The Names of Jesus.

Supt.—Stand up and bless the Lord your God for ever and ever; and blessed be Thy glorious name.

All Rise, Sing.—Music No. 279.

How sweet the name of Jesus sounds
In a believer's ear!
It soothes his sorrows, heals his wounds,
And drives away his fear.

It makes the wounded spirit whole,
And calms the troubled breast,
'Tis manna to the hungry soul,
And to the weary, rest.

Dear name! the rock on which I build,
My shield and hiding-place;
My never-failing treasure, filled
With boundless stores of grace!

I would Thy boundless love proclaim
With every fleeting breath;
So shall the music of Thy name
Refresh my soul in death.

Supt.—By how many Names and Titles is Our Saviour mentioned in the Bible?

School.—Over two hundred and fifty.

Supt.—What are some of the Names given to Him hundreds of years before He was born?

School.—For unto us a Child is born, unto us a Son is given; . . . and His name shall be called Wonderful, Counsellor, Mighty God, Everlasting Father, Prince of Peace.

Supt.—God has highly exalted Him, and given Him a name which is above every name.

Minister.—He is the King of kings, and Lord of lords.

Officers.—Chiefest among ten thousand.

Senior Dept.—Son of the living God.

Young Men's Dept.—Lion of the Tribe of Judah.

Young Women's Dept.—The Bright and Morning Star.

Intermediate Dept.—The Light of the World.

Junior Dept.—The Good Shepherd.

Supt.—Which of all His names is the sweetest?

School.—JESUS.

Sing.—Music No. 324.

Sweetest note in seraph song,
Sweetest name on mortal tongue,
Sweetest carol ever sung,
Jesus, blessed Jesus.

Supt.—Why was He called Jesus?

School.—Thou shalt call His name JESUS; for it is He that shall save His people from their sins.

Minister.—And in none other is there salvation: for neither is there any other name under heaven, that is given among men, wherein we must be saved.

Supt.—He is the Captain of our Salvation.

Officers.—The Author and Finisher of our Faith.

Senior Dept.—The Head of the Church.

Young Men's Dept.—He is the Way, the Truth and the Life.

Young Women's Dept.—The Precious Corner Stone.

Intermediate Dept.—The Friend of sinners.

Junior Dept.—The Man of Sorrows.

Supt.—But of all His names, which is the sweetest?

School.—JESUS,

Sing.—Music No, 324.

Sweetest note in seraph song,
Sweetest name on mortal tongue,
Sweetest carol ever sung,
Jesus, blessed Jesus,

Prayer.

Supt.—Oh, magnify the Lord with me. and let us exalt His name together,

Sing.—Music No, 309.

All Hail the Power of Jesus' Name!

(*Be Seated.*)

Order of Service. No. 2.

No. 405.

1. Instrumental Music.-(*Go quietly to your places. As soon as the music stops, the doors will be closed.*)

2. Silence.

3. School Stands.—(*At signal of piano or organ, sing, without music, the first verse of "All Hail the Power of Jesus' Name."*)

4. Superintendent's Greeting

Supt.— Good morning, teachers and scholars.

School.—Good morning, Mr. (*Supply the superintendent's name.*)

5. Responsive Service.

Supt.-O come, let us sing unto Jehovah.

School.—Let us make a joyful noise to the rock of our salvation,

Sing.—Music No. 56.

If His love is in the soul,
And we yield to His control,
Sweetest music will the lonely hours beguile;
We may drive the clouds away,
Cheer and bless the darkest day,
If we keep the heart singing all the while.

CHORUS.

Keep the heart singing all the while;
Make the world brighter with a smile;
Keep the song ringing! lonely hours we may beguile,
If we keep the heart singing all the while.

Supt.—And seeing the multitudes, he went up into the mountain: and when he had sat down, his disciples came unto him:

School.—And he opened his mouth and taught them, saying:

Assistant Supt.—Blessed are the poor in spirit:

School.—For theirs is the kingdom of heaven.

Sing.—Music No. 116.

When you look at others with their land and gold,
Think that Christ has promised you His wealth untold;
Count your many blessings, money can not buy
Your reward in heaven, Nor your home on high.

CHO.—Count your blessings,
Name them one by one;
Count your blessings,
See what God hath done.
Count your blessings,
Name them one by one;
Count your many blessings,
See what God hath done.

Supt.—Blessed are they that mourn:

School.—For they shall be comforted.

Sing.—Music No. 284.

What a friend we have in Jesus,
All our sins and griefs to bear!
What a privilege to carry
Everything to God in prayer!
Oh, what peace we often forfeit,
Oh, what needless pain we bear,
All because we do not carry,
Everything to God in prayer!

Supt.—What does Peter say concerning the preciousness of Jesus?

School.—"Unto you who believe he is precious." (1. Pet. 2: 7.)

Sing.—Music No. 66.

So precious is Jesus, my Savior, my King,
His praise all the day long with rapture I sing;
To Him in my weakness for strength I can cling.
For He is so precious to me.

CHO.—For He is so precious to me,
For He is so precious to me,
'Tis heaven below
My Redeemer to know,
For He is so precious to me.

6. Show of Bibles.

7. Reading of Lesson.

8. Prayer.

9. Song.

10. Lesson Study.

11. Song.

12. Scripture Drill.

13. Reports.

14. Closing Word.

15. Closing Song.—See No. 42.

Will There be any Stars?

Order of Service. No. 3.

No. 406.

1. Instrumental Music.

2. Silence.—(*Doors closed.*)

Supt.—The Lord is in his holy temple.

School.—Let all the earth keep silence before him.

3. Prayer.—(*Bowed heads.*)

Minister.—This is the day which the Lord hath made.

School.—Let us be glad and rejoice in it.

All Sing.—Music No. 292.

"Come we that love the Lord,
And let our joys be known;
Join in the song with sweet accord,
Join in the song with sweet accord,
And thus surround the throne,
And thus surround the throne.

"Let those refuse to sing
Who never knew our God;
But children of the heav'nly King,
But children of the heav'nly King,
May speak their joys abroad,
May speak their joys abroad.

Supt.—Lift up your heads, O ye gates.

Teachers.—And be lifted up, ye everlasting doors.

Scholars.—And the King of glory shall come in.

Minister.—Who is this King of glory?

Boys.—The Lord, strong and mighty,

Girls.—The Lord, mighty in battle.

Boys.—The Lord of hosts.

All.—He is the King of glory.

4. Song.—(*A familiar and popular one.*)

Supt.—What did Jesus say concerning himself?

Boys.—I am the Door.

Girls.—I am the good Shepherd.

Minister.—I am the true Vine.

Girls.—I am the Bread of Life.

Boys.—I am the Light of the world.

Girls.—I am the Resurrection and the Life.

Supt.—I am the Way, the Truth and the Life.

All.—I am Alpha and Omega, the Beginning and the End, the First and the Last.

Minister.—I am the offspring of David, and the bright and morning Star.

School.—I am he that liveth, and was dead, and behold, I am alive forever more.

All.—And his name shall be called Wonderful Counsellor, Mighty God, Everlasting Father, Prince of Peace.

All Sing.—Music No. 309.

"All hail the power of Jesus' name!
Let angels prostrate fall;
Bring forth the royal diadem
And crown Him Lord of all."

5. Roll-call.

6. Show of Bibles.

7. Golden Text.

8. Lesson Read.

9. Instrumental Music.—(*While the classes gather for lesson study.*)

10. Lesson Study.

11. Instrumental Music.—(*While the scholars return from their classrooms*)

12. Song.

13. Birthday Offering.

14. Review or Scripture Drill.

15. Closing Word.

16. Closing Service.

Supt.—Let not your heart be troubled: ye believe in God, believe also in me.

School.—In my Father's house are many mansions; if it were not so, I would have told you; for I go to prepare a place for you.

Supt.—And if I go and prepare a place for you, I will come again, and will receive you unto myself: that where I am, there ye may be also.

All Sing.—Music No. 98.

Jesus is all the world to me,
My life, my joy, my all;
He is my strength from day to day,
Without Him I would fall.
When I am sad, to Him I go,
No other one can cheer me so;
When I am sad He makes me glad,
He's my friend.

Jesus is all the world to me,
My friend in trials sore;
I go to Him for blessings, and
He gives them o'er and o'er.
He sends the sunshine and the rain,
He sends the harvest's golden grain;
Sunshine and rain, harvest of grain,
He's my friend.

Benediction.—(*Sitting.*)

Order of Service. No. 4.

The first part of this service was prepared by Marion Lawrance and is just as he used it so successfully in his own school.

No. 407. Reception of New Members.

1. All Sing.—Music No. 307.

Dear Father, wilt Thou bless,
And lead in righteousness,
Our Bible school;
Grant that each soul may be
Striving continually
To praise and honor Thee,
God bless our school!

'Tis here we love to meet
About our Savior's feet,
Our Bible school;
Now hear us while we pray
On this most sacred day;
Take all our sins away;
God bless our school!

(*Be Seated.*)

Supt.—The doors of our Sunday School are swung open wide again today to give public recognition to the new members who have been enrolled with us during the past quarter. This is to us a most pleasing service, for we gladly welcome to our ranks all who will heartily engage with us in Bible study and blessed service for our King. What is our motto?

School.—"Remember Jesus Christ."

Supt.—What is our watchword?

School.—"What would Jesus do?"

Supt.—What is "Our Aim?"

School.—"Every member present, every Sunday, on time, with his own Bible, a liberal offering, a studied lesson and a mind to learn."

Supt.—What are our Colors?

School.—Blue and White.

Supt.—What is our Flower?

School.—The Pink Carnation.

(*Members are requested to wear our Flower on all special Occasions if convenient to do so.*)

Supt.—What is our Church and Sunday School Salute?

School.—Give Salute. (*Wave the hand.*)

(*Members are requested to use the Salute in recognizing each other on the street and elsewhere.*)

Pastor.—Words of Greeting.

Supt.—(To the New Members.) You have heard the School repeat "Our Motto," "Our Watchword," and "Our Aim." Will you promise that so far as possible you will join with us in carrying out "Our Aim?"

New Members Answer.—I will.

School.—We gladly receive and welcome you into our Sunday School today. We hope you will soon come to love its precious and hallowed associations as we do. Our aims are high, but the Master we serve deserves our best. We promise to help you and expect you to help us. Let us with united hands and hearts labor together to build each other up in every Christian grace, and to make our beloved Sunday School a strength and credit to the Church and a power for God.

Supt.—In the name of Jesus Christ Amen.

Our Love Circle. — (The General Officers of the School and the teachers who have received new scholars will join hands, thus forming a circle enclosing the new members received today.)

Prayer by the Minister.

Supt.—Blessed are ye when men shall reproach you, and persecute you, and say all manner of evil against you falsely, for my sake.

School.—Rejoice, and be exceeding glad: for great is your reward in heaven: for so persecuted they the prophets that were before you.

Sing.—Music No. 116.

Are you ever burdened with a load of care?
Does the cross seem heavy you are called to bear?
Count your many blessings, every doubt will fly,
And you will be singing as the days go by.

CHORUS.

Count your blessings,
Name them one by one,
Count your blessings,
See what God hath done;
Count your blessings,
Name them one by one,
Count your many blessings,
See what God hath done.

2. Show of Bibles.

3. Reading of Lesson.

4. Prayer.

5. Lesson Study.

Order of Service. No. 5.

No. 408.

Instrumental Music.

Silent Prayer.

Supt.—What is the Golden Text of the Bible?

School.—For God so loved the world that He gave His only begotten Son, that whosoever believeth on Him should not perish, but have eternal life.

Sing.—No. 296.

Love Divine, all love excelling,
Joy of heaven, to earth come down,
Fix in us Thy humble dwelling,
All Thy faithful mercies crown;
Jesus, Thou art all compassion,
Pure, unbounded love Thou art;
Visit us with Thy salvation,
Enter every trembling heart.

Supt.—Behold what manner of love the Father hath bestowed upon us that we should be called the children of God.

School.—For God sent not the Son into the world to judge the world; but that the world should be saved through him.

Supt.—Who shall separate us from the love of Christ?

Minister.—Shall tribulation?

Teachers.—Or anguish?

Boys.—Or persecution?

Girls.—Or famine?

All.—Or nakedness?

Ass't Supt.—Or peril?

Sec'y.—Or sword?

All.—Nay, in all these things we are more than conquerors through Him that loved us.

For I am persuaded that neither death, nor life, nor angels, nor principalities, nor powers, nor things present, nor things to come.

Nor height, nor depth, nor any other creature shall be able to separate us from the love of God, which is in Christ Jesus our Lord.

Sing.—No. 338.

I will love Thee in life, I will love Thee in death,
And praise Thee as long as Thou lendest me breath;
And say when the death-dew lies cold on my brow,
If ever I loved Thee, my Jesus 'tis now.

Prayer.—(Followed by Lord's Prayer.)

Announcements.

Song.

Lesson Reading.

Lesson Study.

Song.

Review.

Song.

Instrumental Prayer Hymn.

Benediction.

Order of Service. No. 6.

Prepared by P. H. Welshimer, Canton, Ohio.

No. 409.

1. **Instrumental.**—(*Selection.*)
2. **Song by School.**—No. 147.
   Let the Sunshine In.
3. **Show of Bibles.**
4. **Responsive Reading.**–Ps. 19: 7-14.
5. **Song.**—No. 219.
   Holy Bible, Book Divine.
6. **Prayer.**–(Followed by Lord's prayer.)
7. **Reading of Lesson.**
8. **Lesson Study.**— (*Instrumental selection while classes are retiring to rooms.*)
9. **Reassembling of Classes.**— (*Instrumental selection while reassembling.*)
10. **Song.**—No. 42.
    Will There Be Any Stars?
11. **Five Minute General Supplemental Work.**
12. **Announcing names of visitors present.**
13. **Special Music.**
14. **Report of Secretary,**
15. **Announcements.**
16. **Song.**—No. 255.
    Onward Christian Soldiers.
17. **Prayer and Benediction.**

No. 410. Responsive Reading.

NOTE.—Before the Leader reads, the Organist should play to the * for a prelude. See music below.

Wisdom.

Leader:—Remember now thy Creator in the days of thy youth. Serve Him with gladness, and magnify His name forever.

Response:—What shall I render unto the Lord for all His benefits towards me? I will take the cup of salvation and call upon the name of the Lord.

Leader:—Give us, O Lord, the wisdom from above, which is first pure, then peaceable, gentle, easy to be entreated, full of mercy and good fruits, without partiality, and without hypocrisy.

Response:—Whence then cometh wisdom? and where is the place of understanding.

Leader:—Behold, the fear of the Lord, that is wisdom, and to depart from evil is understanding.

Response:—Happy is the man that findeth wisdom, and the man that getteth understanding.

Leader:—The merchandise of it is better than the merchandise of silver, and the gain thereof than fine gold.

Response:—She is more precious than rubies.

Leader:—And all things thou canst desire are not to be compared unto her.

Response:—Length of days is in her right hand: and in her left hand riches and honor.

Leader:—Her ways are ways of pleasantness, and all her paths are peace.

Response:—She is a tree of life to them that lay hold upon her; and happy is every one that retaineth her.

Leader:—And beside this, giving all diligence, add to your knowledge temperance.

Response:—And to temperance, patience.

Leader:—And to patience, godliness.

Response:—And to godliness, brotherly kindness.

Leader:—And to brotherly kindness, charity.

All sing:—(Sing promptly without interludes.)

How Gentle God's Commands.

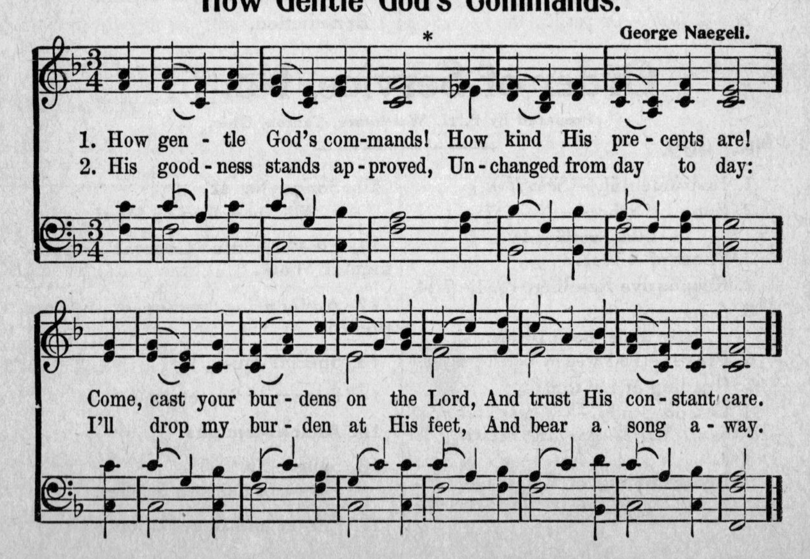
George Naegeli.
*
1. How gen - tle God's com-mands! How kind His pre - cepts are!
2. His good - ness stands ap - proved, Un - changed from day to day:
Come, cast your bur - dens on the Lord, And trust His con - stant care.
I'll drop my bur - den at His feet, And bear a song a - way.

No. 411. Responsive Reading.

NOTE.—Before the Leader reads, the Organist should play to the * for a prelude. See music below.

God's Love.

Leader:—For God so loved the world, that He gave His only begotten Son, that whosoever believeth in Him should not perish, but have everlasting life.

Response:—In this was manifested the love of God toward us, because that God sent His only begotten Son into the world, that we might live through Him.

Leader:—Beloved, if God so loved us, we ought also to love one another.

(*Sing promptly without interludes.*)

1 We praise Thee, O God, for the Son of Thy love,
For Jesus who died and is now gone above.—Ref.

Leader:—But the Comforter, which is the Holy Ghost, whom the Father will send in my name, He shall teach you all things and bring all things to your remembrance, whatsoever I have said unto you.

Response:—When He, the Spirit of Truth, is come, He will guide you into all truth; for He shall not speak of Himself; but whatsoever He shall hear, that shall He speak: and He will show you things to come.

Leader:—He shall glorify me: for He shall receive of mine, and shall show it unto you.

All sing:—

2 We praise Thee, O God! for Thy Spirit of light,
Who has shown us our Savior and scattered our night.—Ref.

Leader:—And I beheld, and I heard the voice of many angels round about the throne, and the living creatures and the elders; and the number of them was ten-thousand times ten-thousand, and thousands of thousands.

Response:—Saying with a loud voice, Worthy is the Lamb that was slain to receive power, and riches, and wisdom, and strength, and honor, and glory, and blessing.

All sing:—

3 All glory and praise to the Lamb that was slain,
Who has borne all our sins and has cleansed every stain.—Ref.

Revive Us Again.

J. J. Husband.

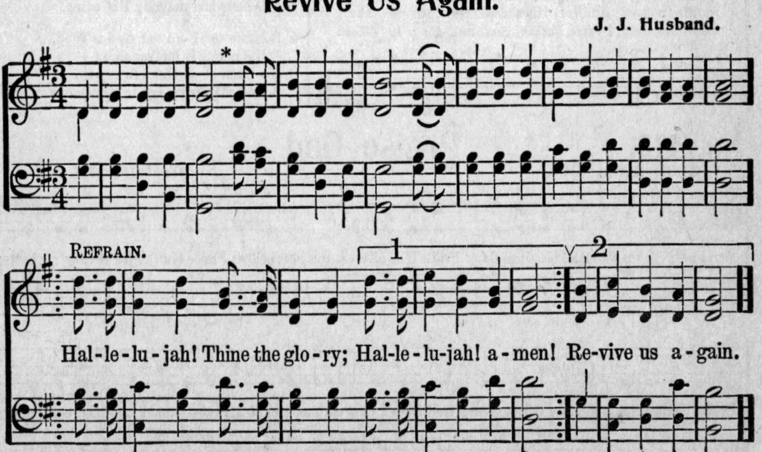
*
Refrain.
1
2
Hal-le-lu-jah! Thine the glo-ry; Hal-le-lu-jah! a-men! Re-vive us a-gain.

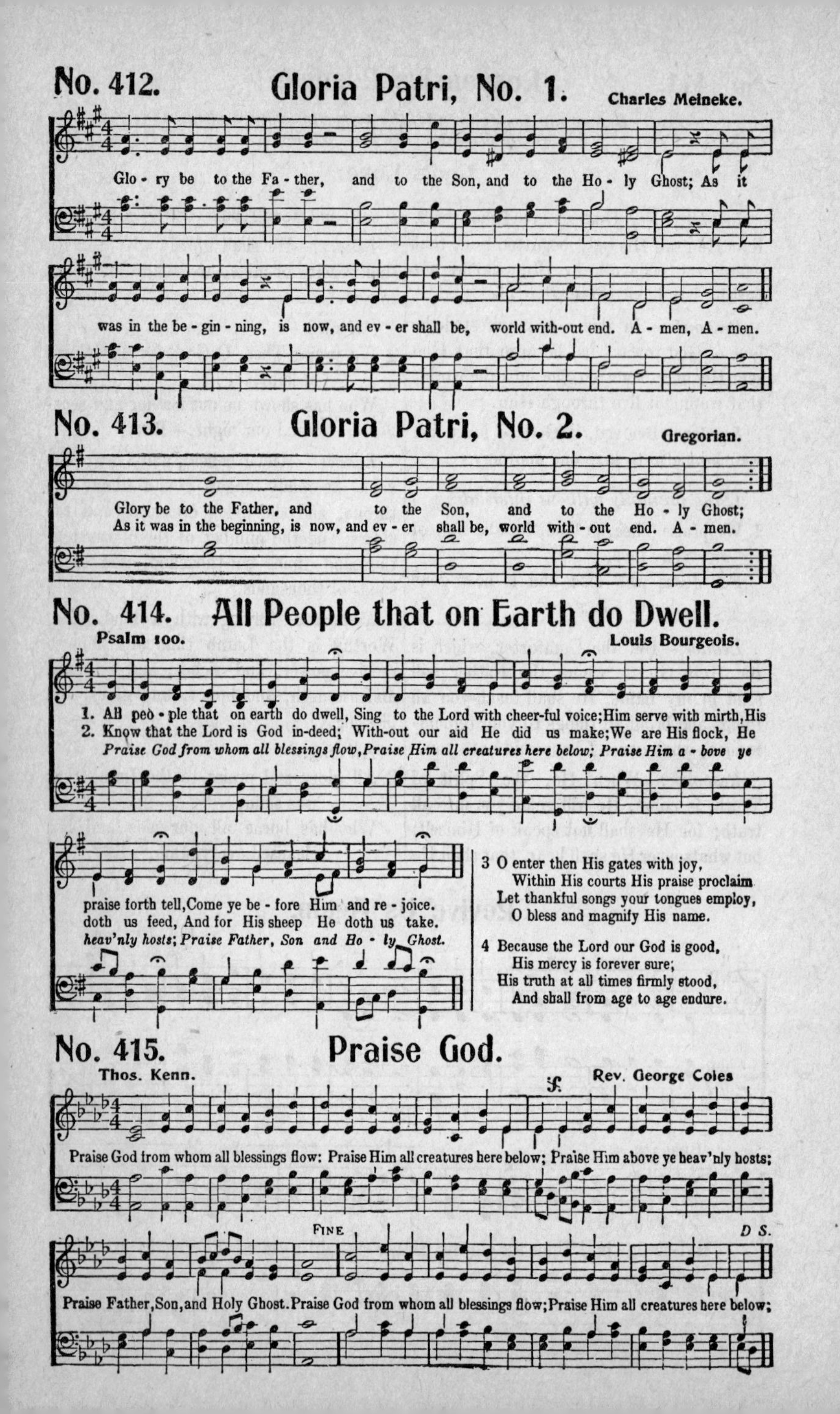
No. 412.
Gloria Patri, No. 1.
Charles Meineke.
Glo - ry be to the Fa - ther, and to the Son, and to the Ho - ly Ghost; As it
was in the be - gin - ning, is now, and ev - er shall be, world with-out end. A - men, A - men.
No. 413.
Gloria Patri, No. 2.
Gregorian.
Glory be to the Father, and to the Son, and to the Ho - ly Ghost;
As it was in the beginning, is now, and ev - er shall be, world with - out end. A - men.
No. 414.
All People that on Earth do Dwell.
Psalm 100.
Louis Bourgeois.
1. All peo - ple that on earth do dwell, Sing to the Lord with cheer-ful voice; Him serve with mirth, His
2. Know that the Lord is God in-deed; With-out our aid He did us make; We are His flock, He
Praise God from whom all blessings flow, Praise Him all creatures here below; Praise Him a - bove ye
praise forth tell, Come ye be - fore Him and re - joice.
doth us feed, And for His sheep He doth us take.
heav'nly hosts; Praise Father, Son and Ho - ly Ghost.
3 O enter then His gates with joy,
Within His courts His praise proclaim
Let thankful songs your tongues employ,
O bless and magnify His name.
4 Because the Lord our God is good,
His mercy is forever sure;
His truth at all times firmly stood,
And shall from age to age endure.
No. 415.
Praise God.
Thos. Kenn.
Rev. George Coles
Praise God from whom all blessings flow: Praise Him all creatures here below; Praise Him above ye heav'nly hosts;
FINE
D S.
Praise Father, Son, and Holy Ghost. Praise God from whom all blessings flow; Praise Him all creatures here below;

Indices

(Alphabetical index arranged by first lines and titles)

A

A call for loyal soldiers.. 92
A happy day 81
A lamp within a stable.240
A land by faith I see....143
A little bit of love.... 99
A little maid with soft..214
A little while and then.. 94
A mother is lonely....356
A sinner made whole...207
A sinner was wandering.210
A stranger stands 198
A thought of him......217
A vision goes before me. 67
A voice is sweetly.......211
A word and a smile.....101
Abide with me.........277
Alas and did my Savior.249
All for Jesus 314
All glory be thine..... 44
All hail Immanuel 227
All hail the power....261
All hail the power....308
All hail the power....309
All hail to Thee.........227
All in all to me....... 11
All of my need He...... 93
All people that on....414
All the way my Savior.241
All thine own 135
All, yes all I give to....314
Almost persuaded 252
Alone at the 191
Alone with God 69
Amazing grace 213
America 367
Angel voices ever 244
Anywhere with Jesus..111
Arise my soul 310
As a volunteer 92
As I cling to the hand...201
As thou once the host.... 53
Ashamed of Jesus 134
Asleep in Jesus 276
At the cross 249
At the feast of.........351
Away in a manger......149

B

Back of every drop of...152
Battle hymn of the...364
Be a hero 170
Be a little sunbeam....163
Be careful 157
Be not dismayed whate'er 22
Beautiful flag 369
Beautiful isle 133
Because his name is....196
Because I love Jesus... 72
Beclouded long my way..186
Behold a stranger at.... 77
Behold I stand at the.174
Behold one cometh in...188
Beneath the cross of..239
Better than I know....220
Blessed assurance 302
Blessed be the......... 36
Blest be the tie......285
Break thou the bread..327
Brightly beams our......115
Bring peace to my soul. 18
But for a moment......218

C

Child of the master..... 10
Christ at the door..... 77
Christ is leading on...232
Christ shall be king... 41
Christ shall be king...231
Clinging close to his...201
Close to thee 109
Cloud or sunshine.....118
Come every soul by sin..330
Come Thou Almighty ..307
Come thou fount 267
Come today 55
Come we that love the..292
Come ye disconsolate...320
Count your blessings...116
Crown him, crown him..230
Crown him, king of....230
Crown him with many...237

D

Day is dying in the....311
Dear little stranger...145
Delay not 344
Did Christ o'er sinners.331
Don't forget to pray... 60
Doxology 414
Do you fear the foe 147
Do you hear the 55
Do you know the 99
Do you know what a ...101
Drifting away from....205

E

Each cooing dove 45
Earthly pleasures vainly. 19
Echoes of old hymns...214
Entire consecration ... 27
Eternity 192
Even me, even me......313
Everybody should know.221
Every sky that glistens..118
Expostulation 341

F

Fade, fade each 323
Fading away like the.. 37
Failing in strength....190
Faith of our fathers...245
Faith will bring the.. 35
Flag of the free........369
Flag of the free 370
Follow all the way....104
Follow your leader.... 65
Forward Christian 363
Forward go 363
From every stormy 334
From Greenland's icy..348
From over hill and plain 80

G

Gently Lord, O gently.316
Gird on your steadfast.106
Gloria Patri, No. 1....412
Gloria Patri, No. 2....413
Glorious things of 306
Glory be to the father...412
Glory be to the father...413
Glory in the cross..... 30
Glory to God for the.... 8
God be with you.......318
God is calling yet..... 76
God is not far away....181
God reaches down 184
God save the king 368
God will take care of.. 22
Go forth! Go forth for.. 47
Going down to the....175
Gone from my heart....250
Grace enough for me... 2
Growing dearer each .. 83
Guide me 297

H

Had we only sunshine...154
Had you dwelt in 183
Hark, hark, my soul...243
Hark the call to arms... 39
Harvest song 108
Have thy affections 25
Have you made the..... 91
Have you seen the......151
Heaven is not far......209
He is so precious to me. 66
He knows it all........224
He leadeth me 315
He loves even me......223
He supplieth all of... 93
He understands 225
He's a drunkard.......354
Held by my Savior's.... 57

HELP SOMEBODY TODAY... 14
HIDING, SAFELY HIDING.. 51
High in the treetop's....162
His gifts are greater ... 6
HIS LOVE CAN NEVER ...208
HIS LOVE FOR ME.......178
HIS LOVE IS ALL I NEED.182
HIS WONDROUS GIFTS TO.128
HOLD MY HAND FAST.... 64
HOLD UP THE CROSS.....130
HOLY BIBLE, BOOK.......219
Holy Ghost comforter ...281
HOLY GHOST WITH LOVE.271
HOLY, HOLY, HOLY 275
HOLY SPIRIT FAITHFUL ..337
HOLY TWILIGHT HOUR ..138
Homeless and friendless.361
HOME, SWEET HOME 349
HOMEWARD AND 228
HONOR BRIGHT CADETS....166
HOSANNA TO THE KING...165
HOW FIRM A FOUNDATION.342
HOW FIRM A FOUNDATION.345
How gentle God's.......410
How many times has 100
HOW SWEET IS HIS LOVE..185
How sweet is the love of. 83
HOW SWEET TO TRUST.... 20
HOW WISE YOU LOOK.....161
HURRAH FOR THE RED,....167

I

I am a stranger here.... 46
I AM GOING ON WITH.... 13
I AM HAPPY IN HIM.....204
I am on the gospel......187
I AM SATISFIED WITH.... 71
I am thinking today..... 42
I can hear my Savior...248
I do not ask to see the..208
I dreamed one night 164
I dreamed that I stood..191
I have a friend more....136
I have a song I love to.. 28
I have seen a mother....352
I have such a wonderful.221
I have toiled all night...179
I KNOW 180
I know my heavenly.....177
I know three little......167
I LOVE HIM 250
I LOVE THY KINGDOM....270
I love to be alone with.. 69
I LOVE TO TELL THE.....312
I love to think my father.224
I must needs go home... 40
I MUST TELL JESUS...... 90
I NEED THEE EVERY 137
I saw one hanging on a.. 29
I SHALL ALWAYS NEED.... 21
I stand all amazed at....197
I stood by the side of...189
I think God gives the....153
I THINK WHEN I READ...173
I want to be more like...131
I want to live closer to.. 48
I WILL NOT FORGET THEE. 49
I WOULD BE LIKE JESUS.. 19
I WOULD NOT LIVE....... 52
I'LL BE A SUNBEAM......146
I'll go anywhere my.....111
I'LL LIVE FOR HIM.......251
I'll sing of a stream.....199
I'M A PILGRIM 200
I'M NOT YOUR JUDGE.....176
I've a message from the.123
I'VE FOUND A FRIEND.....129
I'VE FOUND A FRIEND.....140
If Christ the Redeemer.. 16
If ever Jesus has need...217
IF IT WERE NOT SO....... 43
If we are faithful in.... 15
If you have a kindly....206
If you need uplifting.... 35
In a world where sorrow 59
In days of yore 371
IN HIS SUNLIGHT 50
In looking through my... 2
In the Christian's 319
IN THE CROSS 264
In the cross shall be my. 30
In the light and glory... 50
IN THE SHADOW OF...... 54
In the temple the.......165
In vain I've tried a.....196
IS MY NAME WRITTEN...322
IS THY HEART RIGHT..... 25
IT CAME UPON THE 256
IT IS JESUS 188
IT IS WELL WITH MY..... 87
IT PAYS TO SERVE JESUS.. 89
IT WAS HIS LOVE........ 5

J

JESUS AND HIS LOVE......211
Jesus and shall it ever...134
JESUS BIDS US SHINE.....169
JESUS CALLS US 321
JESUS FRIEND OF SINNERS. 96
Jesus has loved me 357
JESUS I MY CROSS HAVE..287
Jesus is a friend so..... 52
JESUS IS ALL THE WORLD. 98
JESUS IS CALLING 121
JESUS LOVER OF MY SOUL.226
JESUS LOVER OF MY SOUL.332
JESUS LOVER OF MY SOUL.333
JESUS ONLY 24
JESUS ON THE CROSS..... 67
JESUS SAVIOR PILOT ME..272
JESUS SHALL REIGN 262
JESUS THE VERY 260
Jesus wants me for a....146
JESUS WILL 222
Joyfully now our songs...229
JOY TO THE WORLD....... 1
Just a little sunbeam....159
JUST AS I AM...........325
Just as the stars are.....155
JUST FOR HIS SAKE.......179
JUST THE LOVE OF JESUS.. 75
JUST WHEN I NEED HIM.. 7

K

KEEP STEP IN THE MARCH.156
KEEP THE HEART SINGING 56
Kneeling by my trundle.209

L

Lamp of our feet 26
LAND OF THE UNSETTING 68
Lay hold on the hope.... 82
LEAD KINDLY LIGHT.....278
LET HIM IN 97
LET THE LOWER LIGHTS..115
LET THE SUNSHINE IN...147
Let your light shine.... 74
Life wears a different... 4
LIFT HIM UP 350
Like an army we are...233
Like music floating on..215
Little bells of.........158
LITTLE EVANGELS 148
Little feet be very 157
LITTLE STAR 161
LITTLE STARS 155
LITTLE SUNBEAMS 153
Look all around you.... 14
LOOK AND LIVE 123
Look the harvest field...108
LOOK TO JESUS 340
LOOK TO JESUS 355
Lord I care not for.....322
Lord I hear of..........313
Lord Jesus I long to be..263
Lord make today one... 9
Lord take my all 117
LOVE DIVINE 296
Low in a manger 145
LOYALTY TO CHRIST 80
LUTHER'S CRADLE HYMN..149

M

MAJESTIC SWEETNESS 279
March along together ...362
MEMORIES OF GALILEE... 45
Mid pleasures and 349
MINE EYES HAVE SEEN...364
MORE LIKE JESUS 131
MORE LIKE THE MASTER..110
My country 'tis of thee..367
My days are gliding.....141
MY EVER FAITHFUL......136

My faith looks up to..288
My Father knows 177
My hope is built 298
My Jesus as thou......300
My Jesus I love Thee..338
My life I have given... 27
My life, my love I give..251
My mother's song 212
My path may be lonely.. 72
My Savior's voice......215
My Shepherd 343
My soul be on thy....328
My soul is so happy in..204

N

Nearer home 317
Nearer my God to......258
Nearer the cross 236
Neath the shadow of.... 51
Nobody told me of..... 70
No dying there 143
Nothing satisfies but.. 33
No tramp of marching...240
Now the day is over...246

O

O Columbia the gem of.365
O could I speak 290
O day of rest and......305
O eyes that are weary...340
O happy day 294
O how precious are the.. 12
O Jesus I have 238
O Jesus thou art 265
O little town of 286
O love that wilt not..259
O make me pure 186
O sacred head now....280
O sing of his mighty..329
O that will be glory.. 31
O they tell me of a 88
O turn ye 339
O turn ye 341
O where are the......102
O worship the king...283
Oh bliss of the........329
Oh for a clean heart..114
Oh for a heart of 114
Oh for a thousand....266
Oh I love to think of...104
Oh it is wonderful 197
Oh say can you see....366
Oh to be more like ...112
O'er the hills the sun is.317
One day for Thee...... 9
Only remembered 37
Only trust him 330
On the battlefield of.....170
Onward Christian 235
Onward Christian 255
Onward will I journey... 57
Open the door for the. 62
Order of service..404 to 410
Our colors so true.....160
Our Father which art....172
Over and over again...100

P

Praise God from whom.415

R

Raise me Jesus to Thy.202
Refuge 226
Responsive . . ...400 to 412
Rest for the weary....319
Revive us again 301
Revive us again 411
Rock of ages 234
Rock of ages 273
Rose, rose, rose 171

S

Safely through 326
Saints in glory 58
Satisfied 32
Saved, saved 140
Savior go with me..... 53
Savior like a shepherd.269
Savior our hearts shall...135
Savior thy dying love...105
Scatter sunshine 59
Selected ....372 to 400
Servant of God awake.. 85
Service is our 242
Silent night, holy.....291
Since I found my...... 4
Since I have been..... 28
Sing me the song my...212
Sing them over again to.107
Sing with tuneful 150
Sinner why have you ...253
Softly and tenderly ...127
Somebody 194
Somebody did a golden..194
Somebody knows 190
Somebody needs you ... 10
Somebody's boy 361
Somebody voted to ruin..360
Some day I'll reap......353
Some day the sun of ...193
Some happy day 353
Someone is looking.... 74
Some sweet day I shall. 68
Something for Jesus...105
Sometime, somewhere ...203
Sometimes the mists of..113
Sometimes there comes..132
Somewhere the sun is ...133
Somewhere tonight in...354
So precious is Jesus.... 66
Speak it for the......206
Spend one hour with.. 95
Spirit of love divine...281
Stand up for Jesus.....346
Sunbeams bright 159
Sun of my soul 304
Sunshine and rain 154
Sweet by and by.......295
Sweet Galilee 189
Sweet hour of 293
Sweet is the promise ... 49

T

Teach me 17
Tell it o'er mountain.... 78
Tell it wherever you.. 16
Tell me the old, old.. 61
Tell the promises 34
That beautiful stream.199
The apostles creed 402
The banner of the 106
The beacon of the.....113
The Bible 26
The birds' nest 162
The call to arms 79
The children's hosanna.164
The church in the....144
The dream city 195
The field is the 63
The flag of the free..370
The gate ajar 299
The gifts of God...... 6
The glory song 31
The good old fashioned.187
The great Physician ..324
The handwriting on ..351
The home of endless.. 38
The hope set before... 82
The hour of prayer... 8
The King of kings.....229
The King's business ... 46
The life that is to...132
The light of the..... 78
The Lord is my shepherd.343
The Lord's prayer 172
The Love of Jesus..... 23
The Love of Jesus 71
The Love of Jesus 182
The maple leaf 371
The morning light is..347
The night shadows 64
The offering 117
The reapers are loudly.. 63
The red, white and ...365
The shining shore 141
The sinner and the ...210
The slighted stranger..198
The song-land of my ..103
The song of my 125
The Son of God goes...303
The star spangled 366
The temperance army..362
The touch of his 3

The tramp of the 233
The trumpet call 39
The trumpet of battle.... 79
The unclouded day 88
The way of the 40
The whole wide 120
The wondrous cross ...282
There are days so dark.. 3
There are storms the....103
There is a fountain....335
There is a fountain....336
There is a gate that.....299
There's a church in the..144
There's a city I am.....192
There's a city that hath..195
There's a land that is...295
There's a song in my...125
There's a song in my....207
There's a stranger at.... 97
There's danger in the..358
This thought gives 181
Tho' burdens heavy 38
Tho' the way we 73
Tho' your sins be red...355
Thou my everlasting ...109
Thou only art holy 44
Three colors has the....160
Thy saints all stand in.. 58
'Tis dividing the 216
'Tis midnight on 274
Touch not, taste not..358
Traveling on in the.....228
True to my Savior..... 86
'Twas rum that 352
Twilight is falling ...139

U

Unanswered yet 203
Under the snow 168
Upon a hill before me ...119

W

Walk in the light.....268
Wash me in the 335
Was it you 360
Watching over all 152
Weary gleaner whence ..122
Weary soul by sin 95
We have heard the cry..232
We may lighten toil..... 56
We must win them one..124
We plough the fields..289
We praise thee O God ..301
We shall be more 15
We shall see the...... 73
We walk together 126
We're cadets that want..166
We're marching to 292
We've a story to 84
What a friend 284
What is making life so.. 75
What is sweeter tell 171
What they seem to ...151
What wondrous love .. 29
What would you 183
When all my labors and. 31
When earthly cares and.. 18
When He died for me..119
When I gave my heart.. 81
When I go home 94
When I have finished ... 32
When I shall fall ...193
When I survey the 282
When I think of my ...223
When peace like a river. 87
When silently the night.138
When temptation fierce .. 24
When the burden is 34
When the day is dark.. 60
When the last rays of ... 91
When troubled my soul..185
When upon life's billows.116
Where hast thou 122
Where He leads me....248
Where Thou callest .. 12
While shepherds 257
While we pray and 247
Whiter than snow 263
Who is on the Lord's..254
Who will open mercy's..222
Why not come to......253
Why not now 247
Why stand ye here....142
Will there be any 42
Win them one by one..124
With joy we sing 158
Wonderful Savior 357
Working, watching, ... 47
Wonderful words of...107
Would you care if some. 70

Y

Years I spent in sin and.128
Yield not to 359
You ask me how I......180
You have heard of the..178
Your brother has a 350

Order of Services

Order of Service No. 1...............
(The Name of Jesus)............404
Order of Service No. 2 405
Order of Service No. 3 406
Order of Service No. 4.............
(Reception of New Members)....407
Order of Service No. 5 408
Order of Service No. 6 409

Responsive Readings

Prov. 3—My Son Forget Not My Law.400
Matt. 5—And Seeing the Multitudes.401
I Cor. 13—Though I Speak with the Tongues 403
God's Love 411
Reception of New Members 407
The Apostles' Creed 402
The Name of Jesus 404
Wisdom 410

Selected Psalms

I Blessed is the Man.........372
V Give ear to my words......373
VIII O Lord how excellent is....374
XV Lord, who shall abide......375
XVII Hear the right, O Lord.....376
XIX The law of the Lord.......377
XXIII The Lord is my shepherd...378
XXIV The earth is the Lord's.....379
XXVII The Lord is my light.......380
XXXII Blessed is he..............381
XXXIV I will bless the Lord........382
LI Have mercy upon me.......383
LXI Hear my cry, O God.......384
LXIII O God thou art my God....385
LXV Praise waiteth for thee..386
LXVII God be merciful unto...387
LXXXIV How amiable are Thy..388
XCI He that dwelleth in the..389
XCIII The Lord reigneth 390
XCV O come, let us sing.....391
XCVIII O sing unto the Lord...392
CIII Bless the Lord, O my...393
CXIX Blessed are the undefiled.394
CXXII I was glad when they....395
CXXXVIII I will praise Thee......396
CXXXXII I cried unto the Lord...397
CXXXXIX Praise ye the Lord 398
CL Praise ye the Lord 399

Topical Index

Activity (See Conflict).

Advent (See Christmas).

Aspiration: 9, 12, 13, 15, 17, 18, 19, 24, 27, 33, 48, 52, 53, 64, 86, 105, 109, 110, 112, 114, 117, 131, 135, 137, 186, 202, 258, 263, 300, 314, 335.

Assurance: 2, 4, 6, 7, 11, 13, 22, 28, 32, 43, 49, 51, 71, 72, 73, 87, 93, 140, 177, 180, 181, 182, 208, 222, 223, 224, 241, 298, 302, 315, 323.

Atonement: 2, 28, 29, 36, 67, 71, 105, 117, 119, 223, 239, 249, 250, 273, 282, 298, 310, 313, 325, 330, 335, 336.

Bible: 26, 34, 44, 107, 115, 219, 327.

Children: 62, 107, 145, 146, 147, 148, 149, 150, 151, 152, 153, 154, 155, 156, 157, 158, 159, 160, 161, 162, 163, 164, 165, 166, 167, 168, 169, 170, 171, 172, 173, 269, 284, 359, 362, 363, 366, 367.

Choruses: 134, 136, 140, 142, 174, 197, 198, 199, 200, 201, 219, 225, 226, 227, 228, 229, 230, 231, 232, 233, 234, 235, 308.

Christ: 1, 3, 4, 7, 13, 15, 41, 77, 78, 80, 174, 197, 198, 296, 331.

Christmas: 1, 41, 78, 134, 136, 145, 149, 158, 164, 165, 183, 188, 197, 198, 227, 229, 230, 231, 237, 240, 243, 244, 256, 257, 261, 262, 280, 286, 291, 308, 309.

Citizenship (See Patriotism).

Cleansing: 36, 110, 114, 199, 263, 294, 329, 335, 336.

Closing: 246, 285, 318, 412, 413, 414, 415.

Communion (See Fellowship).

Conflict: 39, 47, 57, 63, 65, 79, 80, 85, 92, 102, 106, 108, 124, 130, 142, 147, 156, 166, 170, 194, 206, 232, 233, 235, 242, 254, 255, 292, 303, 346, 362, 363, 364.

Consecration: 11, 17, 19, 27, 48, 105, 110, 114, 117, 131, 135, 248, 251, 314.

Cross: 2, 29, 30, 40, 67, 71, 106, 113, 130, 236, 239, 249, 259, 264, 280, 282, 287.

Devotion (See Worship).

Duets: 64, 120, 122, 126, 132, 134, 136, 138, 142, 149, 150, 197, 198, 202, 203, 204, 205, 206, 207, 208, 215, 221, 222, 224, 353, 355, 359.

Easter: 1, 41, 78, 84, 132, 168, 171, 183, 218, 227, 229, 230, 237.

Faith (See Trust).

Fellowship: 3, 4, 5, 6, 7, 8, 9, 11, 12, 13, 20, 21, 27, 33, 48, 49, 50, 51, 52, 53, 54, 57, 64, 69, 71, 75, 83, 90, 93, 95, 96, 98, 109, 110, 111, 126, 129, 135, 136, 137, 236, 238, 241, 248, 258, 259, 260, 277, 284, 293, 315, 323, 332, 338.

Gloria: 412, 413.

God: 6, 22, 25, 69, 76, 85, 93, 100, 115, 116, 128, 177, 181, 184, 205, 208, 224, 258, 259, 297, 315, 329, 339.

Grace: 2, 3, 5, 6, 8, 11, 18, 31, 66, 93, 95, 178, 213, 248, 267, 279, 288, 306, 308, 309, 332, 333, 344.

Gratitude: 5, 6, 8, 11, 23, 27, 29, 30, 33, 44, 51, 66, 72, 100, 105, 116, 129, 135, 217, 251, 282, 283, 289, 290, 292, 301, 312, 314, 338.

Guidance: 7, 9, 11, 13, 18, 21, 22, 23, 26, 49, 52, 53, 57, 64, 65, 83, 93, 109, 111, 126, 136, 152, 184, 190, 208, 241, 248, 259, 268, 269, 272, 277, 278, 297, 315, 326, 337, 343.

Heaven: 31, 32, 38, 40, 42, 43, 58, 68, 73, 88, 94, 132, 141, 143, 192, 193, 195, 209, 218, 228, 299, 317, 319.

Helpfulness: 14, 16, 47, 56, 59, 62, 74, 85, 91, 99, 101, 102, 118, 124, 142, 147, 194, 206, 209, 220, 242, 346, 350.
Holy Spirit: 17, 69, 77, 271, 281, 337.

Invitation: 10, 16, 25, 29, 33, 35, 36, 40, 55, 66, 67, 76, 77, 82, 96, 97, 121, 123, 127, 134, 202, 205, 248, 249, 252, 253, 254, 259, 263, 265, 271, 273, 282, 284, 287, 294, 298, 299, 310, 313, 314, 320, 321, 325, 330, 339, 340, 344, 355.

Jesus: 1, 3, 7, 11, 13, 15, 19, 20, 23, 24, 27, 29, 31, 33, 43, 48, 49, 51, 52, 54, 65, 66, 67, 70, 71, 72, 73, 75, 85, 89, 90, 95, 96, 98, 105, 110, 111, 112, 119, 120, 121, 126, 127, 129, 131, 134, 135, 136, 145, 149, 169, 174, 178, 182, 185, 188, 190, 196, 197, 202, 204, 207, 208, 211, 217, 221, 222, 223, 226, 227, 229, 230, 238, 239, 243, 250, 259, 260, 262, 265, 272, 273, 276, 284, 287, 300, 308, 309, 312, 314, 324, 329, 330, 332, 333 338, 340, 346, 355.
Joy: 1, 20, 23, 31, 50, 54, 58, 128, 196, 259.

Love: 5, 23, 29, 32, 75, 83, 113, 128, 178, 182, 185, 208, 223, 259, 338.

Male Voices: 134, 136, 142, 197, 198, 204, 205, 206, 207, 208, 221, 222, 355.
Memorial: 68, 88, 94, 132, 133, 141, 143, 177, 181, 185, 192, 193, 195, 200, 202, 218, 224, 258, 272, 273, 276, 277, 278, 295, 300, 304, 317, 319, 320, 323, 332, 333, 334.
Missions: 10, 14, 16, 41, 56, 59, 63, 70, 74, 78, 84, 99, 102, 108, 115, 120, 130, 147, 231, 262, 346, 347, 348.
Motion Songs: 157, 158, 159, 160, 161, 162.

Patriotism: 160, 167, 349, 364, 365, 366, 367, 368, 369, 370, 371.
Praise: 44, 266, 267, 290, 294, 301, 307, 308, 309.
Prayer: 8, 9, 12, 47, 60, 90, 95, 137, 172, 203, 257, 284, 293, 313, 334.
Promises: 34, 43, 49, 93, 174, 208, 223.

Quartets: 45, 51, 69, 96, 117, 133, 199, 200, 202, 243, 259, 278, 281, 308, 317, 332, 341, 358, 361.

Sabbath: 9, 305, 326.
Sacrament: 105, 109, 117, 119 251, 258, 259, 260, 273, 274, 279, 280, 282, 314, 320, 332, 333, 338.
Salvation: 4, 16, 28, 29, 71, 81, 123, 128, 140, 180, 184, 196, 204, 249, 250, 294, 298, 299, 310, 339, 340, 344.
Savior: 1, 3, 4, 12, 21, 27, 29, 31, 49, 50, 51, 53, 54, 57, 64, 66, 73, 83, 86, 97, 109, 110, 119, 126, 129, 135, 136, 137, 174, 179, 189, 198, 201, 205, 206, 207, 210, 215, 217, 221, 223, 227, 229, 230, 241, 248, 249, 259, 269, 273, 274, 279, 280, 288, 290, 313, 329, 335.
Service: 13, 14, 16, 39, 59, 85, 89, 92, 102, 108, 115, 122, 124, 142, 194, 206, 236, 242.
Solos: 68, 70, 72, 88, 94, 99, 117, 125, 133, 175, 176, 177, 178, 179, 180, 181, 182, 183, 184, 185, 186, 187, 188, 189, 190, 191, 192, 193, 194, 195, 196, 209, 210, 211, 212, 214, 216, 217, 218, 220, 223, 350, 351, 352, 354, 356, 357, 360.

Temperance: 92, 170, 350, 351, 352, 353, 354, 356, 358, 359, 360, 361, 362, 363, 364.
Trust: 17, 20, 22, 24, 27, 35, 43, 93, 111, 117, 208, 241, 245, 259, 269, 273, 284, 288, 298, 300, 302, 314, 315, 323, 328, 330.

Warfare (See Conflict).
Worship: 1, 7, 8, 9, 12, 17, 19, 20, 21, 27, 33, 40, 44, 48, 60, 66, 69, 75, 83, 85, 86, 87, 90, 93, 95, 96, 97, 98, 105, 107, 109, 110, 111, 112, 114, 116, 117, 126, 129, 131, 135, 137, 172, 236, 237, 238, 239, 241, 248, 250, 251, 258, 259, 260, 261, 262, 264, 265, 266, 267, 268, 269, 270, 271, 272, 273, 275, 277, 278, 279, 280, 281, 282, 283, 284, 285, 286, 287, 288, 290, 293, 296, 297, 298, 300, 301, 302, 303, 304, 305, 306, 307, 309, 310, 311, 312, 313, 314, 315, 316, 317, 320, 321, 322, 323, 324, 325, 326, 327, 328, 329, 332, 333, 334, 336, 337, 338, 342, 343, 346, 347.